# HOW TO IDENTIFY TREES

## IN SOUTHERN AFRICA

## Braam van Wyk & Piet van Wyk

In memory of
**Piet van Wyk**
05/07/1931 – 02/04/2006

Published by Struik Nature
(a division of Random House Struik (Pty) Ltd)
Reg. No. 1966/003153/07
80 McKenzie Street, Cape Town, 8001
PO Box 1144, Cape Town, 8000 South Africa

Visit us at **www.randomstruik.co.za**

Log on to our photographic website
**www.imagesofafrica.co.za**
for an African experience

First published in 2007
5  7  9  10  8  6  4

Publisher: Pippa Parker
Managing editor: Rod Baker
Editor: Gill Gordon
Designer: Robin Cox
Illustrator: Jaco van Wyk

Reproduction by Hirt & Carter Cape (Pty) Ltd
Printed and bound in Dubai by Oriental Press

ISBN: 978 1 77007 240 4

**PHOTOGRAPHIC CREDITS**
All photographs by Piet van Wyk, with the exception of the following, which are by Braam
van Wyk (unless stated, all photographs on a page are by BvW): pp7, 8, 9, 13, 17–19, 27–32,
34, 36, 37, 38 bottom left, 39–42, 44–47, 51–53, 57, 58 bottom, 68, 73 top, 90 centre, 32 bottom, 93 bottom, 95 bottom, 103 bottom, 108 centre & bottom, 137, 145 top left & right, 157.

**Front cover:** (clockwise from top left) *Croton sylvaticus*: fruit; *Elaeodendron croceum*: fruit;
*Maerua cafra*: fruit; *Dovyalis caffra*: female flowers; *Hippobromus pauciflorus*: fruit
**Back cover:** (top) *Canthium inerme*: fruit; (bottom) *Erythrina humeana*: flowers
**Spine:** *Cussonia spicata*: tree
**Title page:** *Acacia tortilis* subsp. *heteracantha*: tree

# Preface

Southern Africa is rich in trees, with about 2 100 native species, plus several hundred more that have been introduced from other parts of the world. Therefore, identifying specific trees presents a challenge to the professional botanist and layperson alike. When starting out, many tree enthusiasts are disheartened by having to come to grips with such extraordinary diversity. Disappointment sets in when realizing – after several failed attempts at identification – that the acquisition of a tree book is no guarantee for success. Not surprisingly, tree identification is seen by many beginners as a skill that is almost impossible to master. **The principal aim of this book is to demystify the subject and to present knowledge that will enable the novice to become competent in tree identification**.

Instead of responding to the question 'What is that tree?' with a name, this book attempts to answer the more fundamental question 'How do I establish the name of a tree?' Knowing a tree's name is but a small part of what tree identification is all about. In fact, names are not a prerequisite for classification and identification. Far more important is understanding the characters that are used to classify trees. One must, in the first instance, be able to explain what characters distinguish one species from another. Unlike the identification of larger animals, plant identification requires the use of characters that are not always very obvious. We also, at least initially, tend to be constrained in the way we look at trees for identification clues.

Getting to grips with the seemingly bewildering range of trees requires a classification framework. Based on shared features due to common descent, plants and animals are classified by biologists into larger units, one of which is the family. Identifying the family to which an unknown organism belongs is one of the first steps towards establishing its species. By knowing the family, many other possible species can be eliminated and the search for a name becomes more directed. It is easier to conceptualize animal families than plant families, because the identifying differences can often be seen in the shape of the whole organism. (Think, for example, of bird families such as doves, parrots, owls or sunbirds.) This, however, is not the case with trees. Tree families are based on less obvious features that involve details of flowers, fruit, anatomy and chemistry. With few exceptions (the palm family is one) it is not possible to recognize a tree family purely from the shape of its trees.

To compensate for the limitations posed by family recognition, we offer an alternative, more practical approach. Based on easy-to-observe stem and leaf features, 43 tree groups are recognized. These 'groups-of-convenience' might not be natural entities, as is the case with families, but their advantage lies in the fact that they are much easier to identify than formal botanical families. An additional benefit is that they allow the construction of a simple pictorial representation of the principal characters of each group in the form of an icon. These icons make it considerably easier for beginners to conceptualize the observed tree diversity. As your familiarity with trees increases, you will find it easy to recognize some of the widespread tree families.

Identifying an unknown organism, or confirming the identity of a familiar one, is part of the enjoyment of nature. It is also an essential activity, as a name is the key with which all that is known about the organism can be retrieved from the literature or the Internet. It is our hope that this book will further a general understanding of trees and inspire more individuals to take on the challenges of tree identification and, in so doing, increase awareness of the wonderful world of trees.

*How to Identify Trees in Southern Africa* has been prepared to complement the authors' *Field Guide to Trees of Southern Africa*; we strongly recommend that you acquire the latter and use it in conjunction with this book.

BRAAM VAN WYK
PIET VAN WYK
Pretoria, February 2006

*Bauhinia galpinii*: flowers

# Contents

*Albizia anthelmintica* [wormbark false-thorn; wurmbasvalsdoring].

# PART 2: TREE GROUPS  56–169

# PART 1

## PRINCIPLES OF TREE IDENTIFICATION

*To begin the process of identifying trees, it is necessary to understand how a tree is constructed, and to be familiar with the terminology used to record and interpret tree characters. This section presents an illustrated overview of the most important characters used in tree classification and identification. It also offers tips on how to handle samples of tree material gathered for identification purposes.*

**Above** *Rothmannia capensis* [false-gardenia; valskatjiepiering]: flower.
**Left** *Adansonia digitata* [baobab; kremetart].

# Our animal impediment

Most people find it easier to identify animals than plants. Perhaps this is because we are animals ourselves, whereas plants are a completely different form of life. Our approach towards the world, including biology, is clearly animal-centred (zoocentric), resulting in us having an 'animal impediment' governing the way we look at plants. The fact that trees are anchored in one place, and do not show active movement or produce noises makes it difficult for us to think of them as living beings. Yet they have all the senses we normally associate with animals; in their own special way plants can see, taste, smell, hear, feel and communicate. Being fixed in place, plants have to confront adversity instead of fleeing from it, as animals are inclined to do.

Traditionally, the notion of intelligence has rarely been applied to plants. Their responses to external stimuli were seen as progammed, not made by choice. However, the newly emerging scientific field of plant neurobiology depicts plants as intelligent, social organisms possessing complex forms of communication and information processing. Since biology as a field of study is largely founded on animals, including humans, many aspects of plant 'behaviour'(a term to which some people object) remain poorly understood, but it is important that we should not judge plant behaviour and intelligence in human terms, but within the framework of the capability of each organism.

Because of our natural animal-centred disposition, when it comes to plants we tend to search for the same type of identification clues as those we instinctively respond to when identifying fellow members of our own species or other animal species. As the old saying goes: 'We are prone to see what lies behind our eyes rather than what appears before them'. But plants are constructed very differently from animals, and understanding this fact helps considerably to make tree identification easier. One must learn how to look at plants.

Our animal-orientated recognition approach is partly inborn and partly acquired through learning. It is probably correct to claim that most children grow up in an environment where our biological

*Acacia sieberiana* var. *woodii* [paperbark thorn, paperbark acacia (Z); papierbasdoring] has the umbrella-shaped canopy characteristic of many African savanna trees. (Regional common tree names are reflected as follows: SA: South Africa; N: Namibia; Z: Zimbabwe; see p65.)

identification skills are heavily focused on animals, resulting in our natural inclination to recognize animals being reinforced. However, in societies where children learn from an early age to distinguish different plants, plant identification becomes almost as easy as animal identification.

Whereas some aspects of our evolutionary past may hinder our ability to identify trees, other facets of this inheritance may be at the root of our innate propensity to emotionally affiliate with nature in general, and trees in particular, a phenomenon termed biophilia. Given enough time, aspects of the evolutionary history of an organism are written into its genes.

Evidence points to sub-Saharan Africa as being the Cradle of Humanity. The question can be asked whether anything in contemporary human behaviour reflects our interaction with the environment during our comparatively brief history on the planet. Some students of human behaviour claim they can identify behavioural patterns in people today that most probably reflect the conditions of their ancient environment. As far as plants are concerned, perhaps the most interesting indication is the almost universal preference humans have for the savanna-type landscape and for trees that have a relatively low, layered, spreading, umbrella-shaped canopy.

## The tallest, largest and oldest trees

Trees currently hold three important records among living organisms.

**Tallest:** *Sequoia sempervirens* [coast redwood]. Evergreen conifer, living for up to 2 000 years. The tallest, named 'Hyperion', measuring 115.55 m, was discovered in Redwood National Park, California, in 2006. Due to physical constraints in raising water to the leaves, tree height is unlikely to exceed 130 m.

**Largest volume:** *Sequoiadendron giganteum* [sierra redwood]. An evergreen conifer, able to live for up to 3 200 years. In terms of total volume, the largest tree is the 'General Sherman', in Sequoia National Park, California. It has a volume of 1 473 m³ (trunk only), a height of 83.6 m, a base circumference of 31.27 m and a diameter at chest height of 8.25 m. Sierra redwoods are confined to the Sierra Nevada Mountains.

**Oldest** (nonclonal): *Pinus longaeva* [great basin bristlecone pine]. A relatively small, stunted conifer with a gnarled stem, up to 16 m high. The oldest living tree, nicknamed 'Methuselah', grows in the White Mountains, California. It is at least 4 789 years old.

[Source: Gymnosperm Database – www.conifers.org]

*Sequoiadendron giganteum* [sierra redwood], the largest tree species in terms of total volume, is confined to California.

# Plants and their three basic organs

Understanding the form and external components of plants is essential for tree identification. Here we adopt the classic view that a plant has only three basic organs: roots, stems and leaves (see opposite). These three organs correspond to the three fundamental functional units required by plants to exist as self-sustaining (autotrophic) life forms. Roots anchor the plant to one spot, absorb water and minerals from the soil, and store nutrients. Leaves produce food from sunlight and carbon dioxide. Stems carry the leaves, direct them through growth towards the light and act as a conduit between the leaves and the roots.

Each organ is an extremely flexible unit that, through evolution, can change its form substantially to assume functions that are often quite different from the basic ones. Therefore, the seemingly bewildering variety of forms seen in plants are merely developments and modifications of these three organs and their parts. A flower, for example, is a shortened stem with determinate growth and whorls of highly modified leaves, the whole forming a functional unit aimed at sexual reproduction.

Perhaps the greatest difficulty experienced by budding tree watchers is to correctly identify stems and leaves. Roots are rarely used in tree identification, hence they will not receive much attention, but stems and leaves are very important and their structure and variety of forms are considered in more detail further on. Here we explain and illustrate the key features that define roots, stems and leaves.

## Root

An axis, usually below ground, that lacks nodes and internodes and does not carry leaves. A root increases in length due to the growth activities of a group of actively dividing cells (apical meristem) at the root tip. The root's apical meristem is protected by a covering of cells, called the root cap (calyptra), which is usually not visible to the naked eye.

The outer cells of the root cap produce a slimy substance (mucigel) that is important in lubricating the root's passage through the soil. Root hairs, which develop from the surface of young roots, last for one to three days and form part of the complex environment surrounding the root (rhizosphere).

## Stem

An axis, usually above ground, that has nodes and internodes and carries leaves. A node is the region on the stem where leaves are attached. An internode is the portion of stem between successive nodes. Shoots are composed of stems and leaves, the stems being the axis of the shoot. A stem increases in length due to the growth activities of a group of actively dividing cells (apical meristem) at its tip.

The stem's apical meristem, or growing point, is usually protected by developing young leaves and is easy to identify with the naked eye. An undeveloped stem containing the embryonic meristem is called a bud; it is often enclosed by bud scales, these being modified leaves that are specialized for the protection of resting buds.

## Leaf

A usually green, more or less flattened structure formed at a node as a lateral outgrowth of a stem. It commonly consists of a blade and petiole. The upper angle between the leaf and the stem on which it is carried is called the leaf axil. A leaf carries in its axil at least one axillary bud. In seed plants, leaves do not have a distinct apical meristem (although this is present in ferns, at least in young leaves), hence they do not have the potential to grow in length from the tip, as roots and stems do. Growth in size is by cell divisions that occur throughout the entire young expanding blade (lamina). All leaves have a limited, determinate size; they do not expand indefinitely. The axillary bud is an undeveloped stem. On any particular shoot some axillary buds may be resting (dormant), while others may already have developed into new stems with leaves (side shoots).

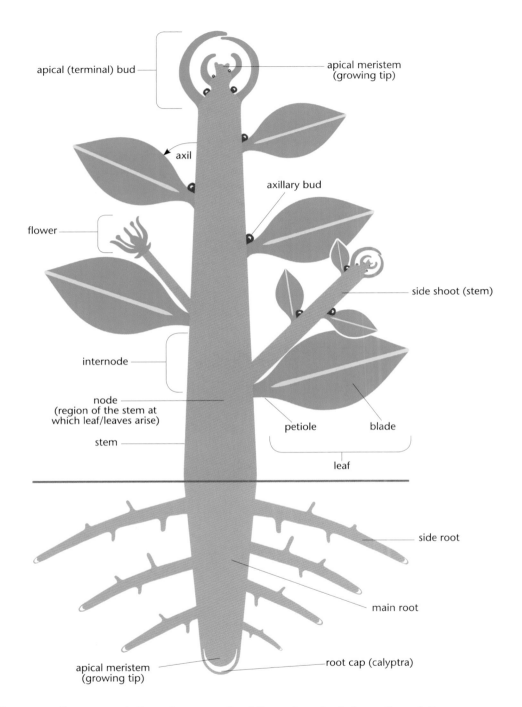

apical (terminal) bud

apical meristem
(growing tip)

axil

axillary bud

flower

side shoot (stem)

internode

node
(region of the stem at
which leaf/leaves arise)

petiole

blade

stem

leaf

side root

main root

apical meristem
(growing tip)

root cap (calyptra)

This diagrammatic representation of a generalized flowering plant shows the relative position of the three basic organs: root, stem and leaf. The flower is a modified stem with highly specialized leaves. Resting apical meristems (axillary buds) are shown in dark green.

# The tree as life form

The concept of a tree is a popular rather than a scientific one. In southern Africa, the term 'tree' is usually applied to any perennial, woody plant growing to a height of at least 2 m. Although typically a tree has a single trunk and a distinct canopy, it may be multistemmed. The term 'shrub' is widely applied to multistemmed, woody plants usually reaching a maximum height of about 2 m. However, in our region, the distinction between a shrub and a tree often breaks down in practice.

Regular outbreaks of fire are a natural phenomenon in many local vegetation types, resulting in otherwise proper trees often being maintained as multistemmed shrubs for years, if not permanently. Furthermore, over half the subcontinent is semi-desert or desert, with trees from these regions tending to be generally smaller and multistemmed. Moreover, all proper trees are less than 2 m tall when young and, at that stage, many are shrub-like. There is no way a beginner can tell whether a shrub is a proper shrub or a shrubby version of what could potentially become a tree later on. Hence the tendency has been for tree books to adopt a broad concept of what constitutes a tree and to include not only species that are technically closer to shrubs, but also robust, woody climbers.

Energy from the sun is essential for the existence of plants and animals. Plants take their energy directly from the sun, whereas animals obtain it indirectly, via plants. In a sense, plants 'eat' sunlight, together with carbon dioxide, water and minerals (a process called photosynthesis). The tree growth form (see below) probably evolved as a means to intercept sunlight before it reaches competing plants. In any environment, outgrowing and over-shadowing the competition must impart a distinct advantage to the tallest plants.

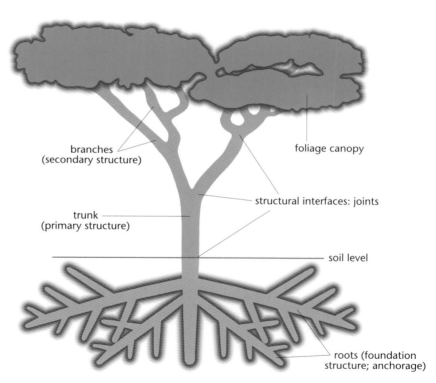

**A typical tree showing the main structural features that combine to provide an efficient and strong support system for a canopy of leaves. Mechanically, the interfaces between the foundation, primary and secondary structures constitute the structural joints, which connect all the different load-carrying elements. The red glow depicts the large external surface through which 'food' is absorbed. Trees have a relatively small volume compared with their vast external surface which interfaces with both the aerial and underground environments.**

*Olea europaea* subsp. *africana* [wild olive (N, SA); african olive (Z); olienhout]. Typical tree shape with a distinct trunk and canopy. The even height of the canopy from the ground, known as a browse line, is due to the removal of stems and foliage by cattle.

The earliest-known modern tree form, that of *Archaeopteris*, a type of tree fern, appeared about 370 million years ago. The canopy of a tree can be likened to a large solar panel for capturing sunlight. The intensity of the radiant energy from the sun that arrives on earth is rather weak. Photosynthesis is not very efficient in capturing this energy. Plants therefore need a large surface area relative to their volume to optimize solar absorption; they also have to capture energy continuously during daylight hours. Moving large surfaces is cumbersome and this may be one of the reasons why plants adopted a stationary way of life. In essence, plants are small volumes with vast external surfaces. Animals, on the other hand, are large volumes with small external surfaces, but vast internal (digestive; breathing) surfaces.

To be large, long-lived and fixed to the ground comes at a cost. A tree must build a structure using the least amount of self-produced material, yet be sufficiently strong to withstand the forces of nature it will encounter during its lifetime, wind being one of the most significant. From an engineering point of view, trees are marvels of structural efficiency. Various features combine to become a very efficient support system to the heavy canopy of leaves. Wood, the main structural material, is ideally suited for this purpose and, at the same time, it provides other functions such as water transport.

Engineers have shown that trees adjust their growth in response to the stresses produced by mechanical loading. Structural features, such as trunk diameter, branch pattern, angles between branches, relative length and thickness of stems and root features are not coincidental, but optimized to reduce stress and minimize the chance of breaking or uprooting. Even the shape and construction of leaves is mechanically optimized to keep the upper surface facing towards the sunlight, despite wind-bending moments.

> It has been estimated that for a tree 40 m high, the external surface area is about one hectare above ground and 130 hectares below ground. The internal leaf surface, which allows gas exchange with the atmosphere through the stomata, would be about 30 hectares, giving the tree a total surface of exchange with the environment of 160 hectares!
> [From Hallé 2002: 44.]

# Trees as modular organisms

Tree identification becomes a bit easier if you understand the differences in the way plants and animals are constructed. In most animals the form, or outline, of the organism is highly determinate. The animal's size may change considerably as it grows, yet the basic form stays essentially the same. Organisms in which the body plan is fixed are called unitary organisms. Not only is the outline of the animal fixed, but also the number and position of organs. A mammal always has one heart, two kidneys, one brain and two eyes, for example.

If shape does change during growth, such as when a caterpillar turns into a butterfly, it happens in a highly fixed and predictable way. Growth in animals stops once a species-specific size has been reached. This is called determinate growth. If an animal accidentally loses a part of its body, the missing tissues and organs usually cannot be replaced, at least in most higher animals.

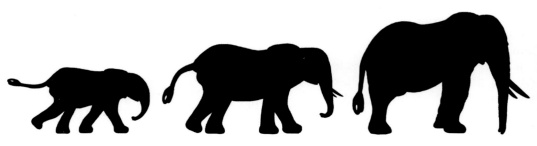

Young elephant                                              Mature elephant

**Unitary organisms, for example mammals, have a highly fixed mature form. Growth proceeds by a determined pathway of development from birth to adulthood and comes to an end when the organism reaches its final form.**

Young tree                                                    Old tree

**Modular organisms, for example plants, do not have a fixed mature form. Plants continue to grow for as long as they live. The outline of trees changes constantly throughout their lifetime. Branches may be lost by natural pruning, as well as through diseases, fires and storms.**

Plants differ fundamentally from most animals in that the form or outline of the whole organism is flexible, not fixed. Growth in plants is not due to an increase in size of a predetermined body form, but involves the repeated addition of component parts, almost in the fashion of stringing together many similar building blocks (see opposite). Each unit of construction is called a module, hence plants are described as modular organisms. Unlike animals, plants continue to grow for as long as they live. This is called indeterminate growth. Shoots are constructed of a series of modules, each consisting of a section of stem, one or more leaves and their associated axillary buds.

The modules themselves increase in size while retaining their shape, as if they are distinct individuals in the sense of unitary animals, even though they are genetically identical. Following the addition of each new module, elongation of its internode results in some lengthening of the shoot, but once the module has fully increased in size, the shoot cannot be lengthened further unless a new module is added by the growing tip. (The stem of the module can increase in girth with age, but this is a different story; see p39.) Although a module's size increase happens within limits, it is under a much stronger influence of the environment than in the case of unitary animals (see p18). Occasionally, the plant will produce temporary, highly specialized reproductive modules, called flowers, which are subsequently shed after developing into fruit.

Indeterminate growth in plants is possible because they retain some unspecialized embryonic cells in the form of meristems that never mature (apical meristems and axillary buds, for example, see p11). If a plant accidentally loses a part of its body, it can easily replace the damaged part by adding new modules. In fact, a plant can lose a substantial part of its body without dying. A tree can be chopped down to ground level and still be able to survive. If such drastic damage was inflicted on a unitary animal it would certainly die!

Indeed, a plant may be interpreted as being a community of many similar organisms, each comprising a module. This explains why small stem cuttings, comprising one or two modules, or even a graft of a single axillary bud, can develop into a whole new plant.

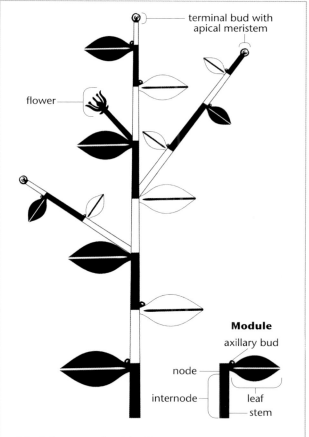

**Modular growth: this diagrammatic representation of a tree shoot depicts the individual modules. Modular organisms, such as plants and corals, do not have a fixed mature form; instead, they grow by means of an ongoing process in which modules are added step by step to the existing structure.**

Clearly, modular organisms are ideally suited to a sedentary form of life. Some sedentary animals are also modular and behave very much like plants, the best known example being the corals.

But how does the distinction between unitary animals and modular plants relate to tree identification? In unitary animals, shape remains fairly constant throughout growth and development. Not surprisingly, visual recognition in insects and higher animals relies heavily on shape, colour patterns and postural displays. Just a silhouette outline of an animal is often sufficient to elicit a recognition (identification) response (see box on p17).

Humans, true to their animal nature, mainly use shape and colour to identify objects. Thanks to their fixed shape, size and colour, clues by which to identify animals are learned almost intuitively. In bird identification, for example, silhouette diagrams depicting general shape and posture are often sufficient to identify major bird families (see p16).

The general impression a bird makes is known as its 'recognizing jizz' and its importance for bird identification is widely acknowledged. If additional details, such as shape and especially colour, are added, most birds can be readily identified from a distance with the help of a good field guide.

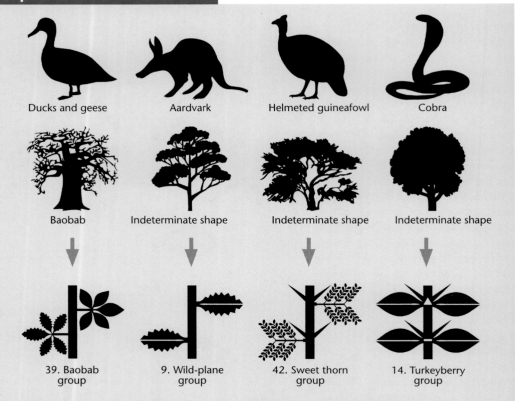

Ducks and geese | Aardvark | Helmeted guineafowl | Cobra

Baobab | Indeterminate shape | Indeterminate shape | Indeterminate shape

39. Baobab group | 9. Wild-plane group | 42. Sweet thorn group | 14. Turkeyberry group

**In the case of animals, the shape of an organism is often enough to identify species, genera or families. In contrast, tree shape is not very useful for identifying species or families (with a few exceptions, such as baobabs and palms). However, placing the emphasis on the modular construction of the plant (bottom row), makes it easier to identify a tree as one of the 43 groups promoted in this book.**

The considerable significance of colour in identification by humans becomes evident when confronted with some of those small nondescript birds with plumage colours in various tones and shades of brown, for example many cisticolas, larks and pipits. Known affectionately as 'LB Js' or 'little brown jobs', identification of species in this group is a challenge, even to the experienced birder, although habitat, calls and flight displays may provide useful additional identification clues.

Now let's look at trees as objects for identification. Being modular organisms, trees do not have a fixed shape. In fact, even among the same species no two trees have exactly the same outline. Yet, what many budding tree watchers hope to find in a field guide is a pictorial image of the growth form of specific trees. If trees of a single species don't all have the same shape, then what are we to use as the 'typical' image for the species?

Unlike animals, growth form is of limited importance when it comes to identifying an unfamiliar tree. The vast majority of trees are nondescript in outline and almost all trees come in various shades of green and brown. In the bird world, the frustrating 'LBJs' may be in the minority, but among trees their counterparts are in the majority! (A few trees, such as the quiver tree, baobab, natal strelitzia and wild datepalm, have easily recognizable growth forms and can be identified from a silhouette, but these are the exceptions.) Occasionally a tree will produce showy, colourful flowers that can be identified from afar, like red coraltrees or purple jacarandas, but trees with such glorious mass displays are rare, and their flowering times are brief. More often, at any one time, the majority of trees in an area will either be without flowers, or their flowers will be small and inconspicuous.

To become competent in tree identification requires a mental change: to scale down one's natural inclination towards using the whole tree shape as the primary identification criterion. Not that shape is completely useless, though. *After* a tree has been identified, the colour and texture of the foliage are the two most important attributes to utilize to form a search image for scanning the surrounding vegetation for other individuals of the same species. Growth form may also come in useful for this purpose, and can be taken into account as one's familiarity with a species increases although, in many cases, familiarity may be due more to colour and texture than to outline.

Seeing that, in most cases, the shape of the whole tree is not very helpful for initial identification, and that trees are usually not in flower when encountered, is there any resolution? One practical approach is to focus on the features of the vegetative module that are usually present. Next to flowers and fruit, the leaves and stem are the parts of a tree that most closely display the degree of constancy of form found in animals. By using leaf and stem features as a first step towards identifying trees, you can avoid the unreliability of having to consider the whole tree form for the purpose of identification (see box on opposite page).

Among the ± 2 100 species of southern African trees we have, for convenience, defined 43 groups in which the vegetative modules are more or less similar in form. Identifying the group to which a tree belongs is the first in a series of steps to try and identify a particular tree or species by using a process of elimination. The steps involved are explained on pp22 and 23.

*Cussonia spicata* [cabbagetree]. Large palmately compound leaves make this species easy to identify from a distance.

## Perceptions of shape

In a famous experiment, Dutch animal behaviourist and Nobel Prize laureate, Niko Tinbergen, showed that birds will flee if a hawk silhouette is displayed overhead.

A hawk-like model was used to test birds in their reaction to the direction of movement of a silhouette. When the model is moved to the right it evokes an escape response, indicated by a '+' sign. Moving the model to the left does not stimulate escape, indicated by a '–' sign. The characteristics that are important in the birds' identification of hawks are the wing shape, the long tail, and the short neck. Silhouettes of birds without these specific characters do not elicit escape (after Tinbergen 1951).

Fellow animal behavourist, Austrian Konrad Lorentz, has further shown that shape is important in a phenomenon called imprinting. When ducklings and goslings follow their parents the young birds became responsive to certain characteristics of the adults, one of which is their shape. Lorentz, who shared the Nobel Prize with Tinbergen, showed that these newly hatched birds would follow other objects (including humans) if their parents were not available. Young ducklings raised with other species would direct their courtship behaviour towards the foster species rather than their own species.

# Variation and plasticity

If we examine carefully a group of trees of any species it is soon clear that not all individuals are alike. Hence a feature of tree descriptions is the copious use of words such as 'usually', 'mostly', 'mainly', 'often', 'rarely', 'sometimes' or 'occasionally'. These descriptors are used to indicate frequency and abundance, but reflect one of the frustrating properties of plants in general and trees in particular – their great variability. Not only must the tree watcher deal with the lack of a fixed outline, but also the fact that within the same species individuals can differ considerably from one another, particularly in certain leaf and stem features. With trees, it is therefore important to adopt a broad, flexible concept of a particular species. Three main differences between individuals can be distinguished: developmental, environmentally induced, and intrinsic.

## Developmental variation

Developmental (ontogenetic) variation refers to the differences between young and old individuals. The transition from juvenile to mature stages in trees represents the unfolding of a developmental programme that is genetically determined. There is a tendency for juvenile leaves to be larger and more strongly toothed; in the case of trees with compound leaves, they can even be simple (see below).

Young plants of spinous species often tend to have more and longer spines. In general, mature growth should be used to establish stem and leaf characters. Be aware, though, that coppice growth at the base of a tree often displays juvenile characters; if possible, also look at material from the canopy.

## Environmentally induced variation

Also referred to as 'phenotypic plasticity', this is the most commonly encountered type of variation found in trees. It is a feature of all plants and forms one of the more striking behavioural differences that occur between plants and animals.

The seed of a plant does not have control over where it lands. Likewise, mature plants are fixed to one spot and cannot move away to avoid stress conditions. To compensate for these 'limitations', plants have acquired the ability to change their growth pattern and shape to best cope with their local conditions.

In juvenile plants of *Adansonia digitata* [baobab; kremetart] the leaves are simple, entire or toothed (A), quite unlike the palmately compound leaves with their entire-margined leaflets of mature individuals (B).

Leaflets of young plants of *Sclerocarya birrea* subsp. *caffra* [marula; maroela] have toothed margins (A), whereas in mature plants they are entire (B); an example of developmental variation.

Plasticity responses are a natural consequence of plants' modular growth and construction (see p14) because this permits them to respond to environmental changes through adjustments in the type and placement of new organs. If a module is added whilst the plant is in the shade, for example, the internodes may be long and the leaves large. However, if a similar module is added later, when the same plant is in the full sun, its internodes may be much shorter and the leaves smaller.

Size, shape and the composition of the module may also be influenced by environmental factors, such as the availability of water, air temperature, prevailing winds, soil type or browsing by animals. These changes can be reversed if the environmental conditions change or if the individual tree is transplanted to another environment.

## Intrinsic variation

In trees, as in all sexually reproductive organisms, individuals of a particular species can differ genetically. Genetic differences are not influenced by changes in the environment and will remain constant even if the tree is transplanted to another environment. In other words, this is not a case of temporary environmentally induced plasticity.

A common example of intrinsic variation is the difference in floral colour among individuals of the same species. If a species has a wide geographical range, it is inevitable for individuals to be subjected to different environmental conditions. Some outlying populations may also become genetically isolated. Over a long period, distinct best-adapted local forms will evolve through natural selection. Differences between these local forms are genetically fixed and some populations may eventually develop into separate species. Genetically distinct local forms are referred to as ecotypes.

The differences are retained even when the forms are grown together in a garden (unlike in the case of variants resulting from phenotypic plasticity). If differences between ecotypes are marked and there is some discontinuity in variation, they may be formally recognized as a subspecies or variety of a species (see below).

Plants of *Ekebergia capensis* [cape-ash (SA); dogplum (Z); essenhout] from the Eastern Cape have stout stems and relatively small leaves with a slightly winged rachis (see photo A), whereas plants from the northern parts of its range (see photo B) have more slender stems and larger leaves with a cylindrical rachis. These differences are retained even if both forms are grown together in a garden; an example of inherent genetically-fixed variation.

# Tree classification

The species is the basic unit of classification. Recognizably distinct individuals that form intergrading, interfertile populations constitute the different kinds or species of trees. In nature, species usually do not interbreed, thus ensuring that each maintains a distinct identity.

The great diversity of trees necessitates some form of classification system to help us remember their characters and properties. Horticulturists, for example, may want to classify tree species according to size, foliage colour, or whether they are evergreen or deciduous; whereas a carpenter may group species according to the properties of their wood. This type of special-purpose classification, where only one or a few characters are used to define groups, is called an artificial classification system. Groups formed in this way are useful to predict the properties used in their construction, but in other characters the members of the group may show considerable diversity because they are not necessarily closely related in an evolutionary sense.

Botanical classifications aim to reflect the presumed evolutionary history of species. They are general-purpose classification systems aimed at a wide range of users. For this purpose, all available biological evidence is taken into account, and species are grouped into an ascending series of successively larger and wider categories, ultimately arriving at a single, all-embracing group covering all plants. Such systems are called hierarchical classifications and the technical term for any of the groups is a taxon. Each level in the hierarchy is a rank. These classifications are more natural and their predictive power is high because closely related species or higher taxa have many characters in common.

For example, species are grouped into genera, genera into families, families into orders, orders into classes and so forth until one reaches the all-embracing Kingdom Plantae. The two most frequently used ranks above species are that of genus and family. A family name is derived from one of its constituent genera and takes the ending '-ceae'. A species may contain genetically distinct subpopulations of individuals that are not yet sufficiently differentiated and reproductively isolated to be considered full species. For such entities, a number of subcategories are available under the rank of species, for example subspecies, variety and forma.

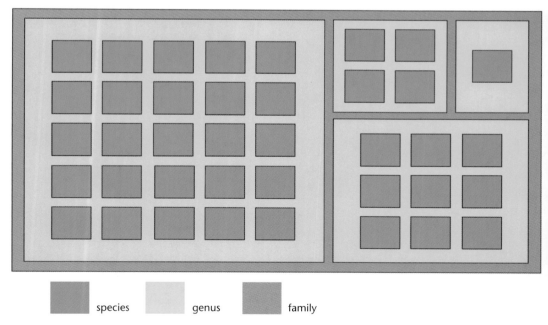

species    genus    family

**Diagrammatic box-within-box presentation of an hierarchical classification of 39 species. At each level one or more groups (taxa) are combined into a single group at the next higher level, this higher group being defined by the sum of the characters of all its subordinate groups. A genus with a single species (upper right-hand one) is called a monotypic genus.**

Naming a tree should not be seen as an end in itself, but as a means towards an end. The species name of a tree is the key with which one can retrieve from the literature or the Internet all the available knowledge on the particular species. Moreover, if the genus, family or other higher category to which a tree belongs is known, one can already infer a great deal of information about it by predicting the possible presence of the characteristics used to define the particular higher taxon. For example, if one knows that a plant belongs to the family Meliaceae [mahogany family; mahoniefamilie], one can predict that it most probably is woody, has alternate compound leaves, flowers with five free petals, stamens fused into a tube, a superior ovary, secretory cells in its tissues and limonoids (bitter-tasting chemical compounds with therapeutic and insecticidal effects).

Normally the first step in identifying an unknown plant is to establish its family. Diagnostic characters of families rely heavily on the morphology of the flowers, fruit and seed, but anatomy and chemistry are also important. In the case of flowers, family recognition is the obvious approach for beginners because flowers are usually noticed at the time of flowering. Unfortunately, this approach is not very practical when it comes to trees, which are conspicuous whether or not they are in flower; in any event, the greatest number of trees are without flowers most of the time. Furthermore, the diagnostic characters of many predominantly woody plant families are rather cryptic and technical. (The last few years have also seen adjustments in the way several large tree families have traditionally been demarcated and this process is continuing.)

In view of the practical limitations of the family approach for the identification of trees in the field, we have classified native trees into 43 artificial groups based on easy-to-observe vegetative features. More obvious leaf and stem features are not always a reliable indication of close relationships because similar vegetative features have evolved repeatedly and independently in unrelated groups of plants. Nevertheless, some of these artificial groups do happen to correspond largely to one or a few families. We strongly recommend that beginners take note of the family to which a species belongs. With experience, and as one's knowledge of trees grows, the ability to recognize certain families will develop.

# How to look at trees and use a field guide

Conventional reference books, such as *Field Guide to Trees of Southern Africa* (see p179), work on the principle that they provide some device to assist in finding the name of a tree, bird or other animal. These devices usually take the form of a key, consisting of a number of paired statements or choices (leads), and one must decide which of two (or more) statements best fits the plant in hand. The longer the key, the more choices you have to make and the greater the chance that you may go astray; only one incorrect answer and you are on the wrong track. It is customary to present the easier choices early on and keep the more difficult ones for later. Ultimately, the keys will lead you to groups, families, genera or species, by means of which to identify your tree or animal.

Unlike other tree books, which arrange trees according to family, the approach promoted in this book is to first classify the tree into one of 43 artificial groups based on easy-to-observe vegetative (stem and leaf) characters. Most of these characters are the primary ones used in all tree identification books.

These groups are called 'artificial' because they are groups-of-convenience and do not necessarily group together related plants, as families would do. A guide to bridge the gap between groups and families is provided on p170, thus allowing you to use the advantages of the group-recognition method in conjunction with other tree books. By using the relatively simple Key to the Groups (pp58–61), you will gain confidence in the use of the often more-daunting keys found in other publications.

In this book, each of the 43 groups has been allocated an icon (pictorial representation) that depicts the outstanding morphological features of the group. These icons are meant to help you remember the key vegetative features of a tree. Each group has also been assigned a name and a number. The names are derived from either an outstanding feature of the group, or from one species, or a group of species (genus), that are members of that particular group.

Although usually not explained as such, most keys work on the principle that they initially lead one to identify the type of modular construction unit that makes up the tree (see p15). In a way, the icons used to characterize Groups 4–43 can be seen as depicting the form of a tree's modular units.

### Looking beyond the obvious

When beginners look at a tree they tend to notice the obvious features, such as growth form, flowers, fruit, bark structure, leaf colour, leaf size and shape. While these characters are useful in identifying the species, most are too general to assist in identifying the group. The secret is to analyze the tree systematically, with the aim of arriving at an icon depicting its basic modular construction. Initially you will need to use the keys on pp59–61 to understand how the groups are defined and how the icons are put together. With experience, it should be possible to only look at the Quick Guide on the inside back cover in order to identify the icon and group applicable to your tree.

Identifying an unknown tree is a process. Like a detective, one has to gather the evidence, after which it is examined and analyzed. The fundamental items of evidence (information) are called characters. Other words used for the same thing include characteristic, feature, property or attribute. When observed, characters are seen to have various states; for example, the states of 'leaf arrangement' might be 'alternate', 'opposite' and 'whorled'.

The best place to start trying to identify trees is in a natural (wilderness) area. Many of the trees found in urban environments are from other parts of the world and few have been incorporated into local field guides. It is important to accept from the beginning that identifying trees is not nearly as straightforward as identifying mammals and birds. With the immense diversity of trees in southern Africa and the inherent limitations of any field guide, it is unrealistic to always expect identification to species level. In many cases, this is simply not possible. For example, flowers and fruit are often required for species recognition, but these may not be present at the time you are looking at the tree. Aim to at least identify the broad group to which the tree belongs; working this out is a challenge in itself and can be quite fun.

### Useful field equipment

- **Notebook and pencil for making sketches and taking notes.**
- **10x hand lens or good magnifying glass.** Useful to check for secretory cavities, stipules and other small objects on the plant material.
- **Binoculars to identify leaf features, flowers and fruit in the canopy of tall trees.** These can also be used as a magnifying glass if reversed and looked through the 'wrong' end.
- **Small, sharp secateurs.**
- **Sturdy plastic bags to collect plant material for later study** (use white or transparent bags, as black plastic becomes too hot in the sun). Plant material enclosed in a plastic bag with a little water can last for several days if kept in a cool, shady place. Never leave bags in direct sunlight. **Note:** Always collect shoots with several leaves attached so you can later check leaf arrangement, stipules and stem characteristics.

### Identifying the group

On p58 you will find more information on how the group key works. When you encounter an unknown tree, start by recording those characters on which the groups are based. By working through the key you will soon become familiar with the characters to look for.

The first three groups are based on obvious and easily established criteria, including succulence, distinctive growth form or unusual leaf morphology. The remainder of the groups are based on a combination of various vegetative features, that are here referred to as the primary diagnostic characters (pp24–37).

## Three-point ID check

This ID check is intended for use with *Field Guide to Trees of Southern Africa*; for guidelines on how to use the group recognition approach with other tree books see p170.
1. Identify the group by using the Quick Guide on the inside back cover or the Key (see pp58–61). Verify the group's identification by checking that it agrees with the concise statement of diagnostic characters at the start of each group treatment. Take account of any special notes and cross-references.
2. Using the distribution maps, compare your tree with the photographs of only those species likely to occur in the area from which your plant comes.
3. Once you have found a picture that seems to match your tree, compare it carefully with the accompanying description. Pay particular attention to the **diagnostic characters** highlighted in bold.

Establishing most of the primary characters requires physical handling of the plant material. This is not a task that can be performed from a distance, and it won't be possible to obtain all the required evidence from, for example, tall forest trees or trees in a game reserve where one is not allowed to leave the vehicle. However, if you do have access to the tree, look at a leafy shoot and systematically perform the following checks:

- **Leaf type: is the leaf simple or compound (p24)?**
- **Leaf arrangement (p26).**
- **Leaf colour: are there differences between the upper and lower surface (p27)?**
- **Venation: this is relevant especially when the leaf is 3- or more-veined from the base (p28).**
- **Secretory cavities: are these present or absent (p29)?**
- **Bacterial nodules: are these absent or present; what is their form and arrangement (p30)?**
- **Hairiness of the leaf blade (p31).**
- **Leaf or leaflet margin: is it entire or variously toothed (p32)?**
- **Stipules: are they absent or present and, if so, what type are they (p33)?**
- **Spines/thorns: absence or presence, type and arrangement (p35).**
- **Latex: is this present and if so, what colour is it (p36)?**

Successfully completing this round of evidence-gathering should result in a first identification: that of the group to which the tree belongs. Knowing the group serves as a summary of the most important vegetative features of the tree and eliminates trees with other combinations of characters. Once a group has been keyed out (selected as the likely one), verify the identification by consulting the outline of group characters on p62 and the summarized treatment of that particular group (see pp66–169). Here you will find examples of typical trees, as well as useful information on members of the group. Do not worry about species identification at this stage; rather, hone your skills to identify the groups and, in the process, gain experience and confidence in the use of identification characters.

For actual species identification you will need a copy of *Field Guide to Trees of Southern Africa* (see p179) which treats the more commonly encountered species in our region. To identify a species additional, more specific characters are required, here referred to as secondary diagnostic characters (see pp38–55). Study the various sources of secondary characters to become aware of what to focus on when gathering evidence from trees. Note whether the tree is in flower or fruit, as this can be very useful when comparing it with illustrations in a book. Characters like domatia and external glands (extrafloral nectaries) are easily overlooked but they can be very useful for species recognition.

The best non-morphological (non-structural) tree character to use for eliminating possibilities is geographical distribution. Only compare the tree you are examining with those species likely to occur in the same area from which your plant comes.

# Simple and compound leaves

Leaf type is the most useful vegetative character for recognizing tree groups. Make sure you know the definition of a leaf (p10); leaves are typically green, expanded and the most obvious photosynthetic organ of most trees. They are borne at nodes and initially carry at least one axillary bud in the angle between the point of leaf attachment and the stem. Unlike stems, leaves do not have an apical meristem (growing tip). Axillary buds are undeveloped shoots and, in the case of older leaves, instead of a bud there is often a side shoot or its modification, such as a spine, inflorescence or flower, in the leaf axil.

For tree identification, it is crucial to be able to distinguish between simple leaves, the different types of compound leaves and between leaves and leaflets (pinnae or pinnulae).

**Simple leaves**  A leaf typically consists of a petiole (stalk) and a flattened blade (lamina). Leaves with the blade undivided are called simple leaves. The blade may be deeply divided into lobes (bilobed leaves) but since the blade remains a single entity, such leaves are still simple. A distinct basal or apical swelling of the petiole is known as a pulvinus and is particularly common in the legumes. Stipules are small scale- or leaf-like appendages at the base of the petiole in some plants. They are part of the leaf and are usually found in pairs. Stipules are very useful for identification and will be receiving more attention on p33.

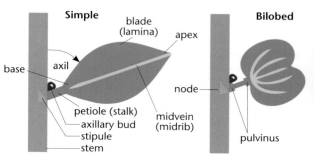

**Compound leaves: pinnately compound**  A leaf in which the divisions of the blade or lamina are completely separate is a compound leaf. Below, we depict a hypothetical sequence of events showing how a pinnately compound leaf is derived through evolution from a simple leaf with pinnate venation (in this example without stipules). What remains of the original midrib is an axis reminiscent of a stem. It is called a rachis because it lacks an apical meristem as well as true nodes and internodes, as is the case of stems. Likewise, the resultant leaf-like divisions are called leaflets (pinnae; singular pinna; Latin: *pinna* = feather) because they lack an axillary bud and are not inserted on a stem, hence they do not comply with the definition of a leaf. The stalk of a leaflet is a petiolule. Pinnate or pinnately compound refers to a compound leaf whose leaflets are arranged in two rows along the rachis. If a pinnate leaf terminates in two opposite leaflets it is called paripinnate (Latin: *par* = equal). An imparipinnate leaf is one that terminates in a single leaflet.

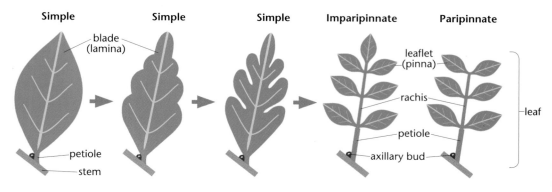

**Compound leaves: palmately compound**
Three or more leaflets arise from a single point and radiate outwards like the fingers of an open hand (Latin: *palma* = palm of the hand). Here we depict a hypothetical sequence showing how a palmately compound leaf is derived through evolution from a simple leaf with palmate venation (in this example without stipules).

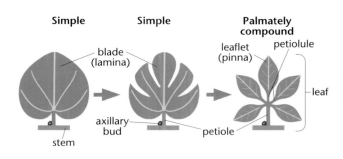

**Compound leaves: trifoliolate**
A compound leaf with three leaflets is trifoliolate. Palmately trifoliolate is when the three leaflets are sessile or stalked by means of petiolules only. If the attachment of the terminal leaflet extends beyond the two basal leaflets on a short rachis, in addition to its petiolule, the leaf is pinnately trifoliolate. In the latter case an articulation indicates the position where the petiolule is attached to the rachis. For convenience both types are usually referred to simply as 'trifoliolate'.

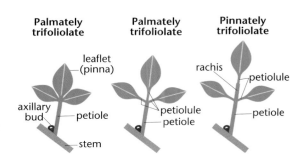

**Compound leaves: bifoliolate**  A compound leaf with two leaflets is bifoliolate. The diagram shows how a bifoliolate leaf may be derived from a paripinnate one through loss of all the leaflets except the terminal pair (here with stipules). Subsequent fusion between the two remaining leaflets will result in a deeply lobed simple leaf. However, the bifoliolate state may derive from the subdivision of a simple leaf (indicated by the arrow). All three types of leaves are common in the Caesalpiniaceae [flamboyant family; flambojantfamilie].

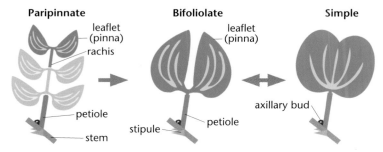

**Compound leaves: bipinnately compound**
The first leaflets (pinnae) of a pinnately compound leaf are further divided, with leaflets (pinnulae; singular pinnule) borne on branches (rachillae; singular rachilla) of the rachis. The diagram shows the changes from a pinnately compound to a bipinnately compound leaf. Palmately compound leaves can become bipalmately compound, but the latter is rare and mainly encountered in *Cussonia*, a genus placed in Group 2 (p70).

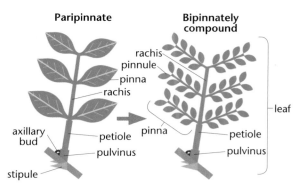

# Leaf arrangement

Leaf arrangement is a very important vegetative character for tree identification and it is often constant for a family. 'Arrangement' refers to the patterns of leaf attachment on the stem and it should not be confused with the arrangement of leaflets along the rachis in pinnately compound leaves (see p24).

The arrangement of leaves on stems (phylotaxis) follows precise mathematical patterns that have long intrigued botanists and mathematicians alike. Here, however, the focus is only on the broad types useful for field identification. The number of leaves per node can vary from one to many. In most trees, leaf arrangement is either constant or follows a single predominant pattern, at least for any one shoot on a plant.

In trees with tufted leaves, the basic arrangement is usually seen in certain upright growing stems, in juvenile plants or in coppice growth. In general, tufted leaves can be taken as alternate unless the tufts themselves are arranged in regular, opposite pairs. The tufted arrangement of leaves is the result of them being spirally clustered on short shoots with extremely reduced internodes. Also known as spur shoots (brachyblasts), these usually develop as side shoots from axillary buds along normal stems. Hence the position of the spur shoots reflects the leaf arrangement in the species. Occasionally the growth tip (apical meristem) of a normal leafy stem may be transformed into a spur shoot. The latter is quite characteristic in certain species of *Terminalia* [clusterleaf trees; trosblaarbome].

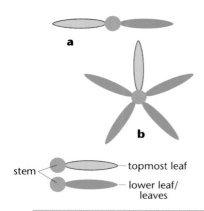

**Alternate leaf arrangement** By far the most common leaf arrangement is the one known as alternate. To assist with identification, two subtypes of alternate leaves are often distinguished: 2-ranked (distichous) and spiral.
(a) When 2-ranked, the leaves are arranged in two distinct rows as seen from the growing point of the shoot (i.e. from above, as illustrated), usually with 180° between the rows.
(b) All other variations of alternate are described in this book as spiral; in most native trees this means more than three longitudinal rows of leaves as seen from above (five illustrated); an arrangement that appears, to the untrained eye, as if the leaves are evenly spaced in a helical pattern around the stem.

## TYPES OF LEAF ARRANGEMENT

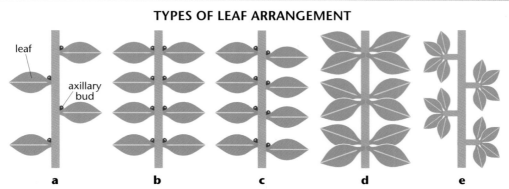

The main types of leaf arrangement are depicted above: (a) alternate: one leaf per node; (b) opposite: two leaves per node. In the case of (c) sub-opposite, the leaves are almost opposite, but not quite – the distance between the two leaves of a pair being considerably shorter than the length of the internode between successive leaf pairs; (d) whorled: three or more leaves per node (axillary buds not shown); (e) tufted (fascicled or clustered): several leaves arranged in a tight cluster, usually on an abbreviated shoot, making it difficult to see the actual leaf arrangement (axillary buds not shown).

The distinction between the two types of alternate arrangement (see illustration opposite) must be used with caution. When a species is described as 2-ranked it refers to the leaves on side shoots; in most cases, the upright primary stems display a spiral arrangement. Leaves on the first few nodes of a new season's growth are often alternate in species with opposite leaves. Opposite and whorled are closely related states and it is common for species with whorled leaves to produce a few opposite ones. Always check the leaf arrangement on a number of nodes and use the predominant state for the particular tree.

# Discolorous leaves

Here we look specifically at the colour of individual mature leaves. General foliage colour, autumn colours and colour changes in ageing (senescent) leaves are covered on p38. Leaves generally are slightly discolorous in being darker green and more glossy on the upper surface compared with the lower surface which tends to be paler green and dull. Of more limited occurrence are leaves where the two surfaces are strikingly different in colour, a feature that has proved most useful in creating the species groups.

We use the term discolorous to refer to leaves that are green above, but white, cream, grey or greyish blue below. The most striking difference is seen in species where the lower leaf surface is covered with a dense felty layer of white, cream or grey hairs. In many species, young leaves are very hairy but become less so as they grow older. In discolorous leaves, however, the hairs on the lower surface persist to maturity.

A bluish green (glaucous) lower surface is often due to the presence of a pronounced powdery waxy coating known as a bloom, a natural surface wax that can sometimes be wiped off. Bloom is common in plants and is seen on the skins of fruits such as plums and grapes and the leaves of cabbage and carnations.

*Buddleja dysophylla* [white climbing sagewood; witranksalie], a species with distinct discolorous leaves due to a dense layer of whitish hairs on the lower surface.

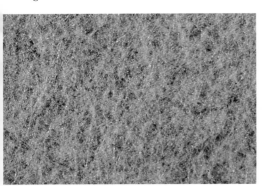

*Brachylaena transvaalensis* [forest silver-oak; bosvaalbos]. The white lower surface of the leaf is due to a dense felty layer of white, cobwebby hairs.

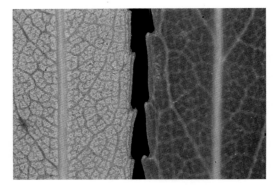

*Salix mucronata* subsp. *woodii* [flute willow; fluitjieswilger]. In this species the white lower surface of the leaf (left) is not due to hairs, but to a waxy layer that adheres to the leaf surface.

# Venation pattern

Venation refers to the arrangement of leaf veins. A system of veins (vascular bundles), spread throughout the leaf blade, transports water and food to and from the leaves. Venation patterns are diverse and usually constant for a species. A rather technical system has been developed to describe venation, but is seldom applied to native trees. To interpret the system, leaves are treated to make them translucent and the veins are selectively stained. In most leaves, the venation is differentiated into vein diameters or size classes. In practice, attention is focused on the primary and secondary veins because they are most readily seen with the naked eye. The former includes the midvein (midrib) and the latter the principal lateral (side) veins that branch off the midvein. Based on patterns formed by the first and second order venation, two distinct groups have been defined for simple leaves: those with a single midvein from the base versus leaves prominently 3–7-veined from the base.

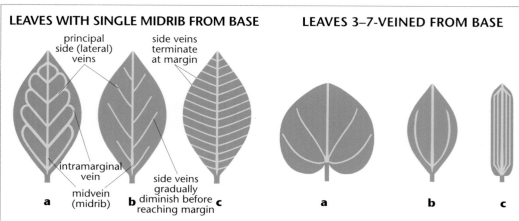

**LEAVES WITH SINGLE MIDRIB FROM BASE**

principal side (lateral) veins — side veins terminate at margin — intramarginal vein — midvein (midrib) — side veins gradually diminish before reaching margin

a    b    c

**LEAVES 3–7-VEINED FROM BASE**

a    b    c

Three common venation patterns occur in leaves with a single prominent midvein (pinnately veined). (a) The side veins do not terminate at the leaf margin, but join together in a series of arches to form an intramarginal vein. This is the most common state. (b) Similar to the previous type but with upturned side veins that diminish before they reach the margin and without forming prominent marginal loops. (c) All secondary veins prominent, often numerous, more or less parallel and terminating at the margin. Secondary veins are said to form a 'herringbone' pattern.

These leaves have three or more primary veins from the base (palmately veined). When leaves are narrow the two basal veins next to the midvein may be only slightly thicker than the side veins that branch higher up from the midvein and can easily be overlooked. (a) Three or more veins radiate from a single point. (b) Two or more strongly developed veins on both sides of the midvein running in convergent arches towards the leaf tip. Arching veins sometimes originate a short distance above the leaf base. (c) Veins run more or less parallel from the base to the leaf tip where they converge.

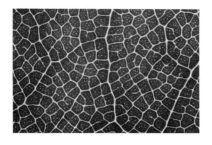

When held up to the light, secondary and tertiary veins can be translucent or obscure. In some families (e.g. Lauraceae and Rhamnaceae), the finest veins anastomose (join) to form a reticulum of minute squares, rectangles or polygons (areolae) that can be useful to identify sterile material. In *Cryptocarya woodii* [cape-quince; Kaapse kweper] (left), note the minute secretory cells, or light dots, in the areolae.

# Secretory cavities

These are minute roundish cavities within the leaf blade (and other tissues) that contain secretions such as resin, mucilage and especially oil (see notes under Group 22, p118). They are usually present in great abundance and their presence is constant for families, but they are very small and easily overlooked.

Secretory cavities should not be confused with secretory cells (see photograph on p28). The latter are specialized individual cells with a storage function similar to cavities but they are even smaller and difficult or impossible to see except with a light microscope.

Always crush a fresh leaf and check its smell (see **Tip**, below). Leaves with secretory cavities are usually strongly aromatic, but it is important to note that not all aromatic leaves have secretory cavities. To test for secretory cavities, hold a leaf up to the sun and look for the presence of tiny translucent dots uniformly scattered over the leaf blade or in a zone adjacent to the margin. The cavities are the size of pinpricks and most people will require a good hand lens to see them clearly. Practise on leaves that are known to contain secretory cavities, such as citrus (Rutaceae) or eucalypts (Myrtaceae), or other members of these families. Leaves with secretory cavities are often described as 'pellucid gland-dotted', 'pellucid punctate' or 'glandular-punctate'.

Occasionally, the cavities may protrude as translucent or coloured dots on the leaf surface and their presence is then easier to detect.

> **Tip** If a tree has milky or watery latex, it should not have secretory cavities and there is no need to check for them.

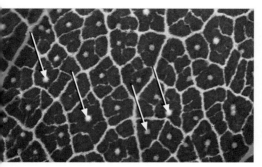

*Calodendrum capense* [cape-chestnut; Kaapse kastaiing]. Secretory cavities are visible as minute light spots (some arrowed) when the leaf is held up to the sun.

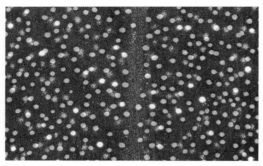

*Callistemon citrinus* [scarlet bottlebrush; skarlakenperdestert]. Secretory cavities are particularly easy to see in members of this Australian genus, several of which are grown as ornamentals in gardens.

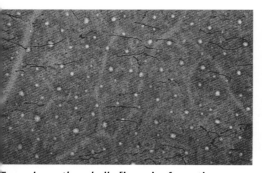

*Eugenia erythrophylla* [largeleaf myrtle; grootblaarmirt]. Secretory cavities may be difficult to see in thick mature leaves. Here they are clearly visible in pinkish bronze young leaves.

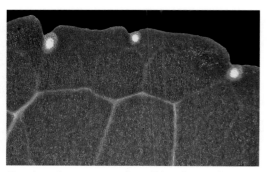

*Zanthoxylum capense* [small knobwood; kleinknophout]. In some small-leaved knobwoods, secretory cavities are best seen along the leaf margin, mainly in the sinuses (small notches) between the teeth.

# Bacterial nodules

Bacterial nodules are dark green knobs seen in the leaf blades of certain members of the Rubiaceae [coffee family; koffiefamilie]. They should therefore only be looked for in plants with opposite, entire-margined leaves with interpetiolar stipules. The coffee family is the largest family of trees in southern Africa and the presence of bacterial nodules was used to define a Group comprising the genus *Pavetta* and a few species of *Psychotria* (see Group 15, p102). Bacterial nodules are much larger than secretory cavities (often 1–2 mm in diameter) and vary from abundant in some species to very sparsely distributed in others.

These structures are consistently present in *Pavetta* and can be seen with the naked eye if a leaf is held up to the sun. Often the nodules are raised as bumps on the leaf surface. In *Pavetta* the bacteria enter the young leaves while they are still enclosed by stipules in the growing point of the shoot. The bacteria enter the blade through some of the stomata and, once inside the leaves, they multiply in a capsular enclosure formed around them by the leaf cells. In older leaves, the bacteria inside the nodule form an amorphous mass that does not seem to divide any further.

Unlike bacterial nodules found in the roots of certain plants, notably legumes, the bacterial nodules in the leaves of Rubiaceae do not fix nitrogen. The nodules may be a pathological reaction by the plant to try to confine the bacteria to a spot below the point of entry into the leaf. The bacteria are nevertheless closely associated with each species of *Pavetta* and are transferred from one generation to the next by the seed.

*Pavetta gardeniifolia* var. *gardeniifolia* [common bridesbush (SA), stinkleaf brides-bush (Z); gewone bruidsbos]. The bacterial nodules are visible as dark spots when the leaf is held up to the sun.

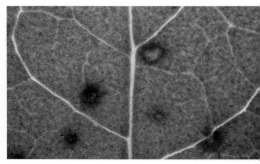

*Pavetta gardeniifolia* var. *gardeniifolia* [common bridesbush (SA), stinkleaf brides-bush (Z); gewone bruidsbos]. Area of leaf blade enlarged to show unevenly scattered, dark-coloured, bacterial nodules.

*Pavetta zeyheri* [small-leaf bridesbush; fyn-blaarbruidsbos]. All the bridesbushes have leaves with bacterial nodules (arrowed) and distinctive white flowers with long, protruding styles.

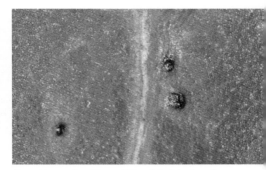

*Pavetta zeyheri* [small-leaf bridesbush; fynblaarbruidsbos]. Upper surface of leaf blade showing bacterial nodules as slightly raised bumps, often with a blackish central depression.

# Hairiness

In many trees the young growth has abundant hairs (trichomes), but it usually becomes less hairy, if not completely hairless, with age. In view of this developmental variation, hair density should be used with caution for identification purposes. Nevertheless, it is useful at species level as the mature growth in some species is consistently hairy whereas in others it is consistently smooth.

The lower surface of leaves is often hairy, especially near or on the larger veins, whereas the upper surface is smooth. This is particularly noticeable in some species with discolorous leaves (see p27). In many members of the Rubiaceae [coffee family; koffiefamilie] the mature leaves are densely hairy; a character used to define Group 16 (see p104).

Hairs are easy to see and feel, and they become even more obvious if they are coloured grey, brownish or white. Hair density is useful mainly at species level, whereas particular types of hair are often characteristic for specific families.

Hairs are broadly classified as non-glandular or glandular. Glandular hairs produce secretions (often sticky or aromatic). They often do not look like typical hairs, but are scale-like without distinct stalks.

Star-shaped (stellate) hairs are non-glandular and often impart a rough texture to stems and leaves. Each stellate hair resembles a star and consists of several arms radiating more or less horizontally from a central point. They are common in *Croton* [feverberries; koorsbessies], Malvaceae [cotton family; katoenfamilie ], Tiliaceae [linden family; lindefamilie] and Sterculiaceae [cacao family; kakaofamilie], among others.

*Vangueria infausta* [wild-medlar; wilde-mispel]. Leaves are densely velvety and hairy on both surfaces. Note the circular scar left by the calyx near the tip of the fruit, a common character in members of the coffee family.

*Chrysanthemoides monilifera* [bush tickberry; bietou]. A layer of loose, white, cobwebby hairs is characteristic for many Asteraceae [daisy family; madeliefiefamilie].

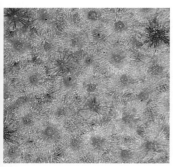

*Croton gratissimus* var. *gratissimus* [lavender feverberry; laventelkoorsbessie]. A dense layer of scales forms the silvery lower leaf surface; each scale decorated with radially arranged striae. Scattered brownish scales are visible to the naked eye.

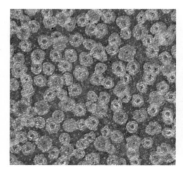

*Combretum imberbe* [leadwood; hardekool; omumborombonga (N)]. Leaves and young twigs are covered with a dense layer of silvery scales, interspersed with the odd brownish one.

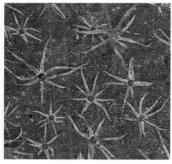

*Grewia flavescens* [sandpaper-raisin (N, SA), donkeyberry (Z); skurweblaarrosyntjie]. Star-shaped hairs are responsible for the harsh sand-papery texture of the leaves in some raisinbushes.

# Leaf margin

Although subjected to developmental variation in some species, the degree of indentation of leaf and leaflet margins is very useful for identification purposes and has been used as one of the characters for defining Groups. Avoid using juvenile growth for this purpose as, in some species, juvenile leaves tend to be toothed while the adult ones are entire (smooth).

Margins are either entire or variously toothed and lobed. Leaves with only a single small indentation or notch at the leaf tip are still considered entire. The term toothed is often used in a generalized sense to refer to a range of indentations for which more specific terms are available (see examples below), but which is sometimes difficult to identify accurately in plant material.

A margin is considered non-entire even if it is toothed along only a part of its length; many leaves tend to be toothed towards either the apex or the base. An undulate (wavy) margin can be entire or toothed and does not refer to any indentations. It describes a margin that is wavy in the vertical plane (compared with the plane of leaf blade); the term should not be confused with sinuous (lobed).

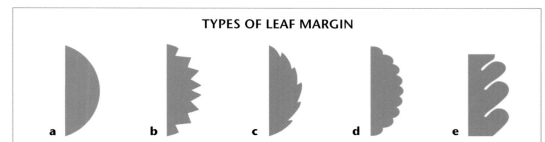

*Euclea undulata* [common guarri; gewone ghwarrie], depicting leaf margins that are entire and conspicuously undulate.

## TYPES OF LEAF MARGIN

a     b     c     d     e

(a) Entire (smooth) – even and continuous without any teeth, lobes or divisions;
(b) Toothed (dentate) – coarse, sharp teeth perpendicular to the margin;
(c) Toothed (serrate) – sharp, forward-pointing teeth, as in a saw;
(d) Toothed (crenate) – shallow, rounded or blunt teeth;
(e) Lobed (sinuate/sinuous) – regular curved indentations or small lobes with rounded recesses, called sinuses, between them; the lobes are usually cut less than halfway to the midvein or base. Any of the preceding states may be superimposed on the margin of the lobes.

# Stipules

Stipules are small scale- or leaf-like appendages at the base of the petiole (leaf stalk) in some plants. They are part of the leaf and generally found in pairs, typically one on either side of the point of insertion of the petiole on the stem. Stipules are important in plant classification and the presence (plants stipulate) or absence (plants exstipulate) often characterizes families or genera. Stipules can be very small; in some cases a 10x hand lens is required to detect them. Hence stipular characters have been introduced fairly late in the Key to the Groups (p58) as they can easily be overlooked.

The stipule may be located at the base of the petiole or be borne on the stem apparently detached from the petiole/leaf base. Stipules often help to protect very young leaves in the bud and may fall off early on, following the unfolding of a leaf, leaving scars on the stems. They are best seen on young, actively growing shoots. Stipules can become modified into spines, making them very conspicuous. Most spines that occur in pairs at the base of leaves are modified stipules (see p35). However, stipules can also be very leaf-like.

Stipules may be fused among themselves or fused with various structures. Interpetiolar stipules are particularly useful in plant identification and their presence has been used as one of the defining characters in Groups 13–18 (see pp98–110). Individual leaflets in the compound leaves of legumes occasionally have small outgrowths at their bases resembling stipules, but referred to as stipels.

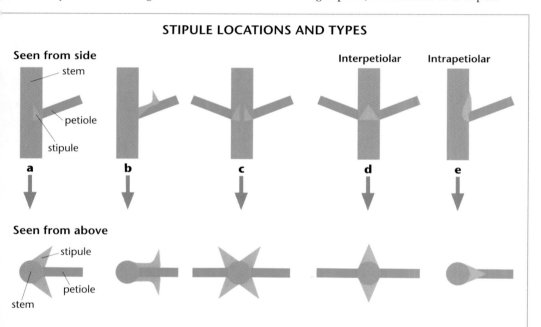

**STIPULE LOCATIONS AND TYPES**

Seen from side

Interpetiolar  Intrapetiolar

stem
petiole
stipule

a   b   c   d   e

Seen from above

stipule
petiole
stem

Diagrams showing the position of stipules (orange) relative to the petiole (green) and insertion of the leaf on the stem (grey), including examples of fusion between stipules.
(a) Stipules borne on the stem apparently detached from leaf base (common);
(b) Stipules fused along part of the length of the petiole;
(c) Stipules borne in pairs between petioles in opposite leaves, each one of a pair belonging to the other leaf;
(d) Single large stipule attached on both sides of stem between the petioles of opposite leaves. Known as an interpetiolar stipule, this has resulted from the fusion of a stipule from each leaf (compare c);
(e) Single large stipule positioned across the axil between the petiole and stem. Known as an intrapetiolar stipule, this has resulted from fusion between the two stipules of the same leaf (compare a).

# EXAMPLES OF STIPULES (see p33)

*Virgilia oroboides* subsp. *oroboides* [keurboom]. Typical stipule (arrowed), stem (a), axillary bud (b) and petiole (c).

*Peltophorum africanum* [african-wattle; huilboom; muparara (N)]. Unusual pinnately divided stipules.

*Cunonia capensis* [red-alder; rooi-els]. Growing tip protected by two large, tightly appressed, spoon-shaped stipules.

*Ficus trichopoda* [swamp fig; moerasvy]. Red conical stipule protecting a young leaf that has started to unfold. Stipule is attached around the stem and leaves a circular scar on falling.

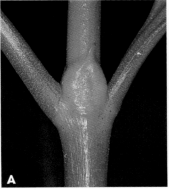

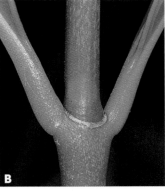

*Psychotria capensis* [birdberry; voëlbessie]. An interpetiolar stipule (A) with the scar left after it was shed (B).

*Bersama swinnyi* [coast white-ash]. Intrapetiolar stipules are rare in local trees.

# Spines, thorns and prickles

Many plants form sharp-pointed hardened structures, supposedly as a mechanical defence against larger animals. The term 'spine' is generally used as a collective term for all sharp structures and is the interpretation followed in the Key to the Groups (see p58). Spines, thorns and prickles may have quite different origins. Most commonly, they are derived through modification from one of the plant's three basic organs (or part of an organ), namely the stems, leaves or roots.

There is considerable confusion in the literature because some authors distinguish between spines and thorns, whereas other authors consider the terms synonymous and use them interchangeably.

According to the first group, the term 'thorn' is applied to sharp structures derived from stems, whereas 'spine' is used for similar structures derived from stipules and leaves. Another approach is to use 'spine' for straight structures and 'thorn' for hooked structures. We will distinguish only between spines and prickles.

Spines are tough structures with their own vascular supply and are usually difficult to break off by hand. Clues to the origin of spines are provided by their position, arrangement and morphology.

Prickles (also called emergences) can occur on stems and leaves and usually do not occur in fixed positions. They do not derive from any organ, but are structures that develop from superficially located tissues and are correspondingly easily broken off; but not in all cases! Good examples of typical prickles are those seen in the rose. Technically, the native species of *Acacia* with hooked thorns have prickles but, especially when paired, they can be very tough and do not come off easily.

The potential to produce spines or prickles is a useful diagnostic character for a species, but the presence of these structures is subject to developmental variation. Spines and prickles are best developed in juvenile and coppice growth and may be absent in mature growth.

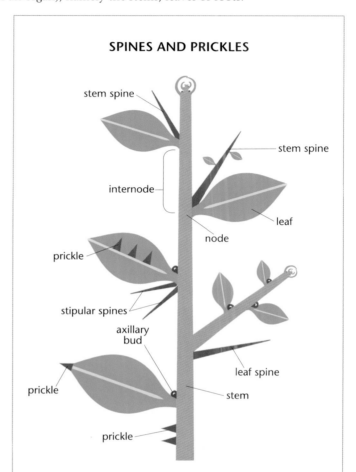

**SPINES AND PRICKLES**

Schematic depiction of part of an imaginary plant showing the range of structures generally described as 'spines'. Stem spines either tip certain shoots or are located in leaf axils (having developed from the axillary bud). Such spines are usually single or branched and may have one or more leaf-carrying nodes. Stipular spines are found at the base of the leaf, are usually paired, and never branch or carry leaves. Spines derived from a leaf or part of a leaf (commonly the petioles) are single and subtend an axillary bud, or a side shoot that has developed from the bud. Prickles are superficial surface structures and can develop in any position.

# EXAMPLES OF SPINES AND PRICKLES (see p35)

*Gymnosporia buxifolia* [spikethorn]. Stem spine (arrowed) with 3 small leaves; spine emerging from axil of leaf (a).

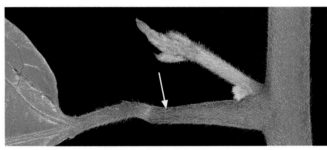

*Combretum microphyllum* [flame-creeper; vlamklimop]. Basal portion of petiole (arrowed), destined to develop into a future spine, differs in thickness from the distal portion that will be shed with the leaf blade.

*Acacia ataxacantha* [flame thorn (N, SA), flamepod acacia (Z); vlamdoring]. Epidermal prickles.

*Acacia robusta* subsp. *robusta* [broadpod robust thorn (SA), robust acacia (Z); enkeldoring]. Stipular spines paired, long, white.

*Sesamothamnus* sp. nov. [largeleaf sesamebush, largeleaf sesametree (N); grootblaarsesambos]. Spines derived from petioles, with one dried leaf blade still attached.

# Latex

In this book, the term latex denotes any abundant liquid exudate, whether watery (clear), cloudy, milky or otherwise coloured. Latex is useful for classification purposes and its presence or absence is often diagnostic for whole families. Latex is contained in an extensive system of special ducts or tubes (laticifers) that pervade most parts of a plant and are particularly associated with the bark and leaf venation. Latex is kept under positive pressure inside the tubes and immediately oozes out when the tissues containing them are cut. It is believed that latex has, among other functions, a protective function in that it serves as a chemical defence against plant eaters.

Based on chemical composition, a distinction can be made between latex and resin (amber is fossilized tree resin). Latex contains rubber which is not always the case with resin. Many resins have distinct and characteristic odours (often turpentine-like), from their admixture with aromatic oils. As it is impractical to expect tree watchers to be able to draw a chemical distinction, we use the term latex for all exudates regardless of their composition.

The white or milky colour of latex comes from small, suspended particles of varying composition, including oils, resins and rubber; such mixtures are known as emulsions. Latex may contain toxic and caustic compounds and should always be handled with caution (see box below).

**Test for latex:** With unknown trees, always test for the presence of latex. Pick a healthy green leaf, preferably from an actively growing shoot; break it off with a snapping action (to create a 'clean' break) at the point where the petiole (stalk) is attached to the stem. Check immediately whether any liquid oozes from the broken end or from the scar on the stem. The exudate needs to be fairly copious, ideally forming a drop that completely covers the wound.

Latex flow is often suppressed during periods of drought, stress or when shoots are dormant, when the presence of latex is sometimes only detected as stickiness when the broken end of a petiole is touched. If no latex is detected, check a few other leaves from different parts of the tree to confirm the fact. Consult the notes on reliability of latex flow under Groups 28 (p132) and 31 (p140).

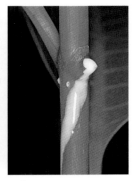

*Strophanthus speciosus* [poison-rope (SA), forest tail-flower (Z); giftou]. Watery latex.

*Tabernaemontana elegans* [toadtree; paddaboom]. Milky latex.

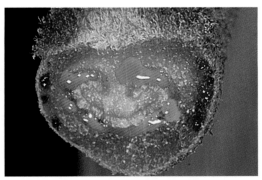

*Harungana madagascariensis* [orange-milk tree; oranjemelkhout]. Bright orange latex.

## ☠ Latex warning

A few native trees, notably species of Apocynaceae [oleander family; selonsroosfamilie] and *Euphorbia* [euphorbias; nabome] contain latex that is extremely toxic and/or caustic. Always handle latex with caution and avoid skin and eye contact. The latex of some euphorbias releases scentless volatile compounds that, upon exposure, can cause extreme irritation to eyes and mucous membranes, even without direct contact. Always wash your hands thoroughly after handling any latex-containing plant.

In a few species of *Commiphora* [corkwoods; kanniedoodbome] from the arid parts of the Northern Cape and Namibia, the latex is under considerable pressure and may squirt up to 300 mm high if a twig is damaged. Take particular care not to get any of this exudate into your eyes. If latex accidentally gets into an eye, wash the area immediately with abundant water and seek medical help. Avoid getting corkwood latex on your skin, clothes or the lenses of cameras or binoculars as it is extremely sticky and difficult to remove.

Also take care when handling certain members of the Anacardiaceae [mango family; mangofamilie] because sensitive people show extremely painful allergic reactions to the resin of two species in particular, *Smodingium argutum* and *Trichoscypha ulugurensis*. See p141 for further information and how to perform the black-spot test to check for this particular toxicity.

# Tree shape, size and foliage colour

The impression created by the whole tree is very useful for recognizing known species, but less so when it comes to identifying an unfamiliar species. Tree shape is useful to help identify species whose shape is distinct enough to be recognized in a photograph (especially Group 2, see p70). Shape alone is often assumed to be important for spotting trees from a distance, especially in bushveld areas – until one is shown a silhouette of the trees, when it becomes clear that shape might not be so important after all.

More significant are the subtle differences in branching pattern, as well as the density, colour, texture and orientation of the foliage. In the veld, these features are best used after identifying a species, to help form a search image to locate similar plants in the same general area. Unfortunately, it is difficult to convey the general effect produced by the foliage of a tree in writing, or in a photograph unless the latter is very sharp and printed fairly large.

Based on height, trees in our region are arbitrarily described as small (up to 5 m height), medium-sized (5–15 m), large (15–30 m) and very large (more than 30 m).

Trees with grey or silvery leaves are particularly easy to identify from a distance. The presence of an occasional bright yellow, orange or red leaf among the prevailing green leaves in the canopy is also very useful, particularly in forest species. Our region has few trees with striking autumn colours, one exception being *Kirkia wilmsii* [mountain seringa; bergsering]. Noteworthy are those trees with a brief flush of conspicuously coloured new leaves at the start of the growing season, such as the cream and white leaves in some species of *Combretum* [bushwillows; boswilge] and shades of copper, pink and red in *Brachystegia* [brachystegias].

Tree architecture refers to the developmental sequence of events that gives rise to a specific branching pattern in a tree, rather than a static shape, and these patterns have been classified into 23 architectural models. (Most native trees have not yet been analyzed in this way and the use of models for identification purposes is still largely of academic rather than practical interest. For a description of some of the models see Van Wyk *et al.* 2000, pp20–23. See p179.)

*Adansonia digitata* [baobab; kremetart]. **One of the most distinctive and recognizable tree shapes in our region.**

*Clutia pulchella* [warty-fruit lightningbush; vratjievrugbliksembos]. **Occasional bright orange leaves appear among prevailing grey-green foliage.**

*Brachystegia spiciformis* [musasa; msasa]. **The flush of new leaves in spring reveals shades of pink, red and bronze.**

# Bark

Bark is a popular term applied to all tissues outside of the wood. Anatomically, a stem consists of a large central woody core surrounded by a thin bark. Between the bark and wood is a remarkable layer of meristematic cells that, throughout the life of the tree, remains in a juvenile state and regularly forms new wood to the inside and bark to the outside. Known as the vascular cambium, this layer is the lateral equivalent of the apical meristem in the stem and root (see pp10 and 11). Whereas the apical meristems are responsible for the growth in length of the stems and roots, the vascular cambium is responsible for their increase in girth. A vascular cambium is present in all dicotyledons, but is absent or poorly developed in monocots, including palms.

Being on the outside of a woody cylinder that is constantly increasing in girth, bark is in an 'awkward' position in that it is constantly subjected to strain. It must stretch like a rubber band around the trunk

*Commiphora harveyi* [copper-stem corkwood; koperstamkanniedood].

*Commiphora multijuga* [purplestem corkwood; persstamkanniedood; omuzunba (N)].

*Commiphora discolor* [stringbark corkwood; reepbaskanniedood].

*Commiphora glandulosa* [tall common corkwood (SA); groot gewone kanniedood].

*Commiphora steynii* [ringbark corkwood; ringbaskanniedood; onangwi (N)].

*Commiphora mollis* [velvet corkwood (N), velvetleaf corkwood; fluweelkanniedood].

*Heteromorpha arborescens* var. *abyssinica* [common parsleytree (SA), parsleytree (Z); gewone pietersielieboom].

Identifying tall forest trees can be frustrating because their canopies are out of reach. Bark characters are therefore widely used under such circumstances. This skill is best learned from an experienced person familiar with the trees in a particular forest.
In parts of the tropics with extensive rainforests the 'slash' (a combination of features detected upon slashing) of the bark can be very informative. A sharp instrument is used to make a cut in the bark to investigate characteristics such as thickness and texture, the colour of the dead outer and living inner bark, the smell of the living bark, and the presence and type of exudate. Because of the restricted occurrence of forests in southern Africa the slash technique is not promoted locally, as bark wounds are the ideal entry points for disease-causing fungi and insect pests such wood borers.

*Boscia tomentosa* [hairy shepherds-tree] showing distinctive white bark.

to accommodate the increase in girth of the wood. Most barks have limited stretching capabilities and, as the trunk becomes thicker, the outer dead layers often split. To minimize cracking, the bark remains relatively thin and often sheds older outer layers in the form of dead scales or flakes. Cracking and sloughing patterns as well as surface colour are widely used to assist in species identification.

Bark can be smooth, fissured, cracked, scaly, dippled-scaly or peeling. Bark features are under strong developmental influence and in most young stems it is thin and smooth. Distinct patterns are only established in older trees which somewhat limits the use of bark features for identification purposes. Mature bark patterns in the same species are also subject to environmental influences. In areas where rainfall is high, the outer dead tissues decay faster and bark patterns and colour may differ from individuals of the same species that grow under drier conditions.

# Twigs and tendrils

Twigs provide many useful characters for identification. They can be round, flattened or more or less square in cross-section. Square twigs are found in trees with opposite leaves, and the angles of the stems are sometimes expanded and are then described as winged. In some cases, the bases of petioles are extended some distance down the stem, forming ridges.

Young twigs are often marked with small, light- or dark-coloured pustules called lenticels – patches of loosely packed cork cells that allow air to penetrate to the underlying tissue. Tendrils are slender, usually coiling, structures that serve as climbing organs. These structures may represent modified stems (usually), leaves, stipules or inflorescences.

In some temperate parts of the world where there are cold winters and an impoverished tree flora, keys based on twig characters have been developed in order to assist with identifying deciduous trees when they are leafless in winter. However, no attempts have yet been made to produce similar keys for our region. Due to the rich diversity of local trees, this method might only work if it is applied to a limited area with a small number of trees.

Detail of *Ochna serrulata* [small-leaf plane; fynblaar-rooihout] showing white lenticels.

# SYMPODIAL GROWTH

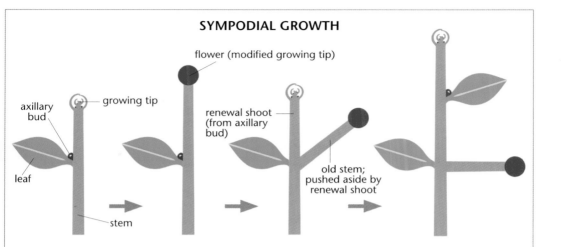

The diagram above shows the series of events that occur during sympodial growth in a plant axis with alternate leaves. In some trees, the tendrils, flowers and inflorescences are borne on stems, opposite or next to the leaves instead of in the leaf axil, as one would expect from structures derived from stems (axillary buds). This is due to a growth pattern known as sympodial growth.

Instead of growing in length for a long time (indeterminate or monopodial growth), some growing tips of shoots develop into a tendril, flower or inflorescence. Once this has happened the plant can no longer grow in length (determinate or sympodial growth). However, the stem continues to extend through the resumption of growth by an axillary bud located in the axil of the last-formed normal leaf.

The renewal shoot thus formed pushes the tendril or flower aside to seemingly emerge from the stem on the opposite side of the leaf petiole. After a period of normal growth, the growing tip of the renewal shoot is also terminated by a tendril or flower, and the whole pattern repeats itself.

Although stems in plants that display sympodial growth look like a single unit, careful scrutiny reveals that the stems are composed of a succession of renewal shoots, or sympodial units.

*Syzygium cordatum* [umdoni (SA), waterberry (N, Z); waterbessie]. Stems square; leaves sessile and stem-clasping at base.

*Rhoicissus tomentosa* [common forest-grape (SA), simpleleaf grape (Z); gewone bosdruif]. The tendril is borne leaf-opposed due to sympodial growth.

# Petioles

Despite its apparent simplicity the petiole, or leaf stalk, provides several characters useful in tree identification. Its length, however, is subject to developmental and environmental variation, but less so if very short or almost absent; the leaves are then described as sessile. Most petioles are grooved along the length of the upper side. This groove allows the leaf to twist in order to reduce the wind drag, without losing resistance to bending. Petioles tinged pinkish, reddish or purplish can be very useful for identifying trees which otherwise have rather featureless leaves.

A distinct swelling is sometimes present at the base of the petiole (or petiolule), especially in legumes. Known as a pulvinus, this structure consists of flexible tissue that responds to internal water pressure resulting in changes in the orientation of the leaf. The pulvinus is responsible for the so-called sleeping movements seen in the leaves of some trees. There is sometimes a second pulvinus at the distal end of the petiole just below its point of attachment with the blade. Winged petioles have expanded margins and are species-specific. Petioles may also carry various glands (see p44). The petiole base may be widened and flattened to form a sheath, the latter often folded partly or completely around the stem (stem-clasping). Petioles show several modifications. In some climbers or scrambling trees the whole or part of a petiole may change into a permanent woody spine (see p35, 36). The apparently simple leaves in some introduced Australian species of *Acacia* [wattles; wattelbome] are flattened petioles functioning as photosynthetic organs (phyllodes).

*Prunus africana* [redstink-wood (SA), african-almond (Z); rooistinkhout]. Petioles reddish purple.

*Steganotaenia araliacea* [carrot-tree (SA), popgun-tree (Z); geelwortelboom]. Petioles stem-clasping. Also note white lenticels.

*Anginon difforme* [common needleleaf; gewone naald-blaar]. Petioles stem-clasping, needle-like, without leaf blades. From a distance the plant can easily be mistaken for a young pine tree.

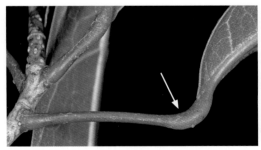

*Cola natalensis* [smooth cola; gladdekola]. Petiole with distinct swelling (pulvinus) at its point of attachment with the blade (arrowed).

*Acacia melanoxylon* [blackwood; swarthout]. Petiole flattened and leaf-like (phyllode), arrowed.

# Leaf shape and size

Shape and size are two of the most obvious and frequently described properties of leaves. Shape is also one of the most variable, being subject, within limits, to developmental, environmental and regional genetic (ecotypical) variation (see p18). Leaf blades come in an incredible array of shapes making shape a valuable tool for tree identification, especially at the species level. Three separate sets of descriptive terms are available for describing the shape of the blade as a whole, the shape of the leaf apex (tip) and the shape of the leaf base. The same terminology is applied to leaflets. Leaf size is even more variable and plastic than leaf shape but variation limits are commonly supplied in tree descriptions.

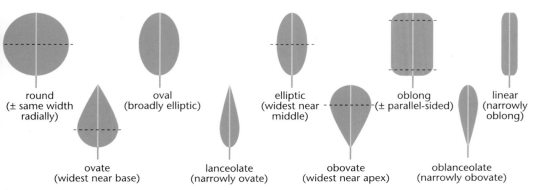

**Major leaf shapes and their variations** The leaf may be considered to have five major shapes depending upon where the blade is the widest (round, oblong, elliptic, ovate, obovate). These terms may be adjusted by the use of modifiers such as broadly or narrowly. It is also common practice to apply a number of well-established descriptive terms to variations of some of the major shapes, as indicated above.

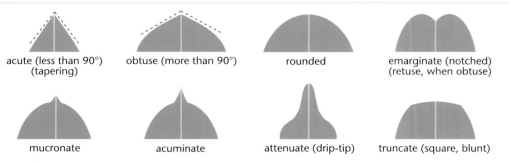

**Apex shapes** Selection of terms relating to the shape of the leaf apex.

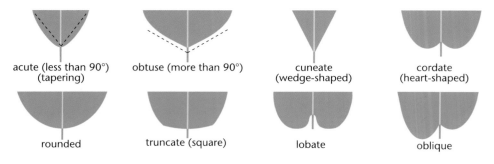

**Base shapes** Selection of terms relating to the shape of the leaf base.

# External glands

Structures on the vegetative organs, notably the leaves, that secrete nectar at one time or another, are called external glands or extrafloral nectaries – because they occur outside flowers yet secrete nectar. These glands are especially active on young growth or under specific environmental conditions, but are still present on older growth, although they have often ceased to be functional. Nectar attracts ants which, in return, guard the plants by dispelling or removing other insects (or their eggs) that may harm the plant. Extrafloral nectaries are large enough to be seen with the naked eye or with a 10x hand lens. On any one organ they are few in number, and should not be confused with secretory cavities, which are minute structures inside tissues (see p29).

Glands may be in pits, level with the surface of the organ on which they occur, and cup-shaped, dome-shaped or distinctly stalked. They are usually located on the lower surface of leaves or, if above, then occur mainly on the petiole or rachis. Some of the principal sites are at the point where the leaf blade is attached to the petiole, on the midvein or other primary veins, in the angles of the larger

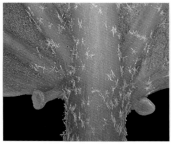

*Croton megalobotrys* [large feverberry (SA), feverberry croton (Z); grootkoorsbessie; murongo (N)]. Extrafloral nectaries paired and located on both sides of midrib at base of leaf blade. Note star-shaped (stellate) hairs.

*Spirostachys africana* [tamboti; tambotie]. Extrafloral nectaries paired and located on upper surface of petiole at junction with blade. They stop functioning at an early stage, then dry out, becoming brownish or blackish in mature leaves.

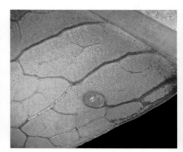

*Sclerocroton integerrimus* [duikerberry; duikerbessie]. Yellowish extrafloral nectary on lower surface of the leaf blade near base.

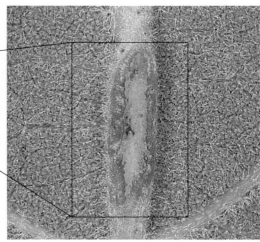

*Azanza garckeana* [azanza; slymappel; monego (N)]. A single elongated extrafloral nectary (shown enlarged on the right) is located on the midrib on the underside of the leaf (similar glands may also occur on some of the other prominent veins that radiate from the base).

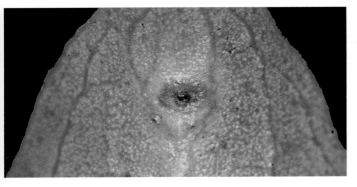

*Galpinia transvaalica* [transvaal-privet (SA), galpinia (Z); brosblaar]. The conspicuous gland on the midrib of the leaf on the lower side near the apex is very characteristic. The gland is rarely functional, although at times secretions can be so abundant as to attract honey bees.

veins or on the surface of the blade but away from veins. Because glands are not widespread among plants, they are very useful for species identification. Although they are consistently present on the leaves of some species, they occur only sporadically in others. Glands are easily noticed when they are active due to the congregation of ants at these sites. (Note that plant-feeders, such as aphids and scale insects, also secrete a sugary liquid, called honeydew, that attracts ants to plants.)

# Domatia

The term domatium (plural domatia) is derived from the Greek word meaning 'little house'. It is applied to depressions (pits), pockets, sacks or distinct tufts of hairs in the axils between the principal side veins and the midrib on the lower surface of leaves in certain woody plants. Domatia are small but clearly visible to the naked eye. The position of domatia is often also reflected by slightly dome-shaped bulges on the corresponding upper surface of the leaf (see below).

Domatia are naturally occurring, genetically determined structures formed by the plant, rather than pathological structures initiated by insects or other outside agents. They are typically inhabited by fungus-eating mites or predatory mites that prey on plant-eating mites. The domatia provide a favourable place for the mites to take refuge and reproduce. The plant, in turn, benefits indirectly from reduced attacks by plant-eating mites and the removal of fungal growth from its leaves, the latter being especially common on evergreen leaves in humid tropical regions.

*Ocotea bullata* [stinkwood; stinkhout]. The tree with the largest pit-domatia in our region, seen here as dome-shaped bulges on the upper surface of the leaves.

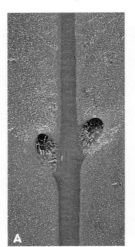

*Rothmannia capensis* [false-gardenia; valskatjiepiering]. Pit domatia with hairs at the orifice, as viewed from below (A) and above (B) the leaf.

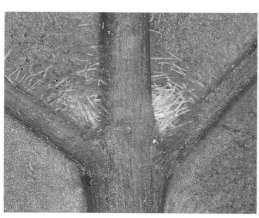

*Mackaya bella* [forest bellbush; bosklokkies-bos]. Hairtuft-domatia. This species has the most colourful 'mite houses' in our region, with their white 'walls' and red 'roofs'.

*Rothmannia globosa* [september-bells; septemberklokkies]. White hair-tuft domatia in axils of side veins. Principal veins are usually reddish.

Domatia are very useful in identifying specific tree species, although they may not be present on all the leaves on a tree. Hollow spines formed by certain, especially East African, species of *Acacia* [thorn-trees; doringbome] to house ants are a special kind of domatium (myrmecodomatia). Swollen spines in some local members of *Acacia* are, however, not considered true domatia because they may only become occupied by ants after being pathogenically hollowed out by other insects.

# Miscellaneous leaf characters

In addition to the universally applied general characters, leaves may have several specialized characters that are useful for identifying species. With increased experience, each person builds up a collection of useful checks to perform on leaves to assist in their identification. Here we describe and illustrate a few additional sources of leaf evidence to help identify trees in our region. (The way young leaves are folded in the bud (ptyxis) and their appearance when they unfold can be very diagnostic for species or families but this character has not yet been recorded in popular tree books for most native trees.)

*Robsonodendron eucleiforme* (=*Cassine eucleiformis*) [false-silkybark; valssybas]. Some members of the Celastraceae [spikethorn family; pendoringfamilie] have very characteristic elastic (rubbery) threads associated with the venation and bark. Crease a leaf blade transversely and slowly, very gently pull it apart along the crease for about 2 mm. If rubber is present, silvery elastic threads will connect the two halves of the blade.

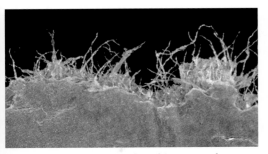

*Chionanthus foveolatus* [pockironwood; pokysterhout]. In addition to the veins, the soft tissues in the leaves of some trees may be pervaded by numerous woody fibres (fibrous mesophyll sclereids). To test for their presence, hold a fresh, mature leaf at the tip and base and pull quickly and vigorously in opposite directions so the blade snaps audibly in two. Using a hand lens, inspect the torn edges for the presence of a dense fringe of protruding fibres, a diagnostic feature for many members of the Oleaceae [olive family; olyffamilie] and *Memecylon* [rose-apples; roosappels].

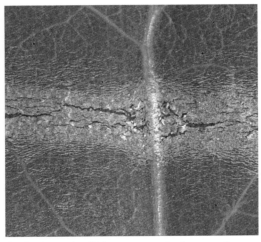

*Scolopia zeyheri* [thornpear; doringpeer]. Fold a mature leaf blade transversely upwards and gently press along the folded edge to create a crease. Open the blade and look for a distinct, white waxy zone associated with the crease. Its presence may indicate a species of *Scolopia* [redpear and thornpear trees; rooi- en doringpeerbome].

*Loxostylis alata* [tarwood; teerhout]. In compound leaves the rachis (and sometimes petiole also) may extend sideways to form 'wings' of variable width. This is an example of a pinnately compound leaf with a distinctly winged rachis.

*Olinia capensis* [cape hardpear; Kaapse harde-peer]. If a tree has opposite leaves without latex, crush a leaf thoroughly and smell it. A strong smell of almonds indicates a species of *Olinia* [hardpear trees; hardepeerbome], not all of which release this characteristic smell.

# Flowers and inflorescences

The sexual reproductive structures of angiosperms are called flowers, hence the common name of flowering plants for the group. A flower is a modified shoot bearing specialized, highly modified leaves. The male sperm is produced in pollen grains and the female egg cell in the ovules inside the ovary. Because they are stationary, plants depend on external forces to transport the sperm from one plant to another, a process referred to as pollination. Flowers are adaptations for specific methods of pollination and function on the principle of advertisement (colour, scent) and reward (nectar, pollen). A fascinating aspect about flowers is that one can often infer the pollen vector from the morphology of a flower.

Most tree flowers are pollinated by animals, with only a small percentage opting for wind pollination. Animal-pollinated flowers are usually brightly coloured, with sticky pollen and contain some form of reward. Wind-pollinated flowers, on the other hand, lack advertisement and reward and are usually small and inconspicuously coloured with long stamens and powdery pollen. Wind-pollinated trees tend to grow gregariously, for example *Colophospermum mopane* [mopane; mopanie].

Flowers come in many forms, are not strongly influenced by environmental variation, and are widely used in plant classification, especially for family recognition. The idealized flower depicted in most books (and also below left) to illustrate its component parts, is rather misleading, as similar-looking flowers are rarely encountered in nature. Many tree flowers are small and their interpretation often requires some botanical background. Hence, in the case of tree identification – especially in photographic guides – flowers are usually compared on the basis of general appearance, such as size, form and colour, rather than the technicalities of actual construction.

Flowers are borne singly or in an arrangement of many flowers called an inflorescence. Inflorescence type is important in routine identification. Flowers can be borne on thick, mature stems, a phenomenon known as cauliflory. A flower is generally interpreted as a short length of stem with modified leaves attached to it. The modified shoot (or floral axis) is called the **receptacle** and the floral stalk is the **pedicel**. Four sets of modified leaves may be present. Outermost are the **sepals**, usually green and leaf-like in the bud stage, enclosing and protecting the other flower parts, and collectively known as the **calyx**. Within the sepals are the **petals**, usually conspicuous and brightly coloured, collectively known as the **corolla**.

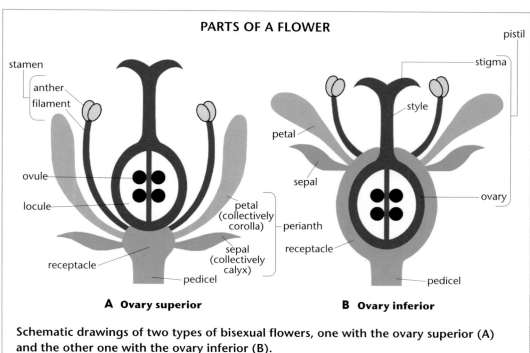

Schematic drawings of two types of bisexual flowers, one with the ovary superior (A) and the other one with the ovary inferior (B).

Within the petals are the **stamens**, male reproductive organs, each comprising a **filament** (stalk) which bears an **anther**, in which pollen grains are produced. In the centre of the flower is the female reproductive organ, the pistil(s). Each **pistil** consists of an **ovary** (derived from modified leaves called **carpels**) at its base, a slender, elongated projection (more than one in some species) called a **style**, and an often enlarged tip, a **stigma**, which acts as the receptive surface for pollen grains. The ovary contains a varying number of **ovules** which, after fertilization, develop into **seeds**.

The male and female parts may be in the same flower (bisexual) or separate flowers (unisexual). A **superior ovary**, borne on top of the receptacle, is visible from above, as sepals, petals and stamens are attached below its base. An **inferior ovary** is completely enclosed by the receptacle and is usually visible as a swelling of the flower stalk below the attachment of the sepals, petals and stamens.

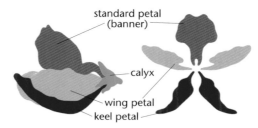

**Floral structure is often characteristic for a whole family. Here we depict a typical butterfly-like flower, as found in the Fabaceae [pea family; ertjiefamilie], and explain the composition of its corolla. The flower can be divided into equal halves (mirror images) along only one plane, a type of symmetry described as irregular. The petals are unequal: the uppermost (standard or banner) are the largest, the side petals (wings) are small and stalked and the basal ones united into a boat-shaped structure (keel) that encloses the ovary and stamens.**

## TYPES OF INFLORESCENCES

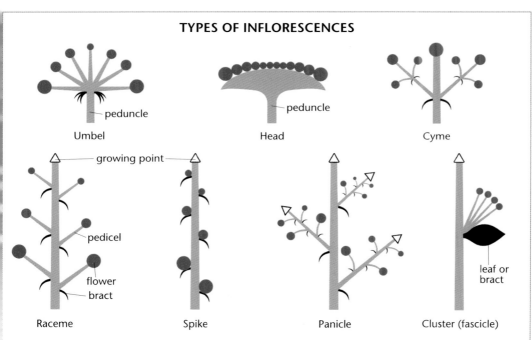

**An inflorescence is a shoot with a collection of flowers (shown as red circles; size indicates sequence of opening). The stalk of an inflorescence is called a peduncle. Each flower develops from a flower bud (the equivalent of an axillary bud) in the axil of a reduced leaf, called a bract (shown in black). Here we depict a few of the more common types. Based on the way inflorescences develop, there are two broad types. On determinate inflorescences (top), the main axis ends in a flower. On indeterminate inflorescences (bottom), the growing point (shown as triangles) produces only lateral flowers.**

# Fruits

A fruit is a matured ovary, along with any fused accessory structures such as the receptacle or calyx. The fruit contains the seeds of the plant. Fruits come in a bewildering range of types, and an elaborate system of classification exists to describe them. Fruit type is very constant for a species, so is important in tree identification. Fruit size and fruit colour are also diagnostic for individual species. Essentially, a primary distinction is made between fleshy and dry fruits, with dry fruits further subdivided into two types: indehiscent (nut, samara) and dehiscent (capsule, pod). The two main types of fleshy fruit are a berry and a drupe (the hard, seed-containing part of which is called a stone). Many specific fruit types are defined in the Glossary (p175). An infructescence is any mature inflorescence with fruits.

## BERRY AND DRUPE

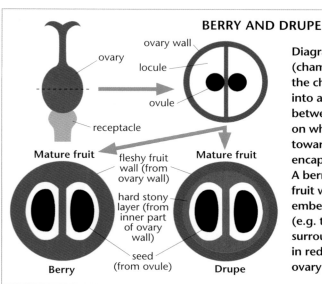

Diagram of an ovary with two locules (chambers) and one ovule per locule and the changes that occur when it develops into a berry or drupe. The distinction between the two fruit types is based on whether the ovary wall contributes towards a hard stony layer that encapsulates the seed in the mature fruit. A berry is a one- or many-seeded fleshy fruit with a soft outer portion and seeds embedded in the fleshy or pulpy tissue (e.g. tomato). In a drupe, the seed(s) is surrounded by a hard stony layer (shown in red) formed by the inner part of the ovary wall (e.g. peach, olive).

## FRUIT FROM SUPERIOR AND INFERIOR OVARIES

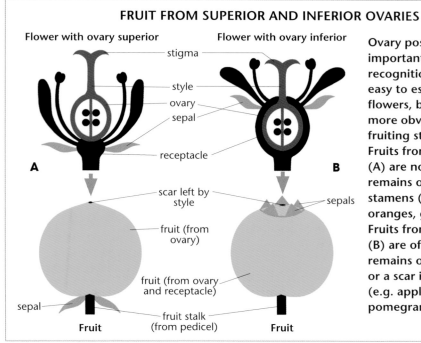

Ovary position is very important for family recognition. It is not always easy to establish in small flowers, but often becomes more obvious during the fruiting stage.

Fruits from superior ovaries (A) are not tipped by the remains of the perianth and stamens (e.g. avocados, oranges, grapes).

Fruits from inferior ovaries (B) are often tipped by the remains of the perianth, or a scar if it is deciduous (e.g. apples, guavas and pomegranates).

# Seeds

A seed is a matured ovule that contains an embryo and, often, nutritive tissues (endosperm). It is found inside a fruit. The seed itself should be seen as a complete miniaturized plant in a phase that allows it to move by external means. Seeds can also protect future generations by suspending their growth, allowing time for dispersal to occur or for the embryo to survive harsh, unfavourable conditions of cold, dryness or both, and sometimes even fire.

Seeds are surrounded by a protective seed coat, the development and microscopic structure of which is very important in plant classification, but essentially useless for field identification. Seeds of fleshy fruits are rather simple because the fruit itself serves as both advertisement and reward for dispersal by animals. However, in dry, dehiscent fruit (see p52, *Turraea*) the seed is often furnished with appendages such as fleshy envelopes, hairs or wings to assist in seed dispersal.

An aril is a fleshy outer covering or appendage that is soft, sometimes oily and often brightly coloured, usually white, yellow, orange or red. Arils develop from the seed coat or funicle (stalk or 'umbilical cord' that attaches the seed to the ovary wall) and are usually associated with seed dispersal by birds. As with other reproductive structures, seed characteristics are very constant, and therefore important in identification.

*Gardenia cornuta* [tonga gardenia; tonga-katjiepiering]. Berry derived from an inferior ovary, tipped by the persistent calyx.

*Diospyros simii* [climbing star-apple; rankster-appel]. Berries derived from superior ovaries, with persistent calyx at the base.

*Euclea natalensis* subsp. *natalensis* [natal guarri; natalghwarrie]. Berries derived from superior ovaries. Fruits that show asynchronous sequential colour changes during ripening are often dispersed by birds.

*Psychotria capensis* subsp. *capensis* [birdberry; voëlbessie]. Drupes derived from inferior ovaries, each tipped by the remains of the calyx.

*Olinia emarginata* [mountain hardpear; berghardepeer]. Drupes derived from inferior ovaries, each tipped by a circular scar left by the floral parts.

*Syzygium cordatum* [umdoni (SA), waterberry (N, Z); waterbessie]. Berries derived from inferior ovaries, each tipped by the remains of the calyx.

*Turraea obtusifolia* [small honeysuckletree; kleinkanferfoelieboom]. Seeds bright orange-red. Fruit a dehiscent capsule.

*Xylotheca kraussiana* [african dogrose; afrika-hondsroos]. Seeds black, partly covered by a bright red aril.

*Commiphora edulis* [roughleaf corkwood; skurweblaarkanniedood]. The blackish 'pip' inside fleshy drupes of the corkwoods is technically a stone and not a seed; the latter is found inside the stone. The hard wall of the stone is derived from the inner part of the ovary wall (see diagram of berry and drupe, p50). Likewise the unusual fleshy, often brightly coloured appendage that envelopes the stone at the base is derived from the ovary wall and is therefore termed a 'pseudo-aril' ('false aril'). A true aril is associated with the seed and is derived from the ovule or its appendages. (A) Ripening drupes. When pressure is applied the soft outer portion of the fruit wall splits into two halves. (B) Drupe with one half removed to show the black stone and red pseudo-aril. (C) Stone and pseudo-aril after shedding both fruit-wall halves.

# Geographical distribution

Every taxon (e.g. species, genus or family) has a particular geographical range. When a new species is described, it is not only defined by its structural features but also by its geographical distribution. Three broad types of distribution are commonly recognized: widespread, very narrow (endemic) or widely separate (disjunct). Knowing where a tree comes from makes identification considerably easier as it allows one to immediately eliminate as potential candidates all trees not commonly known in the particular area.

Field guides usually provide distribution maps which serve as quick visual aids, allowing one to only focus on species likely to occur in the area from which the plant to be identified comes.

In the distribution maps used in this book, coloured areas give a rough indication of the geographical limits of each particular species. The colours show whether a species is endemic (restricted) to southern Africa (shown in green), indigenous to the region but also found further north in Africa (orange), or a naturalized alien (blue), as in the examples opposite.

When describing as 'endemic' those species which have a very restricted or narrow range, one needs to qualify this by noting the 'usually very restricted' geographical area or region to which the taxon is endemic. For example, *Jubaeopsis*

**Green: endemic species; restricted to southern Africa**

**Orange: species is indigenous to southern Africa, but is also found further north in Africa**

**Blue: naturalized alien species**

*Sesamothamnus benguellensis* [kaoko sesamebush; kaokosesambos]. A rare tree endemic to the semi-desert parts of the Kaokoveld Centre in northwestern Namibia and southwestern Angola.

*caffra* [pondo palm; pondopalm] is endemic to Pondoland, while *Leucadendron argenteum* [silvertree; silwerboom] is endemic to the mountains of the Cape Peninsula.

When the distribution of restricted-range plants is mapped, certain recurring patterns may emerge. In this way, key areas can be distinguished that incorporate high concentrations of species with very restricted distributions. Known as 'centres of endemism' (see below), these are of special interest to botanists, conservationists and tree enthusiasts as they indicate areas where it is possible to see rare trees that are found nowhere else in the world.

## REGIONS AND CENTRES OF PLANT ENDEMISM

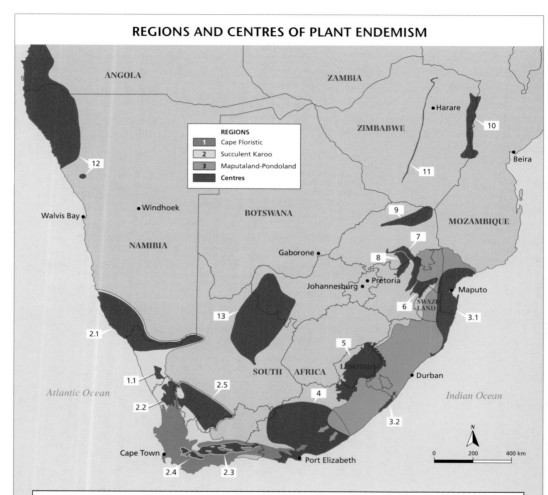

**REGIONS**
1  Cape Floristic
2  Succulent Karoo
3  Maputaland-Pondoland
   Centres

### Key to Regions and Centres

| | | |
|---|---|---|
| 1. Cape Floristic Region | 3. Maputaland–Pondoland Region | 9. Soutpansberg Centre |
| 1.1 Kamiesberg Centre | 3.1 Maputaland Centre | 10. Chimanimani–Nyanga Centre |
| 2. Succulent Karoo Region | 3.2 Pondoland Centre | 11. Great Dyke Centre |
| 2.1 Gariep Centre | 4. Albany Centre | 12. Kaokoveld Centre |
| 2.2 Knersvlakte Centre | 5. Drakensberg Alpine Centre | 13. Griqualand West Centre |
| 2.3 Little Karoo Centre | 6. Barberton Centre | |
| 2.4 Worcester–Robertson Karoo Centre | 7. Wolkberg Centre | |
| 2.5 Hantam–Roggeveld Centre | 8. Sekhukhuneland Centre | (After Van Wyk & Smith 2001) |

Centres in southern Africa that are particularly rich in restricted range (endemic) tree species are: Albany (4), Maputaland (3.1), Pondoland (3.2), Sekhukhuneland (8) and Kaokoveld (12). Areas with exceptional total tree diversity include the Chimanimani-Nyanga (10), Soutpansberg (9), Maputaland (3.1) and Pondoland (3.2) centres.

# Habitat

The habitat of a tree refers to the place where it lives and grows – its environment – incorporating both physical (abiotic) and living (biotic) factors. Significant non-living factors include characteristics of the soil (texture, structure, chemistry, rockiness) and climate (rainfall, temperature, wind, incidence of fire). Living factors include competition from associated plant species and interactions with plant-eaters, pollinators, seed dispersers and pathogens. Tree species display a specific range of tolerance for each of the various environmental factors, but if any factor falls outside the range of tolerance it becomes a

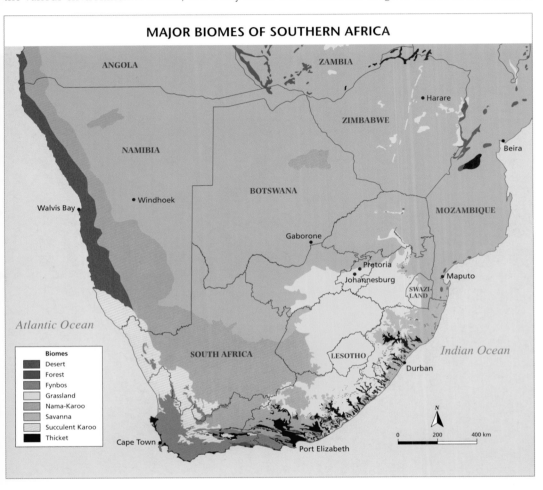

MAJOR BIOMES OF SOUTHERN AFRICA

**Biomes**
- Desert
- Forest
- Fynbos
- Grassland
- Nama-Karoo
- Savanna
- Succulent Karoo
- Thicket

limiting factor, preventing the species' establishment in a particular habitat. Each tree species has its own habitat requirements, and knowing these can be useful for identification. Range maps usually demarcate areas where suitable habitat conditions prevail for a particular species.

Habitat types form an intricate mosaic in nature due to variations in topography, geology and drainage. Soil type is useful for tree identification in so far as certain trees prefer either well-drained, deep sandy soils, or poorly drained, heavy clay soils.

Vegetation is usually determined by climatic conditions, and vegetation type can serve as indication of broad habitat types (biotic zones or biomes). If attributes such as dominant species, plant density and height are considered, biomes can be divided into smaller, more homogeneous ecological units or vegetation types. In our region, most trees are confined to the Savanna Biome (popularly known as bushveld and woodland), in which trees form an important component, as well as the Thicket and Forest Biomes.

# PART 2

## TREE GROUPS

*Trees can be categorized into 43 broadly defined groups, based on easy-to-observe stem and leaf characters. This section begins with a key to the groups, followed by an overview of each tree group, as well as explanatory notes on group characters, icon construction and tips on species identification. Examples of trees belonging to each group are also given.*

**Above** *Grewia occidentalis* [crossberry; kruisbessie]: flowers.
**Left** *Acacia abyssinica* subsp. *calophylla* [nyanga flattop; nyangaplatkroon].

# Key to the groups

The key on the following pages consists of a series of paired statements, called couplets or leads, because they lead one from one statement to another. The couplets are presented in the form of a flow diagram. Because each couplet consists of two leads, this is called a dichotomous key as, at each couplet a decision has to be taken to follow one lead or the other, so that the number of possible groups with which an unknown specimen can be identified is successively reduced until there is only one possibility.

Note that two leads are not printed together, but one above the other. To find the alternative lead one has to look down the page. To make it easier to find the two leads of a couplet, they are connected by a vertical line and, in most cases, are indented the same distance from the left margin. For convenience, the key has been split into three diagrams (labelled A, B and C), but the two leads of any couplet are always on the same page.

Beginning with the first pair of statements in Diagram A, read each carefully. Then examine the tree and decide which lead is most appropriate. At each lead a horizontal line takes you to the next couplet to be examined. At the end of some leads you will be directed to Diagram B or C. Go to the particular diagram and again start with the first pair of statements. Continue in this manner until you

**Flowers of *Schotia brachypetala***

reach the name of a group, then use the index or contents page to locate the relevant pages in this book. Here, you will find more information on the group and the species it contains. (For convenient access, the colour of the text panels corresponds with the Quick Guide on the inside back cover.)

For actual species identification, you will need a copy of *Field Guide to Trees of Southern Africa* (see p179). Turn to the applicable section, then proceed as set out on p23 of this book. You can also use the groups to help identify the possible families your tree might belong to (see Guide to tree families, p170).

One of the weaknesses of using a dichotomous key as an identification tool is that it requires the use of specified characters which may not be conveniently available or easily understood. Hence, in this key, the emphasis is on vegetative characters that are readily available (except during the dormant season, in the case of deciduous trees). Reproductive characters (such as flowers, fruit and seed) have been deliberately avoided because, in many trees, they are only present for part of the growing season, and often briefly so. An overview of the characters and character states used in the key is supplied on pp24–37. (Consult the Glossary on p175 if you do not understand certain terms.)

If you are uncertain whether or not a tree displays specific character states (for instance, whether stipules are present or absent), you could simply follow both leads to their respective groups and then compare the treatments of the two groups to see which best fits your plant. The more difficult statements have been placed towards the end of the various pathways because, if more than one couplet presents difficulties, it becomes easy to get confused.

**Autumn colours of *Kirkia wilmsii***

# Diagram A

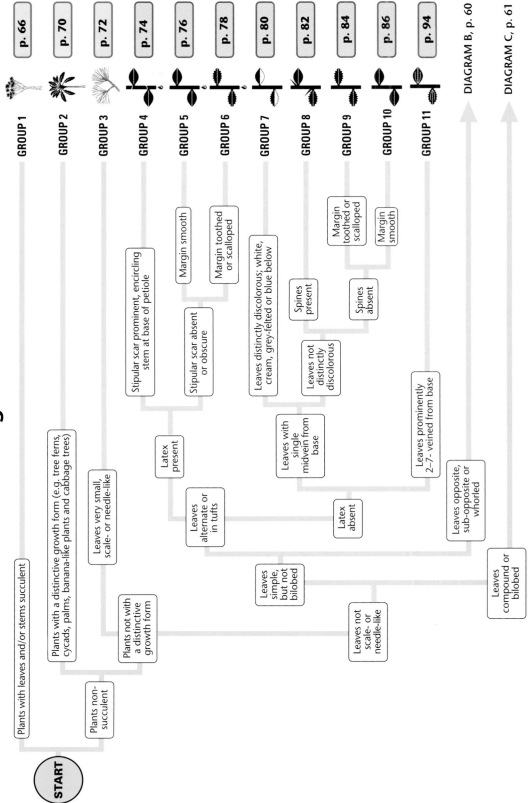

START

Plants with leaves and/or stems succulent

Plants non-succulent

Plants with a distinctive growth form (e.g. tree ferns, cycads, palms, banana-like plants and cabbage trees)

Plants not with a distinctive growth form

Leaves very small, scale- or needle-like

Leaves not scale- or needle-like

Latex present

Latex absent

Leaves simple, but not bilobed

Leaves compound or bilobed

Stipular scar prominent, encircling stem at base of petiole

Stipular scar absent or obscure

Leaves alternate or in tufts

Margin smooth

Margin toothed or scalloped

Leaves with single midvein from base

Leaves prominently 2–7- veined from base

Leaves distinctly discolorous; white, cream, grey-felted or blue below

Leaves not distinctly discolorous

Leaves opposite, sub-opposite or whorled

Spines present

Spines absent

Margin toothed or scalloped

Margin smooth

GROUP 1 — p. 66
GROUP 2 — p. 70
GROUP 3 — p. 72
GROUP 4 — p. 74
GROUP 5 — p. 76
GROUP 6 — p. 78
GROUP 7 — p. 80
GROUP 8 — p. 82
GROUP 9 — p. 84
GROUP 10 — p. 86
GROUP 11 — p. 94

DIAGRAM B, p. 60

DIAGRAM C, p. 61

# Diagram B

|  |  |
|-------|------|
| GROUP 12 | p. 96 |
| GROUP 13 | p. 98 |
| GROUP 14 | p. 100 |
| GROUP 15 | p. 102 |
| GROUP 16 | p. 104 |
| GROUP 17 | p. 106 |
| GROUP 18 | p. 110 |
| GROUP 19 | p. 112 |
| GROUP 20 | p. 114 |
| GROUP 21 | p. 116 |
| GROUP 22 | p. 118 |
| GROUP 23 | p. 120 |
| GROUP 24 | p. 124 |
| GROUP 25 | p. 126 |

Branching key:

. . . Leaves opposite, sub-opposite or whorled

- Leaves opposite or sub-opposite
  - Leaves prominently 3–5-veined from or near the base → GROUP 12
  - Leaves single- or pinnately veined
    - Interpetiolar stipules, scar or ridge present
      - Leaves distinctly discolorous; white or silvery grey below → GROUP 13
      - Leaves not distinctly discolorous
        - Margin smooth
          - Spines present → GROUP 14
          - Spines absent
            - Leaves with blackish bacterial nodules → GROUP 16
            - Leaves without bacterial nodules
              - Leaves densely hairy, at least below → GROUP 16
              - Leaves smooth or sparsely hairy → GROUP 17
        - Margin toothed → GROUP 18
    - Interpetiolar stipules, scar or ridge absent
      - Margin toothed or lobed → GROUP 19
      - Margin smooth
        - Latex present
          - Spines present → GROUP 20
          - Spines absent → GROUP 21
        - Latex absent
          - Leaves with secretory cavities → GROUP 22
          - Leaves without secretory cavities → GROUP 23
- Leaves 3- or more whorled
  - Latex present → GROUP 24
  - Latex absent → GROUP 25

# Diagram C

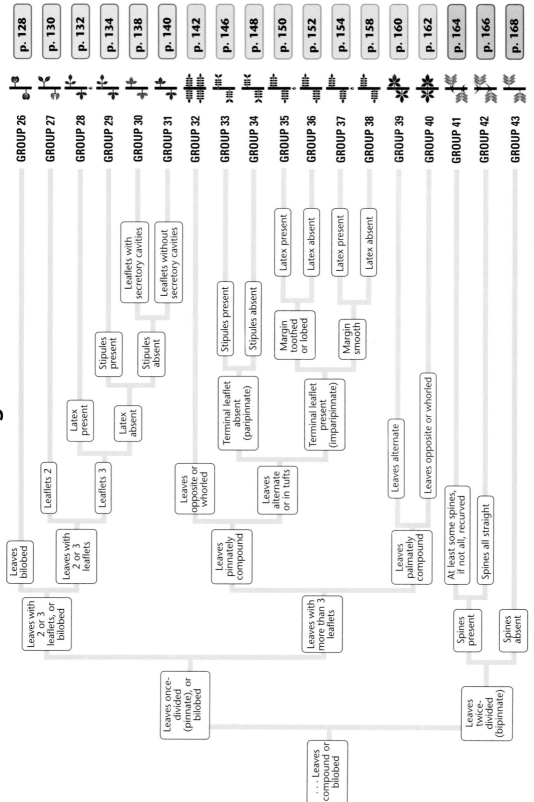

| | | |
|---|---|---|
| GROUP 26 | | **p. 128** |
| GROUP 27 | | **p. 130** |
| GROUP 28 | | **p. 132** |
| GROUP 29 | | **p. 134** |
| GROUP 30 | | **p. 138** |
| GROUP 31 | | **p. 140** |
| GROUP 32 | | **p. 142** |
| GROUP 33 | | **p. 146** |
| GROUP 34 | | **p. 148** |
| GROUP 35 | | **p. 150** |
| GROUP 36 | | **p. 152** |
| GROUP 37 | | **p. 154** |
| GROUP 38 | | **p. 158** |
| GROUP 39 | | **p. 160** |
| GROUP 40 | | **p. 162** |
| GROUP 41 | | **p. 164** |
| GROUP 42 | | **p. 166** |
| GROUP 43 | | **p. 168** |

Leaflets with secretory cavities

Leaflets without secretory cavities

Stipules present

Stipules absent

Latex present

Latex absent

Latex present

Latex absent

Latex present

Latex absent

Stipules present

Stipules absent

Margin toothed or lobed

Margin smooth

Leaflets 2

Leaflets 3

Terminal leaflet absent (paripinnate)

Terminal leaflet present (imparipinnate)

Leaves opposite or whorled

Leaves alternate or in tufts

Leaves alternate

Leaves opposite or whorled

Leaves bilobed

Leaves with 2 or 3 leaflets

Leaves pinnately compound

Leaves palmately compound

At least some spines, if not all, recurved

Spines all straight

Leaves with 2 or 3 leaflets, or bilobed

Leaves with more than 3 leaflets

Spines present

Spines absent

Leaves once-divided (pinnate), or bilobed

Leaves twice-divided (bipinnate)

. . . Leaves compound or bilobed

61

# Outline of group characters

Here we provide an outline of the diagnostic characters for the various groups and clusters of groups. It is a summary of all features selected in the 'Key to the groups' (see pp59–61) that can lead to the identification of a particular group. In the 'Group overviews' (see pp66–169) these diagnostic characters appear as page headers in the case of the collective group characters, and also as icon labels together with the more specific group characters.

Colours correspond with the relevant group panel in the 'Key to the groups', the colour coding on pp66–169 and the 'Quick guide to the groups' on the inside back cover.

## Trees with unusual features

1. **Succulent group:** Leaves and/or stems succulent.
2. **Palm group:** Growth form distinctive.
3. **Cedar group:** Leaves scale- or needle-like.

## Leaves simple and alternate or in tufts, not bilobed

4. **Fig group:** Latex present; stipular scar prominent, encircling stem at base of leaf stalk.
5. **Milkplum group:** Latex present; stipular scar absent or obscure; margin entire.
6. **Tamboti group:** Latex present; stipular scar absent or obscure; margin toothed or scalloped.
7. **Silver-oak group:** Latex absent; leaves with single midvein from base, distinctly discolorous.
8. **Spikethorn group:** Latex absent; leaves with single midvein from base, not distinctly discolorous; spines present.
9. **Wild-plane group:** Latex absent; leaves with single midvein from base, not distinctly discolorous; spines absent; margin toothed or scalloped.
10. **Common group:** Latex absent; leaves with single midvein from base, not distinctly discolorous; spines absent; margin entire.
11. **Raisin bush group:** Latex absent; leaves prominently 2–7-veined from base.

## Leaves simple and opposite or sub-opposite

12. **Monkey-orange group:** Leaves prominently 3–5-veined from or near the base.
13. **Sagewood group:** Leaves single- or pinnately veined; interpetiolar stipules, scar or ridge present; leaves distinctly discolorous, white or silvery grey below.
14. **Turkeyberry group:** Leaves single- or pinnately veined; interpetiolar stipules, scar or ridge present; leaves not distinctly discolorous, margin smooth; spines present.
15. **Bridesbush group:** Leaves single- or pinnately veined; interpetiolar stipules, scar or ridge present; leaves not distinctly discolorous, margin smooth; spines absent; leaves with blackish bacterial nodules.
16. **Wild-medlar group:** Leaves single- or pinnately veined; interpetiolar stipules, scar or ridge present; leaves not distinctly discolorous, margin entire; spines absent; leaves without bacterial nodules, densely hairy, at least below.
17. **False-gardenia group:** Leaves single- or pinnately veined; interpetiolar stipules, scar or ridge present; leaves not distinctly discolorous, margin entire; spines absent; leaves without bacterial nodules, smooth or sparsely hairy.
18. **Onionwood group:** Leaves single- or pinnately veined; interpetiolar stipules, scar or ridge present; leaves not distinctly discolorous, margin toothed.
19. **Spoonwood group:** Leaves single- or pinnately veined; interpetiolar stipules, scar or ridge absent; leaf margin toothed or lobed.

20. **Numnum group:** Leaves single- or pinnately veined; interpetiolar stipules, scar or ridge absent; leaf margin entire; latex present; spines present.
21. **Poisonbush group:** Leaves single- or pinnately veined; interpetiolar stipules, scar or ridge absent; leaf margin entire; latex present; spines absent.
22. **Waterberry group:** Leaves single- or pinnately veined; interpetiolar stipules, scar or ridge absent; leaf margin entire; latex absent; leaves with secretory cavities.
23. **Bushwillow group:** Leaves single- or pinnately veined; interpetiolar stipules, scar or ridge absent; leaf margin entire; latex absent; leaves without secretory cavities.

## Leaves simple and 3- or more whorled
24. **Quininetree group:** Latex present.
25. **Wild-almond group:** Latex absent.

## Leaves once-divided, with 2 or 3 leaflets, or simple and bilobed
26. **Bauhinia group:** Leaves simple, bilobed.
27. **Mopane group:** Leaves once divided, with 2 leaflets.
28. **Corkwood group:** Leaves once divided, with 3 leaflets; latex present (see also Group 31).
29. **Coraltree group:** Leaves once divided, with 3 leaflets; latex absent; stipules present.
30. **White-ironwood group:** Leaves once divided, with 3 leaflets; latex absent; stipules absent; leaflets with secretory cavities.
31. **Karee group:** Leaves once divided, with 3 leaflets; latex absent, or if present, then flow often inconspicuous or inconsistent; stipules absent; leaflets without secretory cavities.

## Leaves once-divided, with more than 3 leaflets
32. **Sausagetree group:** Leaves pinnately compound, opposite or whorled.
33. **Boerbean group:** Leaves pinnately compound, alternate or in tufts; terminal leaflet absent (paripinnate); stipules present.
34. **Soapberry group:** Leaves pinnately compound, alternate or in tufts; terminal leaflet absent (paripinnate); stipules absent.
35. **Peppertree group:** Leaves pinnately compound, alternate or in tufts; terminal leaflet present (imparipinnate); leaflet margin toothed or lobed; latex present.
36. **Knobwood group:** Leaves pinnately compound, alternate or in tufts; terminal leaflet present (imparipinnate); leaflet margin toothed or lobed; latex absent.
37. **Marula group:** Leaves pinnately compound, alternate or in tufts; terminal leaflet present (imparipinnate); leaflet margin entire; latex present.
38. **Kiaat group:** Leaves pinnately compound, alternate or in tufts; terminal leaflet present (imparipinnate); leaflet margin entire; latex absent.
39. **Baobab group:** Leaves palmately compound, alternate.
40. **Fingerleaf group:** Leaves palmately compound, opposite or whorled.

## Leaves twice-divided
41. **Hook thorn group:** Spines present, at least some, if not all, recurved.
42. **Sweet thorn group:** Spines present, all straight.
43. **False-thorn group:** Spines absent.

# Layout of group overviews

With an estimated 2 100 tree species native to southern Africa, and well over 100 more species introduced from other parts of the world and now naturalized in our region, it is not practical to cover more than a fraction of this diversity in a guide like this.

The purpose of the group overviews is not species identification; it is to emphasize the diagnostic characters of the 43 groups and give tips on how to recognize them, with examples of some of the more common trees in our region that belong in each particular group. The group treatments are intended to supplement the comprehensive species treatments provided in *Field Guide to Trees of Southern Africa* (see p179).

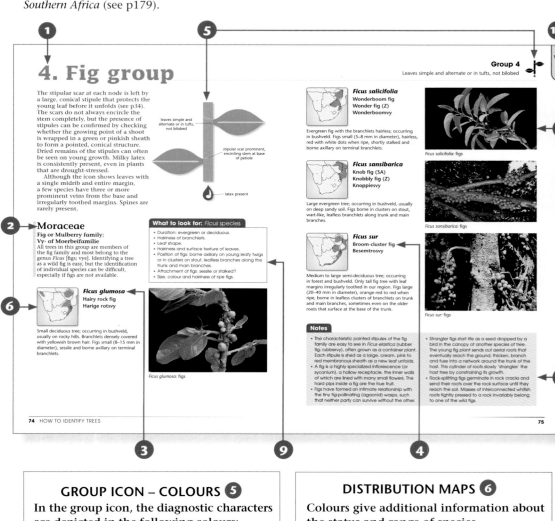

## GROUP ICON – COLOURS ⑤

**In the group icon, the diagnostic characters are depicted in the following colours:**

- veins
- stipule (triangle); stipular scar or prominent ridge (rectangle)
- spines
- leaves
- latex
- stem

## DISTRIBUTION MAPS ⑥

**Colours give additional information about the status and range of species.**

- Green indicates a species endemic (strictly confined) to southern Africa;
- Orange represents a species indigenous to southern Africa but also found further north in Africa;
- Blue represents a naturalized alien species.

# Key to using the group overviews

**1 Group**

Each group has been given a number, as well as a common name derived from one of its constituent genera (for example, Fig group), or an outstanding character of that group. Each group treatment starts with an icon (see 5, below), accompanied by a brief explanation of the group's diagnostic characters, mentioning specific points to note. This is followed by a small selection of trees belonging to the group, arranged according to family (see 2, below).

**2 Family**

Family features are highlighted and mention is made of particularly significant genera, plus the characters useful for their identification (see 3). Because of space restrictions, not all families in a group are covered, but a full list of families in each group is supplied on pp170–174.

**3 Species**

Each species (or subspecies/variety) name (p20) is accompanied by a brief description of the taxon's key characters, at least one photograph, distribution map, and its common names (see 4, below). In a few cases, synonyms are supplied, reflecting fairly recent name changes. They are preceded by an equal sign (=) and placed in brackets. A synonym is a scientific name under which a plant was previously known or by which it is alternatively referred to in different classification systems.

**4 Common names**

Recommended common names are supplied in English and Afrikaans, with names in some cases derived from other local languages. Where applicable, the recommended regional common names of tree species are reflected in the text as follows: SA: South Africa; N: Namibia; and Z: Zimbabwe.

**5 Group icon**

The icon is a pictorial representation of some of the group's diagnostic characters. An explanation of the colours used is supplied on the opposite page. The labelling for each icon essentially summarizes the most important leads you have selected in the Key to the Groups (see p58). The mini icon at the top right is accompanied by the main collective group feature(s) you have selected in the key.

**6 Distribution maps**

Distribution maps show the main areas in southern Africa (south of the Kunene-Kavango-Zambezi rivers) where a species is most likely to be found. See also Geographical Distribution (p53).

**7 Photographs**

Each species is accompanied by at least one photograph showing features that can be used for identification, such as the leaves, flowers, fruits, seeds or bark.

**8 Notes**

Identification hints and anecdotal information are provided in the form of Notes for each group.

**9 What to look for**

For selected larger genera, species identification features are highlighted in an easy-to-locate box. These are characters that are most useful for differentiating between members of a particular genus.

**10 Colour coding**

The background colours match the group panels (see p58 and Quick Guide on inside back cover).

# 1. Succulent group

A succulent is generally defined as a plant with fleshy, juicy leaves or stems. Succulent leaves are usually soft, exude lots of watery sap when squashed and are easy to identify. Because of their supportive function, succulent stems are often less juicy than leaves. Despite an often swollen appearance, the stems can become quite hard and woody. It is debatable whether some trees with thick stems are succulents in the usual sense of the word. Some may better qualify as an unusual growth form (see Group 2, p70). One such case is the baobab, with its thick, but quite woody, trunk. Our inclusion of stem succulents in this group is therefore somewhat subjective and biased towards trees with a less than typical tree-like appearance.

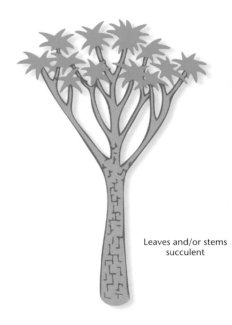

Leaves and/or stems succulent

## Asphodelaceae
### Aloe family; Aalwynfamilie

Plants traditionally classified in an inclusive Liliaceae are now placed in several segregate families. The Asphodelaceae includes the succulent-leaved genus *Aloe* (aloes; aalwyne), several species of which can grow quite tall, though usually with the stems unbranched or sparsely branched.

### *Aloe dichotoma*
Quiver tree
Kokerboom

Small tree with a thickset trunk and dense, rounded crown; occurring in desert and semi-desert areas, usually on rocky ridges. Leaves succulent, blue-green or yellowish green; margin with small, yellowish brown teeth. Flowers bright yellow, borne terminally in spikes above the leaf rosette. Fruit a capsule.

*Aloe dichotoma:* tree

# Euphorbiaceae

**Euphorbia family;**
**Naboomfamilie**

Most succulent trees of the family belong to *Euphorbia* (euphorbias; nabome), a genus of stem succulents with abundant, milky latex. Spines are usually present. Species identification is sometimes tricky.

> **What to look for:** *Euphorbia* species
>
> - Tree distinctly candelabra-shaped or not.
> - Branching pattern of tree.
> - Branchlets constricted or not.
> - Number of mature branchlet angles.
> - Branchlets distinctly winged or not.
> - Horny spine shields on stem margins separate or continuous.
> - Spines present or absent.
> - Number and size of spines.

## *Euphorbia ingens*

**Giant euphorbia (N, Z)**
**Naboom (SA)**

Spiny, succulent tree with a sturdy main stem and massive dark green crown; lower branches not shed with age as in many other species; crown not distinctly candelabra-like. Occurring in bushveld, often on rocky outcrops or deep sand, also on termitaria. Branchlets usually 4- or 5-angled, forming segments with parallel sides; spines paired, borne on separate cushions that do not form a continuous ridge. Flowers (cyathia) in clusters, greenish yellow. Fruit an almost globose capsule, reddish.

*Euphorbia ingens:* flowers

*Euphorbia ingens:* tree

## Notes

- The milky latex of tree euphorbias should be treated as toxic and handled with great caution. In some species, the latex is very caustic and can cause serious injuries on contact. Volatile substances may also be released by the latex. These can cause injury to the eyes and other mucous membranes after brief exposure, even without direct contact with the latex.

- Succulent euphorbias bear a superficial resemblance to South and North American Cactaceae, some of which have become naturalized in our region. Use a sharp object to carefully poke a small hole in the succulent stem; if it is euphorbia, abundant milky latex will flow from the wound. Although latex is present in certain genera of the cactus family, all local tree members of this family lack milky latex.

## *Euphorbia triangularis*
### River euphorbia
### Riviernaboom

Spiny, succulent tree with a sturdy main stem and several stem-like branches, each topped with a small candelabra-like crown. Occurring in thicket and bushveld, often in dense stands. Branchlets usually 3-angled; margins sinuate; spines paired, slender, borne on interrupted or continuous horny cushions along each ridge. Flowers (cyathia) in clusters of up to three, greenish yellow. Fruit a 3-lobed capsule.

*Euphorbia triangularis:* tree

## *Euphorbia sekukuniensis*
### Sekhukhune euphorbia
### Sekhukhunenaboom

Small, spiny, succulent tree with a sturdy main stem and a small, rounded candelabra-shaped canopy. Occurring in bushveld, localized, usually in groups on rocky ridges. Branchlets about 1 m long, slender, 15–20 mm in diameter, 4- or 5-angled; spines in pairs, borne on cushions that unite to form a horny margin along angles of stem. Flowers (cyathia) in clusters, greenish, yellow. Fruit a deeply 3-lobed capsule, shortly stalked.

*Euphorbia sekukuniensis:* tree

# Portulacaceae

**Purslane family; Porseleinfamilie**

A family of mainly leaf succulents and few tree-like members in our region. These belong to *Portulacaria* [spekboombushes; spekboombosse] and *Ceraria* [porkbushes; wolftoonbosse] genera which are sometimes classified in the Didiereaceae.

### *Portulacaria afra*
**Spekboom**

Shrub or small tree; occurring in bushveld and thicket, often in dense stands and dominant over large areas. Leaves opposite, almost circular to obovate. Flowers borne in many-flowered, branched inflorescences, small, pale pink to purplish. Fruit a small capsule, narrowly 3-winged.

*Portulacaria afra:* flowers

# Vitaceae

**Grape family; Druiwefamilie**

A few species of *Cyphostemma* [cobas trees; kobasbome] in Namibia and far southwestern Angola reach tree size. They have pronounced, swollen stems and large, succulent, trifoliolate leaves.

### *Cyphostemma currorii*
**Cobas**
**Kobas**

Small tree with a thick, succulent trunk; occurring in semi-desert and desert areas, usually in rocky places. Bark smooth, whitish to pinkish, flaking in large, yellow, papery pieces. Leaves trifoliolate, fleshy. Flowers small, yellowish green, produced in erect, flat-topped, branched heads. Fruit a berry, oval, red.

*Cyphostemma currorii:* tree with inflorescences

# 2. Palm group

Growth form is of limited use for tree identification. Exceptions include those trees with a single or sparsely branched erect trunk and a small symmetrical canopy of large simple or compound leaves – the type of growth form displayed by many palms. In such trees, the distinct growth form is present from an early age.

Inclusion of some species of *Cussonia* [cabbagetrees; kiepersolbome] in the present group is based more on their distinctive leaves than the growth form, as the latter may change with age. The large, palmately compound leaves borne in clusters at the ends of thick stems and branches are so distinctive that members of the genus can readily be identified among other trees, even from quite a distance. The palm group also includes the tree-like grasses or bamboos. (More conventional trees with a distinctive outline when mature, for example thorn trees with their typically flattened and spreading or umbrella-shaped canopy, are placed among the groups based on stem and leaf characters. Young plants of these trees are often not very distinctive in terms of growth form.)

Leaves and/or stems not succulent

Plants with a distinctive growth form

## Araliaceae
### Cabbagetree family; Kiepersolfamilie

Some species of *Cussonia* [cabbagetrees; kiepersolbome] have large palmately or bipalmately compound leaves that render the plants conspicuous from a distance. The large terminal inflorescences are often umbel-like and assist in the easy recognition of the group.

### *Cussonia paniculata* subsp. *sinuata*
**Highveld cabbagetree**
**Hoëveldkiepersol**

Small tree with a sturdy trunk and blue-green to grey foliage, sparsely branched. Occurring in bushveld and wooded grassland, usually in rocky places. Leaves clustered near the ends of branches, once palmately compound with up to 11 radiating leaflets; margins deeply lobed and often wavy. Flowers small, greenish yellow, borne in branched panicles of spikes. Fruit a fleshy drupe, globose, purple.

*Cussonia paniculata* subsp. *sinuata*: tree

# Arecaceae
## Palm family; Palmfamilie

Palms are poorly represented in our region with only about six native species. They all have unbranched stems, though plants can be multistemmed. The compound leaves are either fan-shaped (palmate) or feather-shaped (pinnate) and this knowledge is essential for species identification.

### *Phoenix reclinata*
Wild datepalm
Wildedadelboom

Palm up to 10 m high with a slender, erect or reclining stem, usually multistemmed; occurring in bushveld and on coastal dunes, often along rivers. Leaves feather-shaped, 3–4 m long, arching, lower leaflets reduced to yellowish spines. Flowers small, cream, produced in broom-like bunches. Fruit an oval drupe, date-like, up to 15 mm long, orange-brown.

*Phoenix reclinata:* tree

# Strelitziaceae
## Strelitzia family; Kraanvoëlblomfamilie

Three rather similar looking species of tree strelitzia occur in our region. They all have predominantly white flowers borne in large, boat-shaped bracts (spathes). Geographical distribution is a good guide to their identification.

### *Strelitzia nicolai*
Natal strelitzia
Natalstrelitzia

Banana-like tree with a conspicuous fan-shaped crown, usually multistemmed; occurring on coastal dunes and adjacent inland areas. Leaves simple, up to 2 x 0.6 m, stalked, often split by the wind. Inflorescence comprises up to five purplish-blue boat-shaped spathes, each at right angles to the preceding one. Flowers with white sepals and a central, narrow, blue, arrow-shaped structure formed by the petals. Fruit a 3-lobed capsule; seeds black with a tuft of bright-orange hairs.

*Strelitzia nicolai:* trees

---

### Notes

- Tree-like members of the genus *Encephalartos* (African cycads; broodbome) have a palm-like appearance. Cycad leaves have a central stalk flanked by narrow leaflets (feather-like; pinnate). Cycads are gymnosperms that reproduce by means of cones; palms are flowering plants. Tree cycads have a limited geographical range.

- The strelitzia family is often confused with the banana family to which the large simple leaves bear a superficial resemblance. Tree strelitzias have a true stem, with leaves arranged in a fan (2-ranked). In bananas, the leaves are borne spirally at the end of a false stem formed by the tightly overlapping leaf sheaths.

# 3. Cedar group

Scale- and needle-like leaves are easy to recognize, but it becomes subjective whether to include in the present group certain trees with very narrow, but flat, leaves. Needle-like 'leaves' may be true leaves, the rachides of pinnately compound leaves that have lost their leaflets, or thin stems with limited growth. Rarely are leaves poorly developed or absent and the plant uses its branched twigs to function as leaves.

Leaves and/or stems not succulent
Plants not with a distinctive growth form

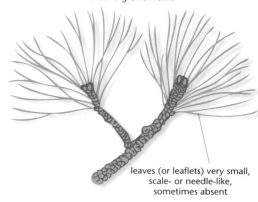

leaves (or leaflets) very small, scale- or needle-like, sometimes absent

## Cupressaceae
### Cypress family; Sipresfamilie

A family of conifers (gymnosperms) with three species native to our region. They all have scale-like mature leaves arranged in opposite pairs. Juvenile leaves tend to be needle-like.

### Widdringtonia nodiflora
**Mountain-cypress (SA)**
**Mountain-cedar (Z)**
**Bergsipres**

Evergreen shrub or small tree, usually with a columnar shape; occurring in fynbos or at high altitude in mountainous areas. Adult leaves scale-like, about 2 mm long, pressed tightly against the branchlets. Male cones up to 4 mm long. Female cones globose, up to 20 mm in diameter, greyish green becoming dark brown with age; scales (valves) four, surface smooth or wrinkled with a few warts.

*Widdringtonia nodiflora*: female cones

## Ericaceae
### Heath family; Heidefamilie

More than 700 species of *Erica* [heaths; heides] occur in our region, the vast majority being low-growing perennial shrublets confined to the Cape Floristic Region. Fewer than 15 reach tree size. Most species have small, rigid, needle-like leaves without stipules.

### Erica hexandra
(=*Philippia hexandra*)
**Petrolbush**
**Petrolbos**

Evergreen shrub or small tree; occurring at high altitude on mountain slopes, often in dense stands among rocks or along streams. Leaves 4-whorled, needle-like, up to 2 mm long. Flowers in clusters at tips of branchlets, small, inconspicuous, greenish tinged with red, wind-pollinated; style protruding from the flower, with stigma saucer-shaped.

*Erica hexandra*: flowers

# Pinaceae

## Pine family; Dennefamilie

A large family of conifers mainly confined to the northern hemisphere and with no native members. Several species of *Pinus* [pines; denne] are grown commercially in plantations for timber and some of these have now become invader weeds in our region.

### *Pinus pinaster*
**Cluster pine**
**Trosden**

Medium to large coniferous tree; a native of Mediterranean Europe, now invading mountain and lowland fynbos. Needles in clusters of two, 80–240 mm long, thick and rigid, dull grey-green. Female cones woody, conic-ovoid, purplish when young, becoming light-brown when mature; cone scales with a prominent ridge, ending in a short, curved point.

*Pinus pinaster:* female cones

# Polygalaceae

## Milkwort family; Melkkruidfamilie

A small family with about four tree species in our region, most with conventional leaves. Flowers in the family superficially resemble those of the Fabaceae [pea family; ertjiefamilie], but what appears to be the two wing-like 'petals' are enlarged sepals.

### *Nylandtia spinosa*
**Tortoiseberry**
**Skilpadbessie**

Multistemmed shrub or small tree with stiff erect branchlets; occurring in fynbos, on sandy soils or rocky slopes. Branchlets sometimes spine-tipped. Leaves simple, small, oval, almost stalkless. Flowers solitary in upper axils, pinkish. Fruit a drupe, round, red, with one or two seeds.

*Nylandtia spinosa:* flowers and fruit

## Notes

- Introduced species of *Casuarina* (beefwood trees; kasuarisbome) are often mistaken for pines. What appear to be needle-shaped leaves in the former are short, thin branches, distinguished from pine needles by being jointed, with several nodes and internodes. True leaves are reduced to a whorl of minute blackish scales at each node. Beefwood trees are flowering plants, but their fruit is clustered together in woody, oval, cone-like structures about 20 mm long.

# 4. Fig group

The stipular scar at each node is left by a large, conical stipule that protects the young leaf before it unfolds (see p34). The scars do not always encircle the stem completely, but the presence of stipules can be confirmed by checking whether the growing point of a shoot is wrapped in a green or pinkish sheath to form a pointed, conical structure. Dried remains of the stipules can often be seen on young growth. Milky latex is consistently present, even in plants that are drought-stressed.

   Although the icon shows leaves with a single midrib and entire margin, a few species have three or more prominent veins from the base and irregularly toothed margins. Spines are rarely present.

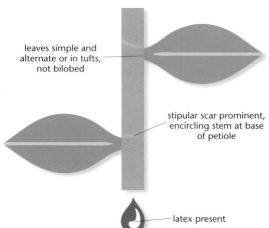

leaves simple and alternate or in tufts, not bilobed

stipular scar prominent, encircling stem at base of petiole

latex present

## Moraceae

**Fig or Mulberry family;**
**Vy- of Moerbeifamilie**

All trees in this group are members of the fig family and most belong to the genus *Ficus* [figs; vye]. Identifying a tree as a wild fig is easy, but the identification of individual species can be difficult, especially if figs are not available.

### What to look for: *Ficus* species

- Duration: evergreen or deciduous.
- Hairiness of branchlets.
- Leaf shape.
- Hairiness and surface texture of leaves.
- Position of figs: borne axillary on young leafy twigs or in clusters on stout, leafless branches along the trunk and main branches.
- Attachment of figs: sessile or stalked?
- Size, colour and hairiness of ripe figs.

### Ficus glumosa

**Hairy rock fig**
**Harige rotsvy**

Small deciduous tree; occurring in bushveld, usually on rocky hills. Branchlets densely covered with yellowish brown hair. Figs small (8–15 mm in diameter), sessile and borne axillary on terminal branchlets.

*Ficus glumosa:* figs

## *Ficus salicifolia*
**Wonderboom fig**
**Wonder fig (Z)**
**Wonderboomvy**

Evergreen fig with the branchlets hairless; occurring in bushveld. Figs small (5–8 mm in diameter), hairless, red with white dots when ripe, shortly stalked and borne axillary on terminal branchlets.

*Ficus salicifolia:* figs

## *Ficus sansibarica*
**Knob fig (SA)**
**Knobbly fig (Z)**
**Knoppiesvy**

Large evergreen tree; occurring in bushveld, usually on deep sandy soil. Figs borne in clusters on stout, wart-like, leafless branchlets along trunk and main branches.

*Ficus sansibarica:* figs

## *Ficus sur*
**Broom-cluster fig**
**Besemtrosvy**

Medium to large semi-deciduous tree; occurring in forest and bushveld. Only tall fig tree with leaf margins irregularly toothed in our region. Figs large (20–40 mm in diameter), orange-red to red when ripe, borne in leafless clusters of branchlets on trunk and main branches, sometimes even on the older roots that surface at the base of the trunk.

*Ficus sur:* figs

## Notes

- The characteristic pointed stipules of the fig family are easy to see in *Ficus elastica* (rubber fig; rubbervy), often grown as a container plant. Each stipule is shed as a large, cream, pink to red membranous sheath as a new leaf unfolds.
- A fig is a highly specialized inflorescence (or syconium), a hollow receptacle, the inner walls of which are lined with many small flowers. The hard pips inside a fig are the true fruit.
- Figs have formed an intimate relationship with the tiny fig-pollinating (agaonid) wasps, such that neither party can survive without the other.

- Strangler figs start life as a seed dropped by a bird in the canopy of another species of tree. The young fig plant sends out aerial roots that eventually reach the ground, thicken, branch and fuse into a network around the trunk of the host. This cylinder of roots slowly 'strangles' the host tree by constraining its growth.
- Rock-splitting figs germinate in rock cracks and send their roots over the rock surface until they reach the soil. Masses of interconnected whitish roots tightly pressed to a rock invariably belong to one of the wild figs.

# 5. Milkplum group

This group is similar to Group 4 (see p74), but the stipules are either absent, small, and difficult to detect; or, if large, then they do not leave a scar that more or less encircles the stem. The milkplum group is also more diverse in its representation. The flow of latex is less consistent, especially under conditions of drought and during autumn (in the case of deciduous trees). In this group, latex can vary from watery to milky (brown-coloured in *Rapanea* [cape-beeches; Kaapse boekenhoutbome], but the latter is put in Group 10 because latex flow is often weak). Because of its greater visibility, milky latex can often be detected at times when flow is low by gently squeezing the broken end of the petiole

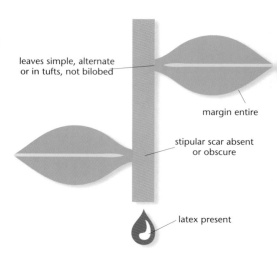

to see if any white liquid oozes out. Watery latex, however, is easily overlooked and it may take longer for enough liquid to be exuded to allow for a positive identification. Several species in this group have discolorous leaves (Group 7, see p80), but the presence of latex takes priority in the key. Spines are rarely present.

## Anacardiaceae
### Mango family; Mangofamilie

Species of *Ozoroa* [resintrees; harpuisbome] from the arid western parts of our region tend to have alternate leaves crowded near the ends of branches, in contrast to the whorled or opposite arrangement of their eastern counterparts (Group 24, see p124). The two groups may represent different genera. All resintrees have leaves with the principal lateral veins numerous, conspicuously parallel and terminating at the margin, instead of merging with an intramarginal vein (forming a herringbone pattern).

### *Ozoroa dispar*
Namaqua resintree
Namakwaharpuisboom

Small to medium-sized tree; occurring in semi-desert regions, usually on rocky ridges. Latex white. Leaves bright green and hairless above, densely hairy and greyish green below; principal lateral veins particularly distinct above. Flowers small, creamy white, male and female on different plants. Fruit a drupe, kidney-shape, black and wrinkled when mature.

*Ozoroa dispar*: fruit

# Euphorbiaceae
### Euphorbia family; Naboomfamilie

As traditionally defined, the euphorbia family is a very heterogeneous one with several subfamilies. To the layman, few features would seem to indicate a common family link among those genera of this family in the present group. Small stipules are usually present and a few genera have 3-lobed capsules. In *Croton* [feverberries; koorsbessies] the brownish colour of young growth is due to the presence of minute, flat, circular scales (specialized hairs; see p31).

### *Croton gratissimus* var. *gratissimus*
**Lavender feverberry (SA)**
**Lavender croton (Z)**
**Laventelkoorsbessie**
**Mbango (N)**

Small to medium-sized tree; occurring in bushveld, usually on rocky ridges. Latex watery or cloudy. Leaves with upper surface dark green, lower surface densely covered with silvery white scales, sparsely dotted with an occasional brown one (see p31). Pair of small, inconspicuous glands present on lower surface of blade, near junction with petiole and next to midrib, or on petiole. Flowers in slender, drooping spikes, small, cream. Fruit a 3-lobed capsule.

*Croton gratissimus:* flowers

# Sapotaceae
### Milkwood family; Melkhoutfamilie

A family well represented in this group. Young growth often has a rusty or brownish colour due to the presence of normal simple hairs. Mature leaves in some genera are congested in rosettes near the ends of branches. All native members have white latex and fleshy, usually edible berries.

### *Englerophytum magalismontanum*
**Stemfruit**
**Stamvrug**

Small to medium-sized evergreen tree; occurring in bushveld, usually in rocky places. Branchlets densely covered with brownish hairs. Leaves dark green, hairless above, with silvery to reddish brown hairs below. Flowers small, cream, borne in clusters mainly on old wood and thick stems. Fruit a berry, ellipsoid, red, single-seeded.

*E. magalismontanum:* flowers

### Notes

- In both the milkwood family and feverberries, very young leaves tend to be folded tightly upward along the midrib (conduplicate), but latex is milky in the former, watery in the latter.
- In this group, the two small glands at the base of the leaf blade at the point of attachment to the petiole are diagnostic for *Croton* (feverberries; koorsbessies). However, they are very small and located on the lower surface and often do not extend beyond the leaf blade (see p44).

- Some non-succulent and leafy tree euphorbias have a smooth bark that peels in yellowish or brownish papery pieces. They can easily be mistaken for a species of *Commiphora* (corkwoods; kanniedoodbome), especially when leafless or sterile.
- *Uapaca* (muzhanje trees; muzhanjebome) were once included in this group but, as the genus lacks latex it is now placed in Phyllanthaceae (see Group 10, p86).

# 6. Tamboti group

The counterpart of Group 5 (see p76), but with the leaf margins variously toothed. Carefully check leaf margins, as the toothed state may be quite obscure, especially when it is shallowly scalloped (crenate). Latex can be watery, cloudy or milky. See also comments about the regularity of latex flow under the previous group. Stipules are often present, but they are usually small and detection is not essential for group recognition, hence they are not depicted by the icon. Spine-tipped branches may be present.

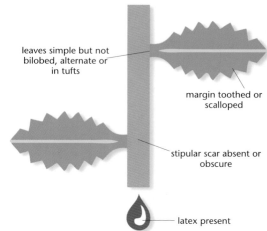

leaves simple but not bilobed, alternate or in tufts

margin toothed or scalloped

stipular scar absent or obscure

latex present

## Burseraceae
### Corkwood family; Kanniedoodfamilie

A greater diversity of leaf types is probably found in *Commiphora* [corkwoods; kanniedood-bome] than in any other local tree genus. Here we include the species with simple leaves and toothed margins. Spinescent shoots are common in the genus.

### *Commiphora viminea*
(=*C. merkeri*)
**Zebra-bark corkwood**
**Sebrabaskanniedood**
**Onangwi (N)**

Small to medium-sized tree; occurring in hot, arid bushveld. Bark grey with distinctive dark blackish warty horizontal bands, hence the common names referring to a zebra. Blue-green leaves are covered by a thin, greyish, powdery layer (so-called bloom). Flowers small, inconspicuous, male and female on different trees. Fruit a drupe, ellipsoid, reddish brown; stone almost completely enveloped by a yellow pseudo-aril.

*Commiphora viminea:* fruit

## Notes

- Latex associated with simple, alternate leaves with toothed margins and glands (extra floral nectaries) is definitive for the euphorbia family.
- Smooth bark that flakes in papery scales is associated with corkwoods, but similar bark patterns are occasionally present in other genera.

- Reddish brown or brown exudate is present in Myrsinaceae (cape myrtle family; mirtingfamilie) and Maesaceae (false-assegai family; valsas-segaaifamilie). Both groups are here treated as without latex (Group 9, see p84) because of the usually poor flow.

# Euphorbiaceae
## Euphorbia family; Naboomfamilie

This is the best-represented family in the group. Always check carefully for the presence of small glands (extra-floral nectaries), usually two per leaf. These are located on the lower surface near the base of the leaf blade, often at its junction with the petiole, and are visible to the naked eye (see p44).

### *Croton sylvaticus*
### Forest feverberry
### Boskoorsbessie

Medium to large deciduous tree; occurring in forest or associated woodland. Leaves with two prominent, green, stalked glands at junction of leaf blade and petiole. Star-shaped hairs present on leaves, often on principal veins (use hand lens). Flowers in sturdy spikes up to 150 mm long, small, cream. Fruit a 3-lobed capsule, bright orange when ripe, often produced in abundance. Latex watery.

*Croton sylvaticus:* fruit

### *Sclerocroton integerrimus*
(=*Sapium integerrimum*)
### Duikerberry
### Duikerbessie

Small to medium-sized tree, often multistemmed; occurring in forest or associated vegetation. Latex cloudy or milky. Leaves dark green above, pale bluish green below, with one or two widely spaced, sessile, yellowish glands on the leaf blade toward the base, but away from the margin and midrib (see p44). Flowers small, pale yellow, borne in spikes of mainly male flowers with few female ones near the base. Fruit a woody 3-lobed capsule with two horns on each lobe.

*Sclerocroton integerrimus:* fruit

### *Spirostachys africana*
### Tamboti
### Tambotie

Medium-sized deciduous tree with a rounded crown. Occurring in bushveld, often in dense stands on heavy soils along streams and rivers. Bark dark grey to blackish, cracked into a regular grid-like pattern of chunky scales. Latex milky. Leaves with two minute, often blackish glands visible on the upper surface at the junction of leaf blade and petiole (see p44); margins finely toothed or scalloped. Flowers small, yellowish, borne in dense spikes. Fruit a 3-lobed capsule.

*Spirostachys africana:* fruit

# 7. Silver-oak group

This group comprises trees with simple, alternate leaves that are distinctly discolorous, usually green above, but white, cream, grey-felted or bluish below. Note that, in most leaves, the lower surface tends to be paler green and less glossy than the upper surface. In the leaves referred to here, however, the colour difference between the two surfaces is very striking and immediately recognized as unusual. This is an easy group to distinguish, although it does not include all trees with discolorous alternate leaves. Make sure the plants are without latex (as in Groups 5, p76 and 6, p78) and that the leaves are not prominently 2–7-veined from the base (Group 11, p94), both features which have been given priority for group recognition in the key. Leaf margins may be entire or toothed and stipules and spines either absent or present.

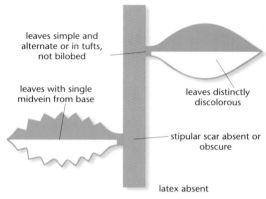

leaves simple and alternate or in tufts, not bilobed

leaves with single midvein from base

leaves distinctly discolorous

stipular scar absent or obscure

latex absent

## Asteraceae
### Daisy family; Madeliefiefamilie

This family is well represented in this group with several species of *Brachylaena* [silver-oaks; vaalbosse] and *Tarchonanthus* [camphorbushes; kanferbosse]. Flowers in both genera occur in heads, male and female on different plants. Species identification is difficult.

### *Brachylaena discolor*
Coast silver-oak
Kusvaalbos

Shrub or small tree, often multistemmed. Confined mainly to coastal bush and associated bushveld. Leaves lanceolate to obovate, dark green above, white-felted below; margin entire or irregularly toothed. Flowerheads creamy white, grouped in large, branched, terminal inflorescences. Fruit a small nut tipped with a tuft of bristly hairs.

*Brachylaena discolor:* flowers

### *Tarchonanthus littoralis*
(previously treated as part of an inclusive and polymorphic *T. camphoratus*)
Coast camphorbush
Kuskanferbos

Grey-green shrub or small tree occurring in mainly forest and coastal dune thicket. Mature leaves bright or dark green, minutely puckered above, densely white-felted below; margins usually shallowly and minutely toothed in distal parts. Crushed leaves have a strong camphorous smell. Flowerheads produced in terminal branched inflorescences, creamy white. Fruit a small nutlet, densely covered with woolly hairs.

*Tarchonanthus littoralis:* fruit

# Hamamelidaceae
## Witch hazel family; Towerhaselaarfamilie

A family represented by four species of *Trichocladus* [underbushes; onderbosse] in our region, three of which have mainly opposite leaves. Flowers in the genus are clustered in dense heads and have distinctive, ribbon-shaped petals.

### Trichocladus ellipticus
**White underbush**
**Witonderbos**

Small to medium-sized evergreen tree; occurring in the understorey of forest. Leaves mainly alternate, glossy dark green above, cream-felted with brownish hairs on venation below; margin entire; petiole often attached to the lower surface of the blade a short distance from the margin (such leaves described as 'peltate'). Flowers in axillary or terminal heads, creamy green. Fruit a small, almost spherical capsule, velvety, dehiscent.

*Trichocladus ellipticus:* flowers

# Salicaceae
## Willow family; Wilgerfamilie

The genus *Salix* [willows; wilgers] is represented by a single species with at least four regional variants (subspecies) in southern Africa. The rather pronounced whitish lower surface is useful to distinguish it from the introduced *S. babylonica* [weeping willow; treurwilger], a species with a pale green or greyish green lower surface.

### Salix mucronata subsp. woodii
**Flute willow**
**Fluitjieswilger**

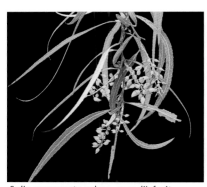

Shrub or small tree with long, somewhat drooping branches; occurring along east-flowing rivers and streams in northeastern South Africa and adjacent regions. Leaves narrowly lanceolate, pale green above, whitish green below due to the presence of a waxy layer (see p27). Flowers small, in spikes, male and female on different trees. Fruit a small capsule with seeds covered in white, woolly hairs.

*Salix mucronata* subsp. *woodii:* fruit

## Notes

- In this group, epidermal prickles on branchlets and leaves almost certainly indicate a species of *Solanum* (bitter-apples; bitterappels).
- Paler lower leaf surface can be caused by a dense layer of hairs, or a white, waxy powdery coating combined with the colour of the under-lying epidermis. A bluish lower surface is usually due to the presence of a pronounced waxy coating, some of which can be removed by gently rubbing the surface.
- In the daisy family, hairs are typically cobwebby. These are layers of long, soft, more or less inter-twined white hairs, especially on young stems and leaves (see p27).

# 8. Spikethorn group

Spinescence (ending in a spine or sharp point) is usually a conspicuous feature, and here its presence is associated with simple, alternate leaves with entire or toothed margins. Many trees in this group have leaves in tufts, which makes it difficult to establish their arrangement. Tufted leaves are usually alternately arranged, unless the tufts themselves are arranged in regular, opposite pairs (rare). Otherwise, look for sucker shoots, which often show leaf arrangement more clearly. Spines are not always present on all parts of a tree; they tend to be smaller and are sometimes absent in older, mature growth. Although single, straight spines (as depicted) are the common state in the group, paired or hooked spines also occur. Stipules may be present or absent.

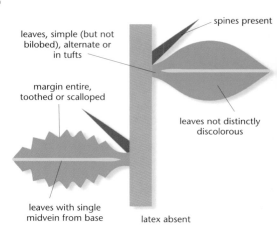

leaves, simple (but not bilobed), alternate or in tufts

spines present

margin entire, toothed or scalloped

leaves not distinctly discolorous

leaves with single midvein from base

latex absent

## Celastraceae

### Spikethorn family; Pendoringfamilie

*Gymnosporia* [spikethorns; pendorings] has many species in the group. Most have small, white flowers that are strongly scented. Sexes are on separate plants. The fruit is a dehiscent capsule, the morphology of which is very useful for species identification. In spikethorns, the seed is partly or completely enveloped by a white, yellow or orange aril.

**What to look for:**
*Gymnosporia* species

- Habitat.
- Growth form: shrub or tree.
- Branchlets round or angular.
- Hairiness of leaves.
- Capsule morphology.
- Colour and size of aril.

### *Gymnosporia buxifolia*
Spikethorn
Pendoring

Shrub or small, untidy tree with somewhat drooping branches. Widespread and occurring in many different habitats. Branchlets green, never angular or ridged. Spines single, straight, small or up to 100 mm long (see p36). Leaves often in tufts, dull-green; margin shallowly toothed, mainly in upper half. Flowers, small, white, produced in abundance, rather unpleasantly scented. Capsules globose, about 5 mm in diameter, rough, white with reddish brown patches. Seeds reddish brown, partly covered by an orange aril.

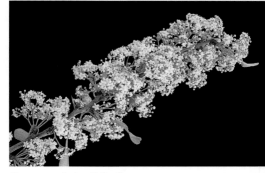

*Gymnosporia buxifolia:* flowers

# Combretaceae
### Bushwillow family; Boswilgfamilie

*Terminalia* [clusterleafs; trosblaarbome] is the only genus of the family in our region with spinescent members, and then only two out of several species (other species can be found in Group 10, see p86). The genus has alternate leaves and the fruit is a nut surrounded by a single wing – compare *Combretum* [bushwillow; boswilge] in Group 23, see p120.

### *Terminalia prunioides*
**Purplefruit clusterleaf (SA)**
**Purplepod terminalia (Z)**
**Sterkbos**
**Muhama (N)**

Shrub or small to medium-sized tree, often multistemmed with long, drooping branches; occurring in hot arid bushveld, usually in dense stands. Branchlets often spinescent. Leaves borne in clusters at ends of reduced side shoots, dark green and hairless when mature. Flowers in slender spikes, small, greenish white to cream, unpleasantly scented. Fruit a flattened, winged nut, bright red to purple red, drying to brown.

*Terminalia prunioides:* fruit

# 'Flacourtiaceae'

Trees previously classified in this family have been reclassified in other families following the realization that Flacourtiaceae was not a natural group. *Dovyalis* and other spiny members of the former Flacourtiaceae are now placed in Salicaceae [willow family; wilgerfamilie], or are retained in Flacourtiaceae (in the narrow sense). Most existing tree books still use the old classification.

### *Dovyalis caffra*
**Kei-apple**
**Keiappel**

Much-branched shrub or small tree; occurring in a wide range of habitats. Spines single, straight, particularly prominent in young plants. Leaves clustered on cushions, hairless; venation prominent on both surfaces; margin entire. Flowers small and inconspicuous, creamy green, male and female on separate plants. Fruit a berry, globose, up to 40 mm in diameter, yellow, shortly velvety.

*Dovyalis caffra:* female flowers

### Notes

- Spines borne singly are usually modified stems that either develop at the ends of shoots or from axillary buds that elongate one or two nodes to form short side shoots (see p35). In both cases, the growing tip stops growing and is transformed into a spine. Spines derived from an axillary bud often reflect leaf arrangement. *Catophractes alexandri* (trumpet-thorn; trompetdoring; ghababos (N)) is one of the few species with opposite spines.

- In *Sesamothamnus* (sesame bushes; sesambosse), the single spines are modified petioles (see p36).
- Spines derived through the modification of stipules are usually paired and positioned at the base of leaves. In this group, stipular spines are found in, among others, Capparaceae (caper family; kapperfamilie).

# 9. Wild-plane group

This is the second-largest group of trees in our region. It comprises trees with simple, alternate leaves with toothed margins and few special features. Although not shown by the icon, stipules are common, but secretory cavities are rare. Always check carefully for the presence of spines somewhere on the tree to ensure it is not perhaps better placed in Group 8 (see p82).

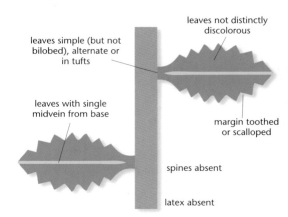

leaves not distinctly discolorous

leaves simple (but not bilobed), alternate or in tufts

leaves with single midvein from base

margin toothed or scalloped

spines absent

latex absent

## Celastraceae
### Spikethorn family; Pendoringfamilie

One of the larger families in this group. Stipules are usually minute, brown and shrivelled. The flowers are small, flat, white, greenish or pinkish, with an exposed nectar-secreting disc around the ovary and a very short style. The presence of elastic threads in the leaves and bark are diagnostic for some members (see Notes). In species with dry capsular fruit, the seed is partly or completely enveloped by a white, yellow or orange aril.

### *Maytenus acuminata*
**Silkybark**
**Sybas**

Shrub or small tree found in forest and associated vegetation, often along streams. Leaves ovate to elliptic, elastic (rubbery) threads evident on breaking the blade; venation, margin and petiole often reddish. Flowers small, creamy green, often tinged pink or red. Fruit a 1–3-lobed capsule, yellow, dehiscent; seed covered by an orange aril.

*Maytenus acuminata:* fruit

---

### Notes

- With few exceptions, identification of wild-plane trees is difficult and the group needs further study to improve demarcation of the species.
- Leaves with secretory cavities, often with brownish content, indicate Myrsinaceae (Cape myrtle family; mirtingfamilie).
- Break a leaf blade by pulling it apart slowly for a millimetre or two. If the two halves remain connected by elastic rubber threads (see p46), the tree is a member of the Celastraceae (spikethorn family; pendoringfamilie).

- Minute golden-yellow surface glands are characteristic for leaves of the Myricaceae (waxberry family; wasbessiefamilie).
- In modern systems of classification, the family Flacourtiaceae (in broad sense) is no longer upheld. Trees traditionally classified in this family are now placed in a number of redefined families; for our region mostly Salicaceae (willow family; wilgerfamilie), Flacourtiaceae (in narrow sense), and Achariaceae or Kiggelariaceae (wild-peach family; wildeperskefamilie).

# Myrsinaceae
## Cape myrtle family; Mirtingfamilie

A small family, some members of which have secretory cavities with a brownish red contents in the leaf (although these are not always easy to see). *Maesa* (below) lacks secretory cavities and is sometimes classified in its own family, Maesaceae.

### *Maesa lanceolata*
False assegai (SA)
Maesa (Z)
Valsassegaai

Shrub or small tree, often multistemmed; occurring along forest margins and in associated vegetation, often along streams. Leaves are large (50–150 x 30–120 mm) with midrib and side veins prominent below. Broken leaves sometimes exude tiny drops of a reddish brown latex from the broken end of the petiole. Flowers small, white to cream, produced in many-flowered heads. Fruit spherical, thinly fleshy, up to 6 mm in diameter, tipped with persistent remains of the calyx and style.

*Maesa lanceolata:* fruit

# Ochnaceae
## Wild-plane family; Rooihoutfamilie

A family characterized by leaves with many closely spaced more or less parallel secondary veins and the marginal teeth tipped by a minute black protuberance. Best known in our region from the many species of *Ochna* [wild-plane trees; rooihoutbome]. All wild-planes have attractive yellow flowers. The calyx persists and enlarges in the fruit, becoming cream, pink or bright red. Leaves are 2-ranked; in most species the young branchlets are densely covered by small whitish lenticels (see p40).

### *Ochna arborea*
var. *arborea*
Cape-plane
Kaapse rooihout

Small to medium-sized tree; occurring mainly in forest. One of the easier species to identify in the field by its smooth bark, conspicuously mottled with large patches of grey, cream, mauve and pink. Leaf margins sometimes almost entire. Flowers bright yellow. Fruit 1–5 kidney-shaped, shiny black drupes on an enlarged receptacle and surrounded by cream to pinkish red, enlarged, petal-like sepals.

*Ochna arborea* var. *arborea:* flowers and young fruit

**85**

# 10. Common group

This is by far the largest group of trees in our region. It comprises those species with simple, alternate leaves with entire margins and few other special vegetative features – the prevailing combination of character states among trees. Although group recognition is easy, species identification can be difficult when only vegetative material is available. It is therefore important to record as many features of a tree as possible, some of which will be highlighted when examples of families and species are supplied below.

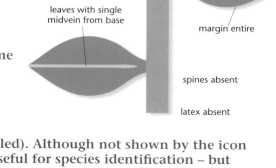

leaves not distinctly discolorous

leaves simple (but not bilobed), alternate or in tufts

leaves with single midvein from base

margin entire

spines absent

latex absent

Note whether the arrangement of the leaves is predominantly 2-ranked (distichous), spiral or clustered (fascicled). Although not shown by the icon (above), stipules are common – and useful for species identification – but secretory cavities are rare. Always check carefully for the presence of spines somewhere on the tree to ensure it would not be better placed in Group 8 (see p82). Also make sure that the leaves are not prominently 3–5-veined from or near the base, as with Group 11 (see p94).

## Annonaceae
### Custard-apple family; Vla-appelfamilie

An easy family to recognize, even when sterile. Leaves arranged in two ranks and without stipules. Very young leaves have the leaf blade folded flat together lengthwise with the upper surface within (conduplicate). Crushed leaves are often slightly aromatic, this being due to the presence of secretory cells (not to be confused with secretory cavities, see p29). Flowers are usually yellowish or greenish and often bend downwards (nodding). Perianth segments are in multiples of three (reminiscent of a monocot) and the stamens are short and stubby. Fruit fleshy, often comprising of finger-like clusters (berries) radiating from the tip of the original flower stalk.

### *Friesodielsia obovata*
**River dwababerry (SA)**
**Northern dwababerry (Z)**
**Rivierdwababessie**
**Mukondekonde (N)**

Shrub or small tree, often with arcuate branches and a tendency to scramble; occurring in bushveld and woodland, often on termitaria. Leaves distinctly 2-ranked, sometimes drooping, velvety when young, becoming less hairy with age; venation prominently raised below, with lateral veins gradually diminishing towards the margin without joining a prominent intramarginal vein. Flowers solitary, borne leaf-opposed and subtended by a leaf-like bracteole, greenish yellow. Fruit a cluster of cylindrical berries, constricted between seeds, bright red when ripe. Could be confused with *Bridelia mollis* [velvet sweetberry (SA), velvetleaf bridelia (Z); fluweelsoetbessie] which has stipules.

*Friesodielsia obovata*: flowers

# Capparaceae

## Caper family; Kapperfamilie

A family characterized by flowers with four free sepals (and petals, if present) and many stamens with long filaments, the latter often comprising the showy part of the flower. The ovary is carried on a distinctive stalk (gynophore), hence fruit stalks in the family consist of two sections demarcated by a scar left by the receptacle and perianth. The portion below the scar is the fruit stalk proper, the portion above it the gynophore. Several species of *Boscia* [shepherdstrees; witgatbome], *Cadaba* [wormbushes; wurmbosse] and *Maerua* [spiderbushes and beadbean trees; witbosse en knoppiesboontjiebome] occur in this group. Leaves in these genera are often tipped by a bristle-like hair. Young branchlets in *Maerua* tend to have numerous, very tiny, slightly raised whitish dots (lenticels). Berries in *Cadaba* and *Maerua* are elongated, often constricted between the seeds in the latter, and strongly reminiscent of the pods in legumes.

### *Boscia albitrunca*

**Shepherdstree**

**Witgat**

Small tree with a much-branched crown and rigid branchlets; occurring in semi-desert areas and bushveld, often on termitaria. Bark smooth, grey to whitish grey. Leaves alternate or in clusters, grey-green to green above and below, secondary veins obscure, often bristle-tipped. Flowers small, yellowish green, with four sepals and a central mass of stamens; petals absent. Fruit a berry, about 10 mm in diameter, round, hairless, yellowish.

*Boscia albitrunca*: fruit

### What to look for: *Boscia* species

- Leaves in tight clusters (fascicles) along branches, or spirally arranged (well spaced).
- Leaf shape and size.
- Leaf texture: soft and leathery or hard and brittle.
- Hairiness of mature leaves.
- Colour of upper and lower leaf surfaces.
- Prominence of venation on both leaf surfaces.
- Presence or absence of petals.
- Hairs on young growth simple or star-shaped.

*Boscia albitrunca*: flowers

### Notes

- In the absence of any special vegetative features and fertile material a pinkish, reddish or purplish petiole (see p42) can be a useful clue to a tree's identity; compare, for example, *Apodytes dimidiata* (white-pear (SA), witpeer), *Faurea* (boekenhout trees; boekenhoutbome), *Ilex mitis* (cape-holly (SA), african-holly (Z); without), *Peddiea africana* (poison-olive (SA), greenflower tree (Z); gifolyf), *Pterocelastrus* (candlewood trees; kershoutbome) and *Rapanea melanophloeos* (cape-beech; Kaapse boekenhout).

- Although not always present, domatia in the axils of the principal side veins (see p45) are a useful field character, occurring in *Cleistanthus schlechteri* (false-tamboti; valstambotie), *Ehretia* (puzzlebushes; deurmekaarbosse), *Heteropyxis* (lavender trees; laventelbome), *Ocotea bullata* (stinkwood; stinkhout), among others.
- Secretory cavities combined with a strong scent when leaves are crushed is found in *Heteropyxis* (lavender trees; laventelbome) and introduced species of *Eucalyptus* (eucalypts; bloekombome).

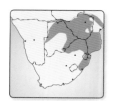

### Maerua angolensis
Beadbean
Knoppiesboontjie

Small to medium-sized tree; occurring in bushveld. Branchlets with numerous, small, whitish lenticels. Leaves elliptic to lanceolate, distinctly stalked; apex rounded, bristle-tipped. Flowers large, white with many long stamens, fading to cream. Fruit a long, slender, pod-like berry, up to 160 mm long, irregularly constricted between seeds.

*Maerua angolensis:* fruit

# Combretaceae
## Bushwillow family; Boswilgfamilie

Whereas *Combretum* [bushwillow; boswilge] has opposite leaves and usually 4-winged dry fruit (Group 23, see p120), the other large genus of the family found in our region, *Terminalia* [clusterleaf trees; trosblaarbome], has leaves that are alternate (spiral), often arranged in clusters, with the fruit surrounded by a single wing. Clusterleaf trees have a very characteristic growth pattern; side branches rapidly elongate for some distance, after which the apical bud is transformed into a slow-growing, reduced shoot with a rosette (cluster) of leaves. For the particular side shoot to continue elongating, an axillary bud from before the last leaf rosette must take over the role of an apical bud. After some growth in length this apical bud is also transformed into a reduced shoot with a rosette of leaves. This sequence is repeated, resulting in a side shoot made up of a series of upturned arcs or many separate stem units, each terminating in a rosette of leaves (so-called sympodial growth; see p41).

### Terminalia sericea
Silver clusterleaf (SA, N)
Mangwe (Z)
Vaalboom

Small to medium-sized deciduous tree with a silvery grey appearance (rarely green in some local variants); crown characteristically layered with more or less horizontal branches; occurs in bushveld, usually on sandy soils. Branches dark brown or purplish, peeling in rings and strips. Leaves clustered towards tips of branches, usually densely covered with silvery silky hairs. Rather unpleasantly scented, small, cream to pale yellow flowers in axillary spikes. Fruit a central nut surrounded by a wing, up to 35 x 25 mm, pink to purplish red when mature, drying to reddish brown.

*Terminalia sericea:* fruit

### What to look for: *Terminalia* species

- Leaves clustered at ends of long branches or at ends of dwarf spur-branches.
- Peeling pattern of bark on young branchlets.
- Size and colour of leaves.
- Hairiness of leaves.
- Presence of glands on lower surface of leaf blade, especially at junction with petiole and on the principal side veins.
- Prominent venation on leaf surface.

*Terminalia sericea:* flowers

# Ebenaceae

## Ebony family; Ebbehoutfamilie

A rather indistinct family with simple, entire leaves and no stipules. Leaf arrangement in *Euclea* [guarri trees; ghwarriebome] is very variable, even on the same plant. Therefore also compare those members of the genus included in Group 23 (see p120).

*Diospyros* [jackalberries and star-apples; jakkalsbessies en sterappels] has many species in our region. Leaf arrangement in this genus is consistently alternate, either 2-ranked or spiral. Active apical growing tips are bent at an angle to the axis of the branchlet and the very young leaves have the leaf blade folded together lengthwise with the upper surface within (conduplicate). Flower buds are distinctly pointed and the petals are basally united and twisted (contorted) in bud. The fruit, a rather tough-skinned berry, is subtended or enclosed by the persistent and often enlarged calyx (see p51).

### Diospyros lycioides
### subsp. *lycioides*
**Karoo bluebush (SA)**
**Western red star-apple (Z)**
**Karoobloubos**

Deciduous shrub or small tree with upright branches; occurring in wide variety of habitats. Bark dark grey, rather smooth. Leaves spirally arranged, usually clustered towards ends of branches, silky-hairy when young, becoming more or less hairless with age; venation not prominently raised. Flowers axillary, drooping, creamy yellow, male and female ones separate on different plants. Fruit a berry, round to broadly ovoid, orange-red to dark red when ripe; calyx persistent, lobes strongly reflexed.

*Diospyros lycioides* subsp. *lycioides*: fruit

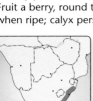

### Diospyros scabrida
**Coast bladdernut**
**Kusswartbas**

Evergreen shrub or small tree; occurring on rocky outcrops in grassland, rarely along forest margins. Leaves 2-ranked, at least on horizontal branchlets, glossy dark green; base square to lobed; silky-hairy when young, becoming almost hairless with age above, but remaining hairy below. Flowers solitary or in few-flowered racemes, white to cream, drooping. Fruit a berry, ovoid, red; calyx lobes persistent, free, usually tinged reddish or maroon towards edges, completely enveloping the fruit. Closely related *D. whyteana* [bladdernut; swartbas] which has the calyx lobes joined to form an inflated, bladder-like structure around the fruit.

*Diospyros scabrida*: flowers

## Notes

- Petioles with a conspicuous swelling just below the lamina (pulvinus), often in addition to a swelling where the petiole attaches to the stem (see p42), are present in *Baphia* (camwoods; kamhout-bosse) and *Cola* (cola trees; kolabome).
- In most leaves, the side veins either stop before reaching the margin, or join an intramarginal vein. Sometimes, principal side veins terminate at or close to the leaf margin, remaining prominent over their full length, resulting in a 'herringbone' pattern (see p28), as in *Annona senegalensis* (wild custard-apple; wildesuikerappel), *Bridelia* (sweetberries; soetbessies), *Friesodielsia obovata* (river dwababerry (SA), northern dwababerry (Z); rivierdwababessie) and some species of *Uapaca* (muzhanje trees; muzhanjebome).
- A large flat gland (extrafloral nectary) on the midrib at the base of the upper surface of the leaf blade indicates a *Monotes* (monotes trees; monotesbome).

| | |
|---|---|
| **What to look for:** *Diospyros* species | |

- Leaves in 2-ranks or spiralling around the stem.
- Hairiness of mature leaves.
- Leaf shape and size.
- Leaf texture and colour.
- Leaf margin wavy (undulate) or not.
- Length of petiole.
- Prominent venation on lower surface of leaf.
- Spines present or absent.
- Morphology of the calyx during fruiting.
- Fruit shape, colour and hairiness.

*Euclea natalensis:* flowers

### Euclea natalensis

Natal guarri
Natalghwarrie

Shrub or small to medium-sized tree; occurring in forest and bushveld. Leaves spirally arranged, usually covered with brownish woolly hairs below, particularly when young; margin wavy. Flowers in dense, branched axillary heads, small, greenish white to cream. Fruit a berry, round, up to 10 mm in diameter, ripening through yellowish, orange and red to black. A very variable species as to leaf shape and size with several subspecies being recognized in our region.

*Euclea natalensis:* fruit

# Erythroxylaceae
## Coca family; Kokafamilie

A family with six species in our region, characterized by alternate leaves and deciduous intrapetiolar stipules. This type of stipule is positioned between the petiole and the stem, thus spanning the leaf axil. The young stems of *Erythroxylum* [cocain trees; kokabome] are conspicuously flattened towards the growing tip. In *Nectaropetalum* [false-cocain trees; valskokabome] the apical buds are covered by long stipules resulting in them being conspicuously spike- or horn-like.

### Erythroxylum pictum

Forest cocain tree
Boskokaboom

Small to medium-sized tree, often with a few bright yellow leaves in the canopy; occurring in forest, often along streams. Branchlets flattened towards tips. Leaves oval to ovate, thinly textured, bluish green above, paler below; apex rounded, slightly notched. Flowers axillary, small, whitish. Fruit a drupe, oval, up to 10 mm long, bright shiny red.

*Erythroxylum pictum:* flowers and fruit

# Euphorbiaceae *in broad sense*

## Euphorbia family; Naboomfamilie

The majority of trees in this group that have been traditionally assigned to an inclusive Euphorbiaceae (subfamily Phyllanthoideae) are now classified in the Phyllanthaceae, a family characterized by an ovary with two ovules per locule (resulting in two seeds per chamber in the fruit), leaves that are alternate, simple and entire with stipules, and the absence of latex. The leaves are 2-ranked in horizontally spreading branches, but with a tendency to be spirally arranged in vertical ones.

Phyllanthaceae includes genera/species such as *Antidesma* [tasselberries; tosselbessies], *Bridelia* [sweetberries; soetbessies], *Cleistanthus* [umzithi trees; valstamboties], *Flueggea* [whiteberries; witbessies], *Heywoodia lucens* [stink-ebony; stinkebbehout], *Hymenocardia* [heart fruit trees; hartvrugbome], *Lachnostylis* [coalwoods; koolhoute], *Margaritaria* [peacockberries; poubessies], *Phyllanthus* [potatobushes; aartappelbosse], *Pseudolachnostylis* [kuduberries; koedoebessies] and *Uapaca* [muzhanje trees; muzhanjebome].

*Drypetes* [ironplums; ysterpruime] is now placed in a separate family, Putranjivaceae.

### Bridelia micrantha
**Mitzeeri**
**Mitseri**

*Bridelia micrantha:* fruit

Medium to large deciduous tree; crown spreading or rounded, usually with a few scattered bright red leaves; occurring in forest and associated vegetation, often in moist places. Leaves 2-ranked, elliptic to obovate, glossy dark green above, paler below, more or less hairless; lateral veins raised below and terminating at the margin to form a 'herringbone' pattern. Flowers in axillary clusters, very small, yellowish green. Fruit a berry, oval, about 8 x 4 mm, black when ripe.

### Phyllanthus reticulatus
**Potatobush (SA)**
**Potatosmell (Z)**
**Aartappelbos**

*Phyllanthus reticulatus:* flowers

Multistemmed shrub or small tree; occurring in bushveld, particularly riverine thicket and in the shade of bush clumps. Leaves oval to elliptic, arranged in two ranks on short, slender side shoots, the latter bearing a strong resemblance to pinnately compound leaves. Flowers in axillary clusters, very small, yellowish, often tinged pinkish red, emitting a strong scent of potatoes in the evening, hence the common names. Fruit a berry-like capsule, up to 6 mm in diameter, black when ripe, dehiscent.

## Notes

- Leaf arrangement in *Phyllanthus* (potatobushes; aartappelbosse) can be very deceptive. Leaves are alternately arranged in 2 ranks along slender side branchlets, creating the distinct impression of large pinnate leaves.
- Fruit type is useful for identification: establish whether fruit is dry, with or without a prominent wing, or fleshy. Berries subtended by a prominent persistent and enlarged calyx are diagnostic for *Diospyros* (jackalberries and star-apples;

jakkalsbessies en sterappels); fleshy fruit with a basal cup-like covering (like an acorn) for *Diospyros natalensis* (acorn jackalberry; akkerjakkalsbessie), *D. nummularia* (lebombo jackalberry (SA), granite jackalberry (Z); lebombojakkalsbessie) and *Ocotea bullata* (stinkwood; stinkhout).
- *Artabotrys* (hookberries; haakbessies) climb by means of very characteristic hooked, flattened inflorescence stalks that twine around branches.

# Lauraceae

## Laurel family; Lourierfamilie

A family with the leaves spirally arranged (opposite in one local species), simple, entire and without stipules. When held up to the light the tertiary (finest) veins of the leaf form a minute grid of squarish enclosures (areolae). Young twigs are usually green and lack prominent lenticels. The crushed leaves are often slightly aromatic due to the presence of oil cells; the latter, however, are much smaller than secretory cavities and are not clearly visible against the light (see p28). In our region the fruit is acorn-like in the two species of *Ocotea* [stinkwoods; stinkhoutbome] and a fleshy spherical or ellipsoid drupe in the seven species of *Cryptocarya* [wild-quinces; wildekwepers].

### Ocotea bullata

Stinkwood
Stinkhout

Medium to large evergreen tree; occurring in forest. Leaves spirally arranged, up to 120 x 50 mm, glossy dark green above, with conspicuous large domatia in axils of some principal side veins below, visible as dome-shaped 'bubbles' on the upper surface; margin wavy. Flowers axillary, very small, yellowish green (see p45). Fruit acorn-like, oval, about 20 mm long, basal part of drupe enveloped by the cup-shaped receptacle, yellowish green to purplish when ripe.

*Ocotea bullata:* fruit

# Podocarpaceae

## Yellowwood family; Geelhoutfamilie

A family of gymnosperms, with four species of *Podocarpus* [yellowwoods; geelhoutbome] in our region. The genus is evergreen and has alternate (spiralled), narrow, stiff and leathery leaves, with a strong midvein and indistinct lateral veins. *P. falcatus* is not closely related to the other local species (compare, for example, seed morphology) and it is sometimes classified in a separate genus, *Afrocarpus*.

### Podocarpus falcatus

(*=Afrocarpus falcatus*)
Outeniqua yellowwood
Outeniekwageelhout

Medium to large evergreen tree; occurring in forest. Leaves spirally arranged, narrow, 30–50 x 3–5 mm, somewhat sickle-shaped, twisted at the base, often with a greyish bloom. Male cones axillary, about 10 x 3 mm, lasting for a short time. Female 'cones' without a fleshy receptacle, comprising of a spherical, fleshy seed about 15 mm in diameter, yellow when ripe.

*Podocarpus falcatus:* seed

## Podocarpus latifolius
**Real yellowwood (SA)**
**Broadleaf yellowwood (Z)**
**Opregte geelhout**

Medium to large evergreen tree; occurring in forest. Leaves spirally arranged, not conspicuously drooping, narrowly elliptic, 60–150 x 5–13 mm, glossy dark green, but dull bluish green in some local forms. Male cones axillary, up to 50 x 5 mm, short-lived. Female 'cones' with a fleshy, swollen, pink, red or purplish receptacle (podocarpium) up to about 10 mm long, on which is carried 1 or 2 round seeds, each about 15 mm in diameter, blue-green often tinged purplish.

*Podocarpus latifolius:* seed

# Proteaceae
### Protea family; Proteafamilie

An ancient, largely southern hemisphere (Gondwana) family of woody flowering plants which, in Africa, has diversified extensively in the Cape Floristic Region. With the exception of the wild-almond, *Brabejum stellatifolium* (see Group 25, p126), all native tree members of the family have leaves that are simple, alternate (spiral), entire (coarsely toothed near apex in some pincushions, *Leucospermum*), leathery and without stipules. The flowers are grouped together in often-showy heads or spikes. Individual flowers are small, but very distinctive. Each has four petal-like sepals with reflexed tips, and four stamens which are opposite and fused to the sepals, often with only the anthers free or with very short filaments. The sexes are on separate plants in *Leucadendron* [cone- and yellowbushes; tol- en geelbosse], the fruiting inflorescences (infructescences) of which bear a remarkable resemblance to gymnospermous cones.

## Protea caffra
**Common sugarbush**
**Gewone suikerbos**

Shrub or small tree with a greyish green appearance; occurring in grassland and bushveld, often on rocky ridges. Leaves spirally arranged towards the ends of branches, narrowly oblong, sometimes slightly sickle-shaped, up to 250 x 45 mm, leathery, pale green to bluish green, hairless, without an apparent petiole. Flowerheads solitary or in clusters of three or four, up to 80 mm in diameter; involucral bracts with inner series oblong to oblong-spathulate, pale red, pink or cream. Fruit a nut, densely hairy. A very variable species with several local forms.

*Protea caffra:* flowerhead (Waterberg form, Limpopo)

### What to look for: *Protea* species

- Leaves distinctly stalked or almost sessile.
- Leaves curving upwards or spread sideways.
- Colour of leaves and midrib.
- Colour and thickening of leaf margin.
- Hairiness of branchlets and leaves.
- Shape and size of flowerheads: solitary or in clusters, with a distinct stalk (stipe) or not.
- Shape, colour, hairiness of involucral bracts.

*Protea caffra:* flowerhead (southern KwaZulu-Natal form)

# 11. Raisin bush group

A large and easy-to-identify group. In some 3-veined leaves the veins on either side of the midrib are not markedly thickened and careful scrutiny is required to detect them. Note that these veins do not branch off from the midrib some distance from the base, but together diverge in a V from the point where the leaf blade joins the petiole. Leaf margins can be entire or toothed. Some strongly palmately lobed leaves superficially resemble palmately compound leaves, but since the lobes are not separately attached to the petiole, these leaves are still simple. Although not shown by the icon, stipules and spines may be present in some species. Latex is supposed to be absent, but see comment in Notes below.

leaves simple
(but not bilobed)

leaves prominently
3–5-veined from or
near the base

leaves
alternate or
in tufts

latex absent

## Malvaceae
### Cotton family; Katoenfamilie

An unmistakable family when in flower; these are usually large, showy, and have five free petals, numerous stamens united into a distinctive tube around the style and the calyx is sometimes subtended by an additional and different-looking calyx whorl (epicalyx). Seed often covered with white, woolly hair (compare cotton).

### *Hibiscus tiliaceus*
**Lagoon hibiscus**
**Kusvuurblom**

Shrub or small tree; occurring in coastal areas along rivers and lagoons. Leaves large, almost circular, velvety white to greyish below. Flowers large, yellow with a dark maroon centre, fading after one day and turn orange-red before they are shed. Fruit an ovoid capsule, covered with golden hairs.

*Hibiscus tiliaceus:* flower

### Notes

- Many trees in this group belong to one of three closely related families: Malvaceae (cotton family; katoenfamilie), Tiliaceae (linden family; lindefamilie) and Sterculiaceae (cacao family; kakaofamilie), sometimes combined into a single inclusive family under the name Malvaceae (in the broad sense). All three have stipules. A useful field character is the frequent presence of star-shaped (stellate) hairs that often impart a rough texture to the leaves and are best detected with the aid of a hand lens (see p31).

- Trees of the Urticaceae (nettle family; brand-netelfamilie) have watery latex and leaves that are prominently 3–5-veined from the base. In the key, the presence of latex is given priority over multiple veins from the base of the blade, so they would normally be looked for in Groups 5 or 6, but because of the dense cover of stinging hairs in *Obetia* (nettles; brandnetels) few people would risk picking a leaf to test for latex, hence the placement of the genus in the present group.

# Rhamnaceae
**Buffalo-thorn family; Blinkblaarfamilie**

Leaves in this family are often glossy and the ultimate venation forms a very fine and regular reticulum of minute polygons, squares or rectangles (best seen with a hand lens when viewed against the light, see p28).

### *Ziziphus mucronata*
**Buffalo-thorn**
**Blinkblaar-wag-'n-bietjie**

Small to medium-sized deciduous tree; widespread and common in many habitats. Leaves glossy dark green above; base strongly asymmetric; margins finely toothed. Stipules spinescent, one hooked, the other straight, or plants unarmed, especially in tall mature trees of some forms in high-rainfall regions. Flowers small, yellowish green. Fruit a subglobose drupe, reddish to yellowish brown.

*Ziziphus mucronata:* flowers

# Tiliaceae
**Linden family; Lindefamilie**

Several species of *Grewia* [raisin bushes; rosyntjiebosse] occur in our region; usually shrubs or small multistemmed trees. Leaves are alternate with asymmetric bases and characteristically arranged in two ranks (two vertical rows when viewed from tip of stems, see p26). The fruit is a drupe, reminiscent of raisins and edible, though thinly fleshy.

### *Grewia flava*
**Velvet-raisin (N, SA)**
**Brandybush (Z)**
**Rosyntjiebos**

Multistemmed shrub or small tree with greyish green foliage; widespread in arid areas, often occurring on deep Kalahari sand. Older stems roundish. Leaves densely greyish hairy. Flowers in axillary clusters, yellow. Fruit globose or faintly 2-lobed, reddish brown. Often grows together with *G. flavescens* [sandpaper-raisin (N, SA); donkeyberry (Z); skurweblaarrosyntjie] also with yellow flowers, but it has harshly hairy leaves and the older stems are 4-angled.

**What to look for:** *Grewia* species

- Habit: creeper or shrub/tree.
- Older stems round or square.
- Hairiness of leaves.
- Flower colour: white, yellow or pink.
- Fruit single, 2-lobed or 4-lobed.

*Grewia flava* and *G. occidentalis* (inset): flowers

# 12. Monkey-orange group

This is an easy group to identify. The outstanding feature, that should not be overlooked, is the presence of additional prominent veins – at least two, one on each side of the midrib – that arise either from the base, or from the midrib in the lower third of the leaf blade. Although not shown by the icon, spines may be present in some species.

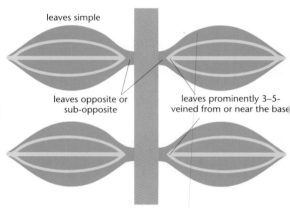

leaves simple

leaves opposite or sub-opposite

leaves prominently 3–5-veined from or near the base

## Strychnaceae
### Monkey-orange family; Klapperfamilie

Most trees in this group are members of the genus *Strychnos* [monkey-oranges and bitterberries; klappers en bitterbessies]. Traditionally classified in the Loganiaceae, some modern classification systems prefer to place the genus in a separate family, Strychnaceae. Ripe fruit is usually yellow to orange, hence the reference to 'orange' in the common name. Fruit size is important for species identification. Monkey-oranges have large fruit (>50 mm in diameter) with many seeds. They are usually found in open vegetation, such as bushveld and thicket. The fruit has a hard, persistent rind and the remains can often be found below trees.

Bitterberries are often associated with forest. They have small fruit (<20 mm in diameter) with one or two seeds and the individual species are rather difficult to identify.

### *Strychnos madagascariensis*
**Black monkey-orange (SA, N)**
**Hairy-leaf monkey-orange (Z)**
**Swartklapper**

A large-fruited (80–100 mm in diameter), spineless species. Plants tend to be multistemmed, with the leaves usually hairy and clustered towards the end of sturdy side shoots. It is locally common in bushveld. The fruit pulp is smoked, dried and stored as food, especially in parts of Maputaland.

*Strychnos madagascariensis:* fruit

### Notes

- Fruit pulp of all large-fruited *Strychnos* species is edible. The fruit is at its best when over-ripe, at which stage the pulp starts to liquefy. Tastiness varies among species, *S. cocculoides* (corky monkey-orange; kurkbasklapper) being superior to the rest. Fruit of this species is often sold in traditional markets, for example, in Botswana.
- Strychnine, an extremely toxic compound, is commercially extracted from the seed of

an Indian species, *Strychnos nux-vomixa* (nux vomica). This compound is probably also present in the seed of native species of *Strychnos*, albeit in lower concentration. Hence it is advisable to avoid chewing or swallowing the seeds when eating the fruit pulp.
- The rose-apple family includes some prominent garden plants, such as the spectacular pink- to purple-flowered tibouchinas or glory bushes.

### Strychnos henningsii
**Red bitterberry**
**Rooibitterbessie**

A small-fruited (up to 12 mm in diameter) species, often single-stemmed and growing in forest. Ripe fruits have a rind that is quite soft, yellow-orange to purplish black. They are single-seeded, bitter-tasting and are not normally consumed by humans.

**What to look for:** *Strychnos* species

- Corkiness of bark.
- Size of ripe fruit.
- Leaf shape and hairiness.
- Spines on stems.
- Prickle on leaf tip.

*Strychnos henningsii:* fruit

# Melastomataceae
## Rose-apple or Tibouchina family; Roosappel- of Tibouchinafamilie

A family poorly represented by trees in southern Africa. All native members are characterized by an inferior ovary, hence the fruit is crowned by the persistent remains of the flower, notably the calyx; in Strychnaceae the ovary is always superior. Most prominent among the trees is *Warneckea*, a genus with two species in our region.

### Warneckea sousae
(=*Memecylon sousae*)
**Tonga rose-apple**
**Tongaroosappel**

Small evergreen tree confined to sand forest and sand thicket, often in dense stands. Flowers greenish yellow, in axillary clusters, usually on older stems. Fruit a berry, oval, up to 10 mm long, purplish black, tipped by the persistent calyx.

*Warneckea sousae:* flower buds

### Dissotis princeps
**Purple wild-tibouchina (SA)**
**Royal dissotis (Z)**
**Perskalwerbos**

Shrub or small tree up to 3 m high; occurring in bushveld and high-altitude grassland, often in moist places. The attractive purple flowers resemble those of the garden tibouchinas.

*Dissotis princeps:* flowers

# 13. Sagewood group

This is a small but easily recognized group. The discolorous appearance of the leaves is due to the presence of a dense, felt-like layer of whitish hairs on the lower surface. The stipules, which in some species are merely a ridge between the petioles, are best observed on actively growing sucker shoots. Leaf margins are mostly finely scalloped, sometimes superimposed on coarse lobes; entire margins are present in one species only.

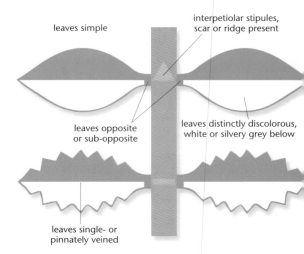

leaves simple

interpetiolar stipules, scar or ridge present

leaves opposite or sub-opposite

leaves distinctly discolorous, white or silvery grey below

leaves single- or pinnately veined

## Buddlejaceae
### Wild-elder family; Wildevlierfamilie

Most species in this group belong to the genus *Buddleja* [sagewoods; wildesaliebome]. Plants are usually large shrubs, rather than trees, and all have soft leaves. The group is also easily recognized by the upper surface of the leaves which are minutely and densely wrinkled (puckered).

### *Buddleja auriculata*
**Weeping sagewood (SA)**
**Eared buddleja (Z)**
**Treursalie**

Semi-scandent shrub or small tree with drooping branches; occurring mainly along forest margins or streams. This is the sagewood with the most prominent interpetiolar stipules in our region; when well-developed they are leafy and often recurved. However, on other stems of the same plant they may be reduced to a weakly developed transverse ridge between the two petioles.

*Buddleja auriculata*: flowers

## Notes

* In *Buddleja saligna* (false-olive; witolien) the interpetiolar stipule/ridge is so weakly developed that it is placed in Group 23 (p120).
* Lebombo ironwood is one of the few trees in southern Africa that grows in almost pure stands, a feature perhaps linked to the fact that it is one of only a handful of native trees that are wind-pollinated. It also occurs in Madagascar, where its nearest relatives are found.

### *Buddleja salviifolia*
Sagewood
Saliehout

Shrub or small tree with a grey-green appearance. One of the most widely distributed sagewoods in our region, occurring along forest margins and in high-altitude grassland, usually along watercourses and in rocky places. Leaves with the minute wrinkling of the upper leaf surface particularly well developed. Flowers white to lilac or purple, with a dark-orange throat, sweetly scented.

*Buddleja salviifolia:* flowers

# Euphorbiaceae *in broad sense*
## Euphorbia family; Naboomfamilie

Only one species, the lebombo ironwood, traditionally classified in this family belongs to the present group. It is the only species in the group with entire leaves and is morphologically quite different from other local members of the family. In modern systems of classification it is placed in the Picrodendraceae.

### *Androstachys johnsonii*
Lebombo ironwood (SA)
Simbitree (Z)
Lebombo-ysterhout

Medium to large tree with an upright habit; occurring in hot, low-altitude bushveld, usually in dense stands. Intrapetiolar stipules are large and distinctive, tightly pressed around the growing bud of shoots to form spoon-shaped structures (compare red-alder, p144, Group 32). As the shoot elongates and each pair of new leaves unfolds, the stipules are shed, leaving an inter- and intrapetiolar scar on the stem. Fruit a conspicuously 3-lobed capsule.

*Androstachys johnsonii:* fruit

# 14. Turkeyberry group

Two interpetiolar stipules, one on each side of the stem, are located at a node. Initially they are green and protect the growing bud of the shoot, but once the shoot has elongated they loose their function and are often shed, leaving a scar or ridge between the two opposite leaves. Spines in this group are derived from axillary buds and therefore represent abbreviated shoots ending in a sharp tip. At a node the spines emerge either from the leaf axils or are placed slightly above the level of insertion of the two opposite leaves.

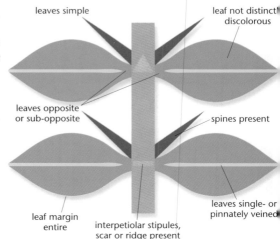

leaves simple

leaf not distinct, discolorous

leaves opposite or sub-opposite

spines present

leaf margin entire

interpetiolar stipules, scar or ridge present

leaves single- or pinnately veined

## Rubiaceae

### Coffee family; Koffiefamilie

The largest family of trees in southern Africa, and one that is usually easy to identify from vegetative material alone. Leaves are usually simple, opposite with entire margins, and interpetiolar stipules are present (see also Notes).

### *Canthium armatum*

**False-turkeyberry**
**Valsdoringklipels**

Shrub or small tree of hot, low-altitude bushveld. Plants are consistently armed with straight spines up to 40 mm long. Until recently it was known as *Plectroniella armata*, but studies have shown that it is best classified as a *Canthium* [turkeyberries; klipelse], a group characterized by either the presence of spines, or the potential to produce spines under certain circumstances.

*Canthium armatum:* fruit

*Canthium armatum:* fruit

## Canthium inerme
### Turkeyberry
### Bosklipels

Small to medium-sized tree occurring mainly in coastal or montane forest. Leaves hairless, rather fleshy and soft leathery with a wavy margin. Spines occur sporadically in this species and their presence is easily overlooked; always look for them by inspecting a number of branchlets and any sucker shoots that may be present.

*Canthium inerme:* fruit

*Canthium inerme:* flowers

## Hyperacanthus amoenus
### Thorn-gardenia
### Doringkatjiepiering

Multistemmed shrub or small tree with short, rigid lateral branches. Leaves often clustered closely together on short lateral shoots, making it difficult to see their opposite arrangement. However, the fact that the spines occur in opposite pairs can be used as an indication that the leaves are opposite.

*Hyperacanthus amoenus:* flowers

### Notes

- All trees in this group belong to the coffee family.
- Flowers in the coffee family have the petals fused into a tube, at least at the base. They are also characterized by an inferior ovary. The latter is reflected by the fact that the fruit is either crowned by the persistent remains of the calyx, or by a circular scar left behind after the shedding of the sepals and petals.

*Hyperacanthus amoenus:* fruit

# 15. Bridesbush group

Two interpetiolar stipules, one on each side of the stem, are located at a node. Initially they are green and protect the growing bud of the shoot, but once the shoot has elongated they loose their function and are often shed, leaving a scar or ridge between the two opposite leaves. The presence of bacterial nodules (see p30) in the leaf blade makes this an easy group to recognize. Moreover, all members of the group have white flowers. Unlike secretory cavities, bacterial nodules are readily visible to the naked eye, especially when a leaf is viewed against a strong light source, for example the sun. They are round, elliptic or linear and usually more than 0.5 mm in longest dimension. Sometimes they can be detected on especially the upper leaf surface as slightly raised bumps, often with a blackish central depression. Arrangement varies from few and randomly scattered to numerous and uniformly spread throughout the leaf blade. In a few species, the nodules are mainly located next to the midrib and can then easily be overlooked.

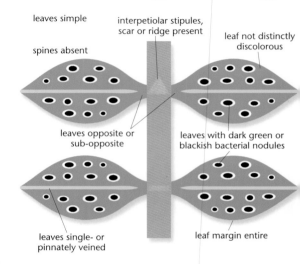

leaves simple

interpetiolar stipules, scar or ridge present

leaf not distinctly discolorous

spines absent

leaves opposite or sub-opposite

leaves with dark green or blackish bacterial nodules

leaves single- or pinnately veined

leaf margin entire

## Rubiaceae
### Coffee family; Koffiefamilie

Most species in this group belong to the genus *Pavetta* [bridesbushes; bruidsbosse]. The common name is inspired by the white flowers that are produced in abundance in most species, usually around November and December. Bridesbushes are mainly shrubs or small trees and, when in full flower, can be detected from afar. All species have fruit crowned by the persistent remains of the calyx. Flowers are very similar in the genus and species identification can be difficult. Also included in this group are about three species of *Psychotria* [birdberries; voëlbessies] from Mozambique and Zimbabwe. In this genus bacterial nodules only occur in some species, and then abundantly so.

### *Pavetta bowkeri*
**Hairy coastal bridesbush**
**Harige kusbruidsbos**

Shrub or small tree, easily recognized by the leaves, being hairless above but densely velvety below. One of the bridesbushes in which the bacterial nodules are often difficult to see; they are elliptic to narrowly elongated and aligned adjacent to, and often parallel with, the midrib. *P. natalensis* [coast bridesbush; kusbruidsbos] has a similar nodule-arrangement but the leaves are hairless. In both species the calyx lobes are very narrow and needle-shaped.

*Pavetta bowkeri*: flowers

## Pavetta edentula
**Glandleaf bridesbush**
**Kliertjiesboom**

One of the few bridesbushes that is easy to identify from a distance, even when not in flower. Plants are sturdy shrubs or small trees with thick, rigid branches and large lanceolate leaves up to 200 x 50 mm. Bacterial nodules are small, often abundant and scattered throughout the lamina, hence the common names.

*Pavetta edentula: flowers*

## Pavetta lanceolata
**Weeping bridesbush**
**Treurbruidsbos**

Perhaps the most-recognized bridesbush because of its mass floral displays and relatively wide distribution. It is often encountered on forest margins and in associated bushveld. Leaves are elliptic, hairless but with minute hair-tuft domatia in the axils of the side veins. Bacterial nodules are irregularly scattered over the leaf blade and sometimes rather difficult to see because they tend to be only slightly darker green than the rest of the leaf. Calyx lobes are shortly triangular with minute, sharp tips.

*Pavetta lanceolata: flowers*

## Psychotria kirkii
**Noduleleaf birdberry**
**Knoppiesblaarvoëlbessie**

Shrub or small tree; occurring in bushveld and woodland, often in rocky places, riverine bush or on termite mounds. Leaves elliptic or elliptic-obovate, densely hairy to hairless; bacterial nodules numerous, dot-like, especially distinct on lower surface of blade. Flowers white or cream, 6–10 mm long. Fruit fleshy, subglobose, up to 8 mm in diameter, bright red, tipped by the remains of the calyx.

*Psychotria kirkii: fruit*

### What to look for: *Pavetta* species

- Shape of the calyx lobes, established in either flowering or fruiting material.
- Shape and hairiness of the leaves.
- Abundance and distribution of the bacterial nodules.
- Presence and type of domatia.

### Notes

- Some bridesbushes make attractive garden subjects but flowering displays are very brief.
- The long, narrow, tubular flowers are probably pollinated by butterflies and/or hawk moths.
- Flowers display secondary pollen presentation, common in members of the coffee family.

# 16. Wild-medlar group

Two interpetiolar stipules, one on each side of the stem, are located at a node. Initially they are green and protect the growing bud of the shoot, but once the shoot has elongated they loose their function and are often shed, leaving a scar or ridge between the two opposite leaves. The most outstanding feature of the group is the densely hairy leaves, at least the lower surface and often involving the young stems as well. Hence the leaves have a velvety or rough feel. Whereas many plants have the young leaves hairy, they become hairless later. In this group, however, the hairs persist in mature leaves.

interpetiolar stipules, scar or ridge present

leaves single- or pinnately veined

leaf margin entire

leaves opposite or sub-opposite

leaf not distinctly discolorous

leaves simple, without bacterial nodules; densely hairy, at least below; spines absent

## Rubiaceae
### Coffee family; Koffiefamilie

This is the largest family of trees in southern Africa, and about the fifth-largest family of flowering plants worldwide (more than 10 000 species). Easily recognized by opposite entire-margined leaves, interpetiolar stipules and flowers with the ovary inferior.

### Afrocanthium gilfillanii
(=*Canthium gilfillanii*)
**Velvet rock-alder**
**Fluweelklipels**

Shrub or small tree common on rocky ridges in grassland and bushveld. Resembles some of the small-leaved wild-medlars (*Vangueria*) but the fruits are asymmetrical black drupes. Often associated with *A. mundianum* [rock-alder; klipels], a plant which is similar, but with more or less hairless leaves.

*Afrocanthium gilfillanii:* fruit

### Crossopteryx febrifuga
**Crystalbark**
**Sandkroonbessie**
**Murombe (N)**

Shrub or small tree of bushveld and growing in sandy soils. Leaves are rough-haired or velvety with the venation prominently raised below. It is rather unusual in the group for having dry capsular fruit; most other members have fleshy fruit that do not split open.

*Crossopteryx febrifuga:* flowers

### *Vangueria infausta* subsp. *infausta*
**Wild-medlar**
**Wildemispel**

Probably the most-recognizable member of this group. It is a deciduous shrub or small tree of especially rocky ridges in grassland and bushveld. Leaves are large (50–240 x 38–150 mm) and densely hairy, often with elongated, papillate insect galls. Fruit subglobose, up to 35 mm in diameter, yellowish brown, with a tough, leathery rind and little flesh. They are edible, though not particularly tasty, and best when still soft; older fruits become dry and tend to persist on the plant.

*Vangueria infausta* subsp. *infausta*: fruit

### *Vangueria parvifolia*
(=*Tapiphyllum parvifolium*)
**Mountain wild-medlar**
**Bergwildemispel**

A shrub or small tree of rocky ridges in bushveld. It resembles a small-leaved version of the wild medlar, with the leaves usually shorter than 20 mm and the globose fruit rarely exceeding 15 mm in diameter. Plants are also easily confused with the velvet rock-alder (see p104), but the latter has thinner leaves and bean-shaped, blackish fruit.

*Vangueria parvifolia*: flowers

## Notes

- All trees in this group belong to the coffee family. As in other members of the family (see p101) the fruit is tipped by the persistent remains of the calyx, or by a circular scar left after shedding of the calyx.
- The coffee family is characterized by so-called species-pairs (e.g. in *Afrocanthium* and *Vangueria*). These are plants that are essentially similar in most features, but in one form the leaves are hairless or sparsely hairy, but densely hairy in the other. Botanists are divided as to whether to treat these two entities as separate species or merely as forms of the same species. In southern Africa, the two forms have traditionally been maintained as separate species.

# 17. False-gardenia group

Two interpetiolar stipules, one on each side of the stem, are located at a node. Initially they are green and protect the growing bud of the shoot, but once the shoot has elongated they loose their function and are often shed, leaving a scar or ridge between the two opposite leaves. Also included in this group are trees without stipules, but with a prominent ridge between the opposite leaves. The outstanding diagnostic feature is the leaves which, at least when mature,

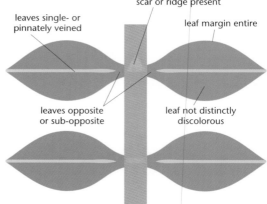

interpetiolar stipules, scar or ridge present

leaves single- or pinnately veined

leaf margin entire

leaves opposite or sub-opposite

leaf not distinctly discolorous

leaves smooth or sparsely hairy; without bacterial nodules; spines absent

appear essentially hairless to the naked eye. Check carefully for the presence of spines though, for these are sometimes confined to sucker shoots only and their presence would place the tree in Group 14 (see p100). In non-stipular species, the ridge between the leaves is sometimes obscure, in which case they may be found in Group 23 (see p120). Species with a ridge between the two leaves, but with three or more prominent veins from the base of the blade, are in Group 12 (see p96).

## Icacinaceae
### White-pear family; Witpeerfamilie

A small family without any outstanding diagnostic features. Leaves tend to be opposite, simple and without stipules. The flowers are small and often whitish. In *Cassinopsis* [lemonthorns; lemoentjiedorings] the inflorescences often seem to arise from between the opposite petioles or from only one of the axils of a leaf pair (see below). The family does not appear to be a natural entity and the two local genera may in future be placed in other families.

### *Cassinopsis tinifolia*
False-lemonthorn
Valslemoentjiedoring

Evergreen shrub or small tree found in forest margins. Stipules are lacking, but the interpetiolar ridge is prominent. The inflorescences always seem to rise from only one axil of a leaf pair. This is because growth in the species is sympodial (see p41), with the apical bud of the shoot developing into an inflorescence. The axillary bud of one of the upper leaf pairs then resumes growth to take over the role of the shoot, in the process displacing the inflorescence to the side.

*Cassinopsis tinifolia:* fruit

# Gentianaceae

### Gentian family; Gentiaanfamilie

A family of non-stipular, mostly herbaceous plants. The only woody genus in our region (*Anthocleista*) was previously classified in the Loganiaceae.

### *Anthocleista grandiflora*

Forest fevertree
Forest bigleaf (N, Z)
Boskoorsboom

Unmistakable tree with a straight, clean bole and a canopy of large, simple leaves. Associated with forest or riverine vegetation, usually in moist or marshy places. Juvenile plants have leaves up to 1 m long, the largest of any dicotyledonous tree native to southern Africa. Ridges between the leaves are not associated with stipules.

*Anthocleista grandiflora*: flowers

# Rhizophoraceae

### Onionwood family; Uiehoutfamilie

Many members of this family are mangroves. They resemble the coffee family in having interpetiolar stipules. Ovaries, however, are superior, hence the remains of the calyx does not tip the fruit, as is the case in the coffee family.

### *Bruguiera gymnorrhiza*

Black mangrove
Swartwortelboom

A mangrove of tidal estuaries and lagoons, with numerous knee-like breathing roots arising from the mud around the tree. The seeds germinate while still on the tree and the resultant, green, cigar-shaped 'fruits' are often washed up on beaches along the tropical east coast.

**Notes**

- Most trees in this group belong to the coffee family. In all members of the family the fruit is tipped by the persistent remains of the calyx, or by a circular scar left after shedding of the calyx.
- Domatia in the axils of the principal side veins are common in woody members of the coffee family. Because of the smooth leaves, pit- and hairtuft-domatia are particularly noticeable in many species included in this group.

*Bruguiera gymnorrhiza*: fruit

# Rubiaceae
## Coffee family; Koffiefamilie

Coffee is made by brewing the roasted seeds of *Coffea arabica* (naturalized in eastern Zimbabwe) and *C. robusta*. Although not native to our region, both species would be classified in this group. Of the five species of coffee native to southern Africa, at least one, *C. racemosa* [mozambique-coffee; mosambiekkoffie], produces a good coffee.

### *Oxyanthus pyriformis* subsp. *pyriformis*
**Hatpins-loquat**
**Hoedespeldlukwart**

Evergreen shrub or small tree, usually with horizontal branches, occurring in the shady understorey of forest. The flowers have long, very slender tubes filled with nectar, an adaptation for pollination by hawk moths at night.

*O. pyriformis* subsp. *pyriformis:* flowers

### *Psychotria capensis* subsp. *capensis*
**Birdberry**
**Voëlbessie**

Shrub or small tree associated with forest or bush clumps in high-rainfall grassland. Leaves somewhat fleshy, with pit domatia in axils of side veins. Fruit ripens sequentially through yellow to red or black (illustrated on p51).

*Psychotria capensis:* flowers

### *Rothmannia capensis*
**False-gardenia**
**Valskatjiepiering**

Small to medium-sized evergreen tree occurring in forest or rocky hillsides in bushveld. Leaves are hairy in juveniles, but hairless in mature plants, with distinct pit-domatia in the axils of the principal side veins (see p45). Flowers attractive, white with maroon markings inside throat of corolla tube (illustrated on p7).

*Rothmannia capensis:* fruit

*Rothmannia capensis:* tree

# 18. Onionwood group

Most trees in this group are without stipules, yet they display a prominent ridge between the opposite leaves. In a few species, however, large stipules (two per leaf; hence two on each side of the stem) or interpetiolar stipules (one on each side of the stem) are located at a node. Initially they are green and help to protect the young leaves in the apical bud, but once the shoot has elongated they loose their function and are often shed, leaving a scar or ridge between the two opposite leaves.

Leaf margins are variously toothed, a term used here in the broad sense to include states technically described as dentate (teeth directed outwards), serrate (saw-like, with teeth directed forward) or crenate (scalloped; teeth rounded). 'Wavy' (undulate) should not be confused with 'toothed'. The former refers to a margin which is wavy (not flat), it may be entire or toothed. Spines are rarely present.

leaves simple

interpetiolar stipules, scar or ridge present

leaf margin toothed

leaves opposite or sub-opposite

leaves single- or pinnately veined

leaf not distinctly discolorous

## Celastraceae
### Spikethorn family; Pendoringfamilie

Most opposite-leaved members of the family have minute stipules and lack an interpetiolar ridge or scar (see Group 19, p112).

### *Catha edulis*
Khat
Boesmanstee

Small to medium-sized deciduous tree with upright crown and somewhat drooping branches; occurring in bushveld, often in rocky places. An interpetiolar scar is formed by the shedding of two relatively large stipules (superficially resembling a single interpetiolar stipule) placed next to one another on both sides of the stem (compare diagram **c** on page 33).

*Catha edulis:* flowers

# Cornaceae
**Dogwood family; Kornoeliefamilie**
A small family with only two species in our region.

### *Curtisia dentata*
Assegai
Assegaitree (Z)
Assegaai

Medium to large evergreen tree associated with forest. Young growth densely covered with grey or brownish hairs. Stipules lacking and the interpetiolar ridge not scar-like. Leaf margins strongly and sharply toothed. Fruit white, and crowned with remains of the calyx.

*Curtisia dentata:* fruit

# Rhizophoraceae
**Onionwood family; Uiehoutfamilie**
Many members of this family resemble the coffee family (Rubiaceae) in having interpetiolar stipules. Leaf margins in the coffee family, however, are always entire.

### *Cassipourea malosana*
Onionwood
Uiehout

Small to medium-sized tree with horizontally spreading branches, usually occurring in the understorey of forest. The fruit is capsular and tipped by the remains of the style.

*Cassipourea malosana:* flowers; petals already shed

## Notes

- Some onionwood trees (*Cassipourea* species) are under threat as a result of bark harvesting. The bark is used extensively in traditional medicine, notably to treat various skin conditions and in skin lightening preparations.
- Fresh leaves of *Catha edulis* are chewed for its habit-forming stimulant properties. Known as 'khat', the drug is usually obtained from cultivars with higher concentrations of the active compounds than in wild plants. The species is extensively grown and traded in parts of North Africa, Arabia and Madagascar. A compound related to khat's most active ingredient (cathinone) is manufactured synthetically (methcathinone) and is used, usually illegally, as a recreational drug worldwide.
- Included in this group is *Lydenburgia abbottii* (pondo bushmans-tea; pondoboesmanstee), the rarest tall forest tree endemic to southern Africa. Previously known as *Catha abbottii*, all known trees of the species, estimated at fewer than 400, are confined to an area with a radius of about 10 km in Pondoland.

# 19. Spoonwood group

A large and diverse group with simple, opposite leaves and the margins variously toothed or coarsely lobed (sinuate). It differs from Group 18 (see p110) in that the stipules are either absent or, when present, are small, inconspicuous and never form a conspicuous scar across the node between the petioles of opposite leaves. Because the stipules are so small and unimportant for the recognition of the group, they are not shown on the icon. 'Wavy' (undulate) should not be confused with 'toothed'; the former refers to a margin which is wavy (not flat), and may be smooth or toothed. Spines are rarely present. If a tree cannot be found in this group, check also under Group 18.

leaves simple

interpetiolar stipules, scar or ridge absent

leaves opposite or sub-opposite

leaf not distinctly discolorous

leaf margin toothed or loded

leaves single- or pinnately veined

## Celastraceae
### Spikethorn family; Pendoringfamilie

A family well-represented in this group. All the species have minute, inconspicuous stipules which usually wither and dry at an early stage.

### *Cassine peragua* subsp. *peragua*
Forest spoonwood
Boslepelhout

Evergreen tree associated with forest. Bark contains a yellow pigment in the dead outer layers. Leaves with venation clearly visible on both surfaces; venation translucent when viewed against the sun. Fruit a round berry, ripening through yellow and red to purplish black.

*Cassine peragua* subsp. *peragua*: flowers

### Notes

- Trees with opposite leaves and yellow pigmented bark invariably belong to the spikethorn family. The layers of yellow pigment usually only become apparent when the outer dead layers of bark are scraped away and are best seen between the living inner and dead outer bark.
- Sequential colour changes during the ripening of fleshy fruits, as seen in members of the spikethorn family, are always associated with seed dispersal by birds. Such fruits ripen asynchronously, often from green through yellow, orange and red to purplish and eventually black.
- *Xymalos monospora* (lemonwood) of the Monimiaceae (lemonwood family) is the only tree in this group with secretory cavities in the leaves. They are very small, usually overlooked.

### *Elaeodendron croceum*
**Common saffron (SA)**
**Forest saffron (Z)**
**Gewone saffraan**

Evergreen forest tree with a yellow pigment in the outer dead layers of the bark, the latter being the source of the common name 'saffron'. Branchlets are covered with numerous raised brown or black dots (lenticels). Flowers greenish and inconspicuous. Fruit a drupe, oval, cream to pale yellow.

*Elaeodendron croceum:* fruit

### *Cassine schinoides*
**(=*Hartogiella schinoides*)**
**Spoonwood**
**Lepelhout**

Small to medium-sized tree associated with woody vegetation in fynbos, often along streams. Flowers white or cream, small and inconspicuous. Differs from the forest spoonwood in having narrow elliptic leaves with the venation obscure when held against the light. Fruit a berry, though not very fleshy; yellow to brownish when ripe.

*Cassine schinoides:* fruit

# Lamiaceae
## Sage family; Saliefamilie

A family of predominantly aromatic herbaceous plants. Recent studies have shown that a number of woody plants traditionally classified in the Verbenaceae are better placed in the sage family. Among these are the genus *Karomia* (chinese-hat bushes; sambreelblombosse).

### *Karomia speciosa*
**Mauve chinese-hats**
**Pers sambreelblom**

Sparsely branched shrub or small tree; occurring in hot, arid bushveld, usually on rocky mountain slopes. Coarse-toothed leaves borne on stalks about 10 mm long. Plants are very showy when in full flower. Each flower consists of a deep blue, 2-lipped corolla inserted in a papery, mauve to pink plate-like calyx, the latter resembling a Chinese hat, hence the common names.

*K. tettensis* [northern chinese-hats; noordelike perssambreel-blom] has seemingly sessile leaves and the flowers are larger. It occurs from the Zambezi River Valley northwards.

*Karomia speciosa:* flowers

# 20. Numnum group

The combination of opposite leaves, milky latex and spines makes this group very easy to identify. Latex flow is very consistent, but the spines are sometimes sparsely distributed, especially in older plants. Spines are usually present in opposite pairs. Regularly forked spines are diagnostic for this group, being present in some of the species only.

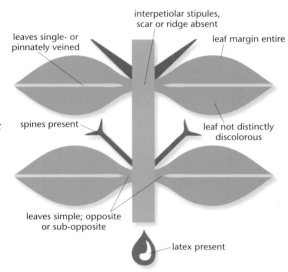

interpetiolar stipules, scar or ridge absent

leaves single- or pinnately veined

leaf margin entire

spines present

leaf not distinctly discolorous

leaves simple; opposite or sub-opposite

latex present

## Apocynaceae
### Oleander family; Selonsroosfamilie

This group is made up of a single genus, *Carissa* [numnums; noemnoems]. Numnums have white flowers and bright red or black to bluish purple berries. In flower buds the petals are twisted either anticlockwise or clockwise, as viewed from the tip.

### *Carissa edulis*
**Climbing numnum (SA)**
**Simplespine carissa (Z)**
**Ranknoemnoem**

Much-branched, scrambling shrub or small tree; occurring in bushveld, often in riverine vegetation or on termite mounds. Spines nearly always simple (not forked). Leaves with or without hairs. Flowers white, often tinged with pink or purple; petals twisted clockwise when in bud. Berries oval, purplish black.

*Carissa edulis*: flowers

*Carissa edulis*: fruit

## *Carissa macrocarpa*
Amantungulu
Grootnoemnoem

Shrub or small tree; occurring on coastal dunes, often in dense stands just above the highwater mark. Spines often forked once or twice. Leaves glossy dark green above, paler below, hairless. Flowers with petals twisted anticlockwise when in bud. *Carissa* species with the largest red berries in southern Africa (up to 50 x 35 mm).

*Carissa macrocarpa:* flowers and fruit

*Carissa macrocarpa:* flowers

## *Carissa tetramera*
Sand numnum (SA)
Sand carissa (Z)
Sandnoemnoem

Much-branched shrub or small tree, usually multi-stemmed; occurring in frost-free bushveld, usually on sandy soil. Spines usually twice-forked, rarely simple. Flowers white, often tinged with red; petals 4 (all other species have 5), twisted anticlockwise when in bud. Fruit a berry, oval, hardly exceeding 10 mm in diameter, purplish black.

*Carissa tetramera:* flowers

### Notes

- Despite belonging to a generally poisonous family, the ripe berries of all numnums are edible. One of the few native fruits that are consumed together with the rind and seed, they are eaten fresh, or made into jam or jelly. The fruit of *Carissa macrocarpa*, a species often grown in gardens, is particularly tasty and has commercial potential.

### What to look for: *Carissa* species

- Spines simple or branched.
- Size and colour of ripe berries.
- Number of petals (4 or 5).
- Direction the petals twist in bud: anticlockwise (to the left; most species) or clockwise (to the right).

# 21. Poisonbush group

Leaves in this group are always entire. Latex is present and may be white, pale yellow, yellow or even bright orange. Latex flow is very consistent. In some latex-containing trees with the leaves predominantly whorled, a substantial proportion of the leaves may be opposite; these species are treated under Group 24 (see p124).

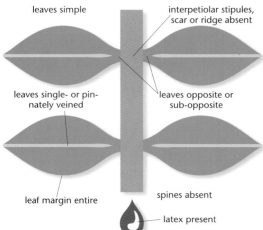

leaves simple

interpetiolar stipules, scar or ridge absent

leaves single- or pinnately veined

leaves opposite or sub-opposite

leaf margin entire

spines absent

latex present

## Apocynaceae
### Oleander family; Selonsroosfamilie

The bulk of the trees in this group belong to the oleander family; most are characterized by white latex. Species of *Acokanthera* [poisonbush; gifboom] are highly toxic and, although the ripe berries are probably edible, they should be avoided.

### Acokanthera oppositifolia
**Bushmans-poisonbush**
**Boesmansgif**

Shrub or small evergreen to semi-deciduous tree; occurring in wooded places in a variety of habitats. Leaves thick and leathery, often tinged with red or purple; apex tapering to a sharp, spine-like point. Flowers white, often tinged with pink, sweetly scented. Fruit a berry, ovoid, pinkish to purplish black.

### Notes

- Some of the most poisonous trees in the region can be found among the oleander family in this group. Particular care should be exercised when handling species of *Acokanthera* (poisonbushes; gifbome); avoid all contact, especially with their latex.
- The yellow or orange latex found in some members of the mangosteen family is used to dye textiles and to extract yellow pigments used in watercolour paints.

*Acokanthera oppositifolia:* flowers

### Diplorhynchus condylocarpon
**Hornpod (SA)**
**Wild-rubber (Z)**
**Horingpeultjieboom**

*Diplorhynchus condylocarpon:* fruit

Sparsely branched tree with slender, drooping branches and more or less drooping leaves; occurring in bushveld, usually on rocky ridges and in sandy soil. Latex white, particularly sticky. Fruit a pair of follicles. Such paired fruit (carpels), sometimes with the individual units long and pod-like, is found in many members of the oleander family, including the oleander itself.

# Clusiaceae
## Mangosteen family; Geelmelkhoutfamilie

The only family in southern Africa which has trees with yellowish or orange latex. This family is not nearly as poisonous as the oleander family; in fact, some of the *Garcinia* species [mangosteens; geelmelkhoutbome] have tasty, edible fruit.

### Garcinia gerrardii
**Forest mangosteen**
**Bosgeelmelkhout**

*Garcinia gerrardii:* fruit

Small to medium-sized evergreen tree; occurring in the shady understorey of forest. Latex pale yellow. Branchlets angled by decurrent leaf petioles. Leaves leathery, glossy on both surfaces. Flowers small, yellowish green. Fruit fleshy, subglobose, orange when ripe. A superficially similar-looking species, *Buxus natalensis* (natal box; natalbuksboom), often shares the same habitat, but it does not have latex and belongs to Group 23 (see p120).

### Harungana madagascariensis
**Orange-milk tree**
**Oranjemelkhout**

*Harungana madagascariensis:* fruit

Shrub or small to medium-sized bushy tree; occurring in forest areas, usually on forest margins or in clearings. Latex highly unusual, thick, bright orange (see p37). Foliage with a brownish yellow appearance. Pairs of youngest leaves at the tips of shoots held tightly pressed together, covered by rusty hairs on the outside. Flowers, small, cream, in many-flowered terminal sprays. Fruit fleshy, globose, 2–4 mm in diameter, ripening through greenish orange to bright red.

# 22. Waterberry group

Crucial for the identification of this group is the ability to recognize secretory cavities in the leaf blade. Because of their very small size (less than 0.25 mm in diameter), most people find it difficult to detect these structures, which are best looked for with the aid of a good hand lens.

Secretory cavities usually only become visible when a leaf is held up to a strong light source, such as the sun. They appear as translucent dots, usually uniformly distributed throughout the leaf blade. It is advisable to practise on familiar trees known to contain secretory cavities to see what they look like (see p29 for more information).

A good indication for their possible presence is that leaves with secretory cavities usually have a strong smell when crushed. On the other hand, not all strongly scented leaves have secretory cavities. When a leaf is held up to the light, turn it around and look at it from both sides, as the cavities may be better visible from one of the two surfaces.

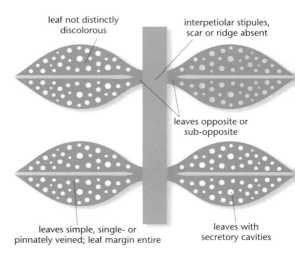

leaf not distinctly discolorous

interpetiolar stipules, scar or ridge absent

leaves opposite or sub-opposite

leaves simple, single- or pinnately veined; leaf margin entire

leaves with secretory cavities

## Myrtaceae
### Guava family; Koejawelfamilie

All members of the guava family have secretory cavities. Native members are also characterized by opposite leaves, hence most of the trees in this group belong to this family.

### *Eugenia capensis*
**Dune myrtle**
**Duinemirt**

Shrub or small evergreen tree occurring on coastal dunes, often in dense stands just above the high-water mark. Its leaves are round to oval, thick and leathery. Several woody plants in this dune habitat tend to have similar leaves, but the combination of opposite arrangement and the presence of secretory cavities makes it easy to separate the dune myrtle from the others.

*Eugenia capensis:* flowers

## Syzygium cordatum
Umdoni (SA)
Waterberry (N, Z)
Waterbessie

Medium to large evergreen tree associated with wet or marshy habitats. One of the easier waterberries to identify due to its sessile or very shortly stalked, elliptic to almost circular bluish green leaves with a heart-shaped base. All the waterberries have 4-angled branchlets and showy terminal inflorescences. The flowers shed their petals on opening and colour is provided by numerous, fluffy white stamens. Fruit an oval berry, purplish black when ripe.

*Syzygium cordatum:* flowers

# Rutaceae
## Citrus family; Sitrusfamilie

Alternate leaves predominate in the citrus family. However, the cape-chestnut is the only tree member of this family in southern Africa with opposite, simple leaves.

## Calodendrum capense
Cape-chestnut
Kaapse kastaiing

Medium to large forest tree, often forming part of the canopy. Flowers large, pink, often produced in profusion, thus rendering the trees visible from afar. Often planted in gardens but cultivated trees are rarely as floriferous as their counterparts in the wild. Fruit is a large woody capsule with a knobby surface.

*Calodendrum capense:* flowers

### Notes

- Simple, entire-margined opposite leaves with secretory cavities are also found in *Hypericum* (currybushes; kerriebosse) of the Clusiaceae (mangosteen family; geelmelkhoutfamilie). In our region, these cavities are difficult to see in woody members of the genus, hence they have been classified in Group 23 (see p120).
- The ovary in the guava family is invariably inferior, resulting in fruit tipped by the remains of the calyx (as in a guava). This is also found in the Rubiaceae (coffee family; koffiefamilie).
- Based on fruit type, the guava family can be divided into two major groups: species with fleshy fruit and species with dry fruit. With the exception of one Cape species (*Metrosideros angustifolia*: lanceleaf myrtle; smalblad), all native African members have fleshy fruit. Species of *Eucalyptus* (eucalypts; bloekoms) are widely planted in our region.

They originate mainly from Australia and belong to the group with dry fruit; they also differ from local species in having the mature leaves apparently alternate (although juvenile leaves may be opposite).
- Species-identification in *Eugenia* (myrtles) and *Syzygium* (waterberries) is difficult and often requires expert knowledge. Waterberries have nectar-producing, bisexual flowers, but in the myrtles the flowers lack nectar and are functionally unisexual, with separate male and female plants. The myrtles are unusual in that flowers of both sexes have stamens and produce pollen. Morphologically, the flowers appear to be either male or bisexual. Pollen in the seemingly bisexual flowers is, however, sterile and produced solely as a reward for pollinators; functionally these flowers are female.

# 23. Bushwillow group

The largest group of trees with simple, opposite leaves. In the absence of any specialized structures it is an easy group to identify. Nevertheless, to eliminate other groups, check carefully for the presence of interpetiolar stipules, scars or ridges (Groups 13–18), latex (Group 21) or secretory cavities (Group 22).

Stipules are either absent or small and inconspicuous; they are not required for group recognition and are therefore not indicated on the icon. Leaves may be discolorous, but among trees with opposite leaves this attribute is only used for group recognition in combination with interpetiolar stipules (Group 13). Spines are rare in this group and their presence is not part of its definition.

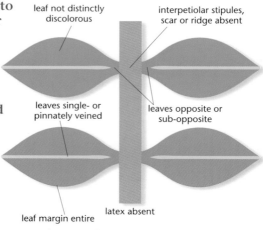

leaf not distinctly discolorous

interpetiolar stipules, scar or ridge absent

leaves single- or pinnately veined

leaves opposite or sub-opposite

leaf margin entire

latex absent

leaves simple; without secretory cavities

## Combretaceae
### Bushwillow family; Boswilgfamilie

*Combretum* [bushwillows; boswilge], the largest genus of trees belonging to this group, are a key component of the warm bushveld vegetation in southern Africa. In many parts, bushwillows form the dominant broad-leaved component of the vegetation, especially on nutrient-poor sandy soils. Trees are usually deciduous, flowering briefly and profusely with the appearance of the new leaves in spring. An outstanding diagnostic feature of the group is the dry, generally 4-winged fruit (technically a samara) which may remain on or below trees for a long time. Leaves and fruit are covered by minute, sessile, scale-like glandular hairs, often difficult to detect without a hand lens (see p31), but they are responsible for the shiny, varnish-like secretions on especially the young leaves and fruit in some species.

### *Combretum kraussii*
**Forest bushwillow**
**Bosvaderlandswilg**

One of the few bushwillows which is a forest species; crown usually with scattered bright red leaves. The flush of new leaves in spring lacks chlorophyll and are white to cream, thus rendering the trees clearly visible in the forest canopy. Fruit is produced in abundance and is usually attractively tinged pink to dark red, eventually drying to brown.

*Combretum kraussii*: fruit

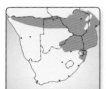

## *Combretum zeyheri*
**Large-fruit bushwillow (SA)**
**Large-fruit combretum (Z)**
**Raasblaar**
**Mukenge (N)**

A characteristic small to medium-sized bushveld tree. Young branchlets are minutely whitish and hairy; the leaves have the venation slightly raised below with hair-tuft domatia in the axils of the principal side veins. The 4-winged fruit is among the largest in the genus, up to 80 x 80 mm, with wings up to 40 mm wide.

*Combretum zeyheri:* fruit

### What to look for: *Combretum* species

- Habit: climber, suffrutex, shrub or tree.
- Shape and size of leaves.
- Hairiness of branchlets and leaves.
- Prominence of venation on both leaf surfaces.
- Flower colour.
- Fruit size.
- Fruit colour.

*Combretum zeyheri:* flowers

*Combretum zeyheri:* tree

### Notes

- This group is represented by at least 24 southern African tree families, only four of which are mentioned here.
- Vegetatively, bushwillows superficially resemble members of the coffee family on account of their simple, entire, opposite leaves. However, unlike the coffee family with its prominent interpetiolar stipules, bushwillows lack stipules. Morphological differences between bushwillows are often slight and species identification can be difficult in the absence of fertile material.
- In bushwillows, the winged fruit develops from an inferior ovary. Ovary position is most notice-able during flowering. The flowers are essentially stalkless, but appear to be carried on short, stout 'stalks', the latter being the ovaries on top of which the other floral parts are borne.
- Leaf arrangement in guarries is not always con-sistent; leaves can be opposite, sub-opposite or alternate, even on the same branch. The most frequent state, as a rule for group identification, is opposite. Species identification is difficult.
- Prominent principal side veins ending at the leaf margin to form a 'herringbone' pattern are diagnostic for *Berchemia* (ivorywoods).
- A conspicuous flat gland terminates the midrib before the apex on the lower surface of the leaf in *Galpinia transvaalica* (see p45).

# Ebenaceae

## Ebony family; Ebbehoutfamilie

*Euclea* [guarri trees; ghwarriebome] comprise many species in our region. They are evergreen, most species tending to have rigid, leathery leaves with a papery texture (they make a dry, rustling sound when shaken); the leaf margins are often wavy (undulate), though not toothed. Young growth in many species is covered by scale-like glandular hairs appearing to the naked eye as minute rusty brown granules. Leaf arrangement in some guarries is very variable, even on the same plant; compare also those species of the genus included in Group 10 (see p86).

### *Euclea undulata*

Common guarri
Gewone ghwarrie

Dense leafy shrub or small tree with a wide distribution, often occurring in rocky places. The leaves are relatively small (20–40 x 5–15 mm), usually dark green with a conspicuously wavy margin (see also p32). Often confused with *E. crispa* [blue guarri; bloughwarrie], a species with the leaves larger, grey- to blue-green above and the margin less wavy.

*Euclea undulata:* flowers

# Rhamnaceae

## Buffalo-thorn family; Blinkblaarfamilie

A family with leaves of which the venation is often diagnostic; the finest veins form a regular grid of minute squares or rectangles (best seen when a leaf is held up to a strong light source, such as the sun). The flowers are usually inconspicuous, with a prominent nectar-secreting disc, and five reduced petals very characteristically borne opposite to, and often embracing, the five stamens.

### *Berchemia discolor*

Bird-plum (N, Z)
Brown-ivory (SA)
Bruinivoor

Medium to large deciduous or evergreen tree; occurring in low-altitude bushveld. Leaves elliptic or elliptic-oblong, shiny dark-green above, pale-green to bluish green below, essentially hairless, principal side veins prominently raised below and ending at the margin without the formation of an intramarginal vein. Flowers in axillary clusters, greenish yellow. Fruit a drupe, ovoid, yellow to pale-orange, with a single stone. Easily confused with *B. zeyheri* (red-ivory; rooi-ivoor) which tend to be a smaller tree with more greyish green leaves and yellow to brownish red fruit.

*Berchemia discolor:* fruit

# Oleaceae

## Olive family; Olyffamilie

Several species of *Olea* [olives and ironwoods; olien- en ysterhoutbome] occur in our region. Most have 4-angled branchlets with scattered, whitish lenticels. The opposite leaves lack stipules and may be slightly discolorous. A useful field test for members of the family is to hold a fresh leaf at the tip and base and pull quickly in opposite directions until the blade snaps in two. Inspect the torn edges (use a hand lens) for the presence of a dense fringe of protruding fibres, a diagnostic feature for many members of the family (see p47).

*Olea europaea* subsp. *africana:* tree

### *Olea europaea* subsp. *africana*
**Wild olive (N, SA)**
**African olive (Z)**
**Olienhout**

Evergreen tree with a dense rounded crown and greyish green foliage. Leaves with the lower surface paler than the upper due to a dense cover of silvery or brownish scales. Flowers are small, white and, characteristically for the family, each has two stamens. This tree is often confused with *Buddleja saligna* [false-olive; witolienhout], a completely unrelated species which has leaves with the lower surface white and prominently veined.

*Olea europaea* subsp. *africana:* flowers

# 24. Quininetree group

Trees with a mainly whorled leaf arrangement often produce a few opposite leaves on the same plant and vice versa. If a twig has opposite leaves, always check additional branches for the possible presence of the whorled state. This group is for trees in which the whorled state predominates. Latex colour varies according to the species; it can be watery, cloudy, white or yellow.

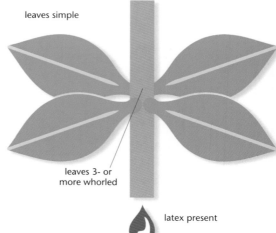

leaves simple

leaves 3- or more whorled

latex present

## Anacardiaceae
### Mango family; Mangofamilie

Some species of *Ozoroa* [resintrees; harpuisbome] have predominantly 3-whorled leaves. In resintrees the main side veins of the leaf are prominent on the lower surface and arranged more or less parallel to one another. Each side vein ends at or near the leaf margin without joining an intramarginal vein, resulting in a 'herringbone' pattern (see p28). Identification of the individual resintree species, however, is difficult.

### *Ozoroa paniculosa*
**Resintree (SA, Z)**
**Common resintree (N)**
**Harpuisboom**

Small to medium-sized deciduous tree; occurring in bushveld, often on rocky hillsides. Leaves grey- to blue-green above, silvery to silky (due to densely appressed hairs) below. Flowers small, creamy white, male and female ones on separate plants. Fruit a drupe, elliptic or kidney-shaped, ripening hard, black and wrinkled.

*Ozoroa paniculosa*: flowers

*Ozoroa paniculosa*: fruit

# Apocynaceae
### Oleander family; Selonsroosfamilie

Opposite or whorled leaves with entire margins and watery or milky latex is diagnostic for the oleander family.

### *Rauvolfia caffra*
**Quininetree**
**Kinaboom**

Large, stately tree; occurring in riverine bush and along forest margins. Leaves in whorls of 3–6, bright glossy green above. Flowers small, white, sweetly scented. Latex white, very sticky. Fruit fleshy, almost spherical, green with white spots, ripening to black and wrinkled. Resembles *Breonadia salicina* [matumi (SA), breonadia (Z); mingerhout] of the coffee family, but the latter lacks latex (Group 25, see p126).

*Rauvolfia caffra:* fruit

# Clusiaceae
### Mangosteen family; Geelmelkhoutfamilie

The only family which has trees with yellowish or orange latex in southern Africa. Most members have opposite leaves.

### *Garcinia livingstonei*
**African mangosteen**
**Afrikageelmelkhout**
**Ushika (N)**

Rather untidy tree with short rigid branches; occurring in low-altitude bushveld, often on floodplains of rivers. Latex pale-yellow. Leaves borne towards the ends of short, stiff branches, 3–4-whorled or opposite, blue-green, thick, stiff and leathery. Flowers axillary or on knobbly side spurs on older stems, male and female ones on separate trees. Fruit fleshy, bright orange-red, edible, with a delicious acid-sweet taste.

### Notes

• For reasons of safety, trees of the oleander family should be considered poisonous unless proven otherwise. Avoid contact with the latex, particularly. The family is rich in alkaloids and several members are used medicinally.

*Garcinia livingstonei:* fruit

# 25. Wild-almond group

A very distinct and easily recognizable group whose species have either entire or toothed leaf margins. Note that trees with predominantly whorled leaves often have at least a few opposite ones on the same plant. This is especially the case when the leaves are 3-whorled.

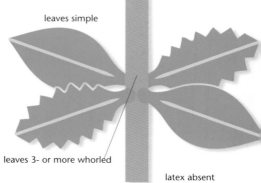

leaves simple

leaves 3- or more whorled

latex absent

## Buddlejaceae
### Wild-elder family; Wildevlierfamilie

In the past, members of this family were classified under the Loganiaceae. Whereas *Buddleja* [sagewoods; wildesaliebome] have consistently opposite leaves, those of *Nuxia* [wild-elders; wildevlierbome] are usually 3-whorled. Modern evidence suggests that the sagewoods might be best classified under Scrophulariaceae [snapdragon family; leeubekkiefamilie] and the wild-elders under the closely related Stilbaceae.

### *Nuxia floribunda*
**Forest elder**
**Bosvlier**

Evergreen tree with a somewhat rounded crown; occurring in and around forest. Twigs are slightly angled with swollen nodes. Leaves are 3-whorled or opposite, more or less drooping and more than three times as long as broad. The slender petiole (15–45 mm long) and the midrib are often tinged pink or purplish. When in full flower, trees are visible from a distance due to the large much-branched terminal sprays of small white flowers.

*Nuxia floribunda:* flowers

### Notes

- In the wild-elders, opposite and 3-whorled leaves are often present on the same branch. The first leaves of a new shoot tend to be opposite. Always check several leaf positions and use the predominate state for identifying the group.
- The wild-almonds' rather aberrant leaf arrangement among native Proteaceae is reflected in the fact that its closest living relatives are not in Africa, but in Madagascar, South America and Australia. Its presence in the Cape flora may indicate the connection that existed between these land masses when they were united in the super-continent Gondwana.

- In the gardenias, the leaves are usually borne in dense clusters on short lateral twigs, making it difficult to establish their whorled (sometimes opposite) arrangement. In trees with clustered leaves, look for sucker shoots, as these have longer internodes, making it easier to see the arrangement of leaves at a node.
- Fruit in the coffee family develop from inferior ovaries; this is clearly seen in the fruit of gardenias which is tipped either by the conspicuous persistent calyx or by a circular scar left after the shedding of the calyx and other floral parts.

# Proteaceae

**Protea family; Proteafamilie**

The wild-almond is the only native member of the protea family in this group. The rest of the family in our region have alternate leaves.

### *Brabejum stellatifolium*
**Wild-almond**
**Wildeamandel**

Multistemmed shrub or medium-sized tree, usually confined to stream banks in fynbos. Leaves 4–9-whorled with the margin irregularly and often sharply toothed. The small, white and fragrant flowers are borne in dense, axillary spike-like racemes. An outstanding feature is the indehiscent, almond-shaped (hence the common names) fruit which, when mature, is covered with a velvety layer of rusty-brown hairs.

*Brabejum stellatifolium:* flowers

# Rubiaceae

**Coffee family; Koffiefamilie**

The vast majority of trees in this family have opposite leaves and interpetiolar stipules, but whorled leaves do occur in some species, hence its inclusion in this group. Imagine the interpetiolar stipules becoming leaf-like and it becomes easy to imagine how the whorled state could have been derived from the more typical opposite state.

### *Breonadia salicina*
**Matumi (SA)**
**Breonadia (Z)**
**Mingerhout**

Imposing tree up to about 40 m tall with a tall straight trunk and rather narrow crown, invariably associated with riverine fringe forest along near-permanent rivers and streams in hot, low-lying bushveld. Leaves are usually 4-whorled and superficially resemble those of *Rauvolfia caffra* [quininetree; kinaboom] of the oleander family, a species with which it can be confused. The latter, however, exudes abundant milky latex (Group 24, see p124).

*Breonadia salicina:* flowers

### *Gardenia volkensii*
**Bushveld gardenia**
**Bosveldkatjiepiering**

Shrub or small tree with rigid branches; occurring in bushveld. Leaves usually 3-whorled and clustered in whorls at the end of short, sturdy, side twigs. The large flowers are white when they open, but soon start to whither and fade to cream. They are pollinated by hawk moths at night. Fruit is oval, shallowly ribbed longitudinally and tipped by the persistent calyx; they are greyish green with numerous small, whitish warts.

*Gardenia volkensii:* fruit

# 26. Bauhinia group

A very distinct and easily recognizable group. The leaves are simple, although always shallowly to deeply notched apically. If the degree of division is such that there are two separate leaflets, each with its own 'stalk', then the leaf is considered to be compound and the plant is placed in Group 27 (see p130).

All the trees in this group have leaves with a pair of small deciduous stipules at the base; these are not shown by the icon as their detection is not essential for group recognition.

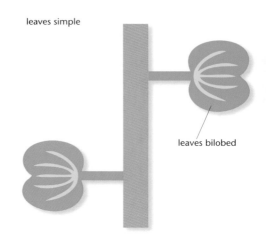

leaves simple

leaves bilobed

## Caesalpiniaceae
### Flamboyant family; Flambojantfamilie

One of three families characterized by a pod (legume) as fruit type – the other two being the Mimosaceae and Fabaceae. In the past, most local members of this family with simple bilobed leaves were classified under the genus *Bauhinia*. Today three different genera are recognized, based mainly on floral details. Examples of all three are treated below.

### *Adenolobus garipensis*
**Butterflyleaf**
**Gariepbauhinia**
**Omukandakanda (N)**

Rather untidy multistemmed shrub or small tree with long, slender branchlets. It grows in arid semi-desert and desert areas, often along dry watercourses or on rocky hills. Leaves are small, very shallowly lobed and clustered on dwarf side-shoots. Flowers are tubular, slightly curved, with petals pale yellowish or pinkish to red with conspicuous dark reddish venation; they are pollinated by sunbirds. Dry pods are dehiscent.

*Adenolobus garipensis:* flowers and fruit

### *Bauhinia galpinii*
**Pride-of-de-kaap (SA)**
**Red bauhinia (Z)**
**Vlam-van-die-vlakte**

The only red-flowered bauhinia in our region. It tends to be a scrambling shrub or climber rather than a tree. Occurs in bushveld and thicket, usually along streams or on rocky hillsides. Leaves are clearly notched at the apex. The very showy flowers are produced in large branched sprays near the ends of branches. Dry pods are dehiscent.

*Bauhinia galpinii:* flowers

## *Bauhinia petersiana*
**Coffee/Kalahari bauhinia**
**Koffie-/Kalaharibauhinia**
**Koffiebeesklou (N)**

*Bauhinia petersiana:* flowers

Of the three white-flowered bauhinias in our region, this one has the largest and most showy flowers. It is a rather low-growing scrambling shrub or small tree of bushveld, usually on deep Kalahari sand. Leaves are lobed for about half their length.

## *Bauhinia tomentosa*
**Yellow bauhinia**
**Geelbauhinia**

*Bauhinia tomentosa:* flowers

The only yellow-flowered bauhinia in our region. It is usually a multistemmed shrub of coastal forest and bushveld. Leaves are apically divided for one-third to half their length. The yellow flowers are bell-shaped, with or without a central dark brown or maroon blotch. Dry pods are dehiscent.

## *Piliostigma thonningii*
**Camelsfoot (SA)**
**Monkeybread (Z)**
**Kameelspoor**
**Mupapama (N)**

*Piliostigma thonningii:* flowers

Shrub or small tree of bushveld, usually on sandy soil. Leaves are large (up to 120 mm long), thick and leathery with the venation conspicuously raised on the lower surface. They are apically divided for about one-eighth to one-third of the length of the blade. Young branchlets and lower leaf surfaces are covered by short, reddish brown hairs. Flowers are rather inconspicuous, with crinkly white or pinkish petals. Pods are large, woody and indehiscent.

## Notes

- All trees in this group belong to the flamboyant family, whose leaves are usually paripinnate with opposite leaflets. Bilobed leaves can readily be derived from this state by postulating first a reduction of the number of leaflets to a single pair, followed by their partial lateral fusion into a single blade, the apical notch reflecting the still unfused portion of the once separate leaflets.

- Such a sequence is illustrated on p25, under 'Compound leaves: bifoliolate'.

- Because of their attractive flowers, several species of bauhinia are planted in gardens. The red-flowered pride-of-de-kaap is one of the most widely used; its common name is derived from De Kaap Valley, near Barberton in Mpumalanga, where the species is particularly common.

# 27. Mopane group

This easily recognizable group represents trees with the simplest form of compound leaf – one that is once-divided with two leaflets; technically such leaves are described as bifoliolate. It is a small group, with few southern African species.

The leaflets are either sessile at the tip of the petiole (the leaf is then popularly referred to as butterfly-like because of the resemblance of the leaflets to butterfly wings), or each leaflet is distinctly stalked. Stalked leaflet pairs may be mistaken for two opposite leaves, the petiole being confused with a short branchlet.

Pay particular attention to the position of the axillary bud (or to the side shoot/spines if the latter has grown out). An axillary bud is located in the axil of the true leaf; neither of the leaflets have axillary buds, nor is there an apical bud between the points of leaflet attachment that would indicate the presence of a stem. Butterfly-like leaves of the flamboyant family (see below) always have secretory cavities as well as a pair of small deciduous stipules at the base, but neither of these are shown by the icon as their detection is not essential for group recognition. Spines may also be present, but they are not shown for the same reason.

leaves compound, once divided

leaves with 2 leaflets

## Balanitaceae
### Torchwood family; Groendoringfamilie

A family comprising the single genus *Balanites* (torchwoods; groendorings). Torchwoods have green branchlets and prominent simple or forked spines, the latter being modified short stems. Leaflets in the four native species are shortly stalked to almost sessile.

### *Balanites maughamii*
**Greenthorn (SA)**
**Y-thorn torchwood (Z)**
**Groendoring**

Tall deciduous tree occurring in warm, dry bushveld and sand forest, often along riverbanks. The trunk in old trees is characteristically fluted. Branchlets are grey green and often more or less zigzag. They bear simple or conspicuously forked spines. Leaflets are velvety-hairy and shortly stalked. Fruit is oval, 40–60 x 20–30 mm, thinly fleshy and yellowish when ripe. The fruit is edible but not popular.

*Balanites maughamii*: fruit

# Caesalpiniaceae
## Flamboyant family; Flambojantfamilie

One of three families characterized by a pod (legume) as fruit type – the other two being the Mimosaceae and Fabaceae. Most native trees with butterfly-like leaves belong to this family.

### Colophospermum mopane
Mopane
Mopanie

Shrub to medium-sized deciduous tree occurring in hot, low-lying areas, often on alluvial or lime-rich soils. Leaflets are stalkless, butterfly-like, with a small protuberance between the pair. The leaflets contain secretory cavities which are visible as minute pellucid dots against the light and smell strongly of turpentine when crushed. Flowers are greenish cream and inconspicuous. Pods are flattened, weakly kidney-shaped and indehiscent.

*Colophospermum mopane: fruit*

### Guibourtia coleosperma
Large copalwood (SA)
Large false-mopane (Z)
Umtshibi (Z); Ushivi (N)
Grootvalsmopanie

Evergreen tree with a large, dark-green, rounded crown with drooping branchlets. Almost exclusively confined to tropical bushveld on deep Kalahari sand. Branchlets are reddish. Leaflets are very shortly stalked and somewhat sickle-shaped. They contain numerous secretory cavities and smell of turpentine when crushed. Flowers are small and white or cream. Pods are oval, thickly woody and split down one side to release a single seed that dangles on a slender stalk. The seed itself is covered by a conspicuous scarlet layer (aril).

*Guibourtia coleosperma: fruit and seed*

## Notes

- The mopane is among the few wind-pollinated trees in our region. As part of its pollination strategy the species tends to form almost pure stands in a vegetation type dominated by it and known as mopane veld, which covers more than 50 000 square kilometres in southern Africa.
- Leaves in the flamboyant family are usually paripinnate with opposite leaflets. Evolutionary

bifoliolate leaves in this family can readily be derived from this state by a reduction in the number of leaflets to a single pair. The minute protuberance between the two leaflets (for example, in mopane) may be the vestigial remains of the axis (rachis) of the ancestral paripinnate leaf (compare 'Compound leaves: bifoliolate' on p25).

# 28. Corkwood group

This group represents trees with the leaves divided into three leaflets (trifoliolate) and with abundant watery or cloudy latex. The leaves are alternate in all local members of the group. Occasionally, leaves on the same tree may have three to five leaflets, or be simple; in such cases only trees where the predominant state is three leaflets are included here. Leaflets may be variously stalked or sessile and the margins entire or variously toothed. Spinescent twigs are sometimes present.

**Important:** All local tree species of *Rhus* [karees and wild-currants; kareebome en taaibosse] have three leaflets and contain ducts with watery or cloudy latex (resin). Technically they all belong in this group. However, in these species latex flow is very inconsistent and is particularly difficult to detect in older leaves as well as in plants that are drought-stressed. Hence, for practical reasons, all karee trees and wild currants are treated as if without latex under Group 31 (see p140). If an unknown tree with trifoliolate leaves and latex is encountered, start looking under the present group, and if not found, continue searching under Group 31.

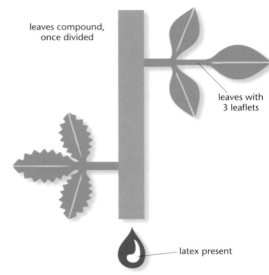

leaves compound, once divided

leaves with 3 leaflets

latex present

## Burseraceae
**Myrrh family; Mirrefamilie**

Locally this family is only represented by species of *Commiphora* [corkwoods; kanniedoodbome]. The latter genus shows great diversity in leaf characters, and members of the genus can also be found in Groups 5, 35 and 37. In all species, the fruit is a fleshy, subglobose drupe of which the outer fleshy part is shed to reveal a hard blackish stone surrounded by a fleshy bright yellow, or usually, red appendage (pseudo-aril, see p52).

### *Commiphora africana*
**Poison-grub corkwood (SA, Z)**
**Hairy corkwood (N)**
**Gifkanniedood**

Shrub or small deciduous tree of hot bushveld. Bark green or greyish, smooth and often peels in papery scrolls. Branchlets may be spine-tipped. Leaves are finely velvety and the leaflet margins are coarsely toothed. The two side-leaflets are about a third the size of the terminal one.

*Commiphora africana*: fruit

## *Commiphora neglecta*

**Greenstem corkwood (SA)**
**Sweetroot corkwood (Z)**
**Groenstam-kanniedood**

Small to medium-sized tree of bushveld, often found on rocky hillsides. The bark peels in brownish papery strips to expose a green underbark. Branchlets are often spine-tipped. Leaves are hairless, glossy, with margins of leaflets usually entire.

*Commiphora neglecta:* flowers

## *Commiphora schimperi*

**Glossyleaf corkwood**
**Blinkblaar-kanniedood**

Shrub or small deciduous tree with rather drooping crown; occurring in hot, arid bushveld, often on sandy soil. Bark green, peeling in yellowish brown papery flakes. As in the previous two species, the branchlets are often spine-tipped. Leaves hairless, glossy, with side-leaflets about half the size of the terminal one; leaflet margins are deeply toothed.

*Commiphora schimperi:* fruit

## Notes

- Corkwoods, many with a shrubby habit, are partic-ularly common and diverse in the arid parts of the Northern Cape and the western half of Namibia, notably the Kaokoveld. A useful field character is the bark which, in many of the species, exfoliates in thin, papery flakes (see p39). In most cases, peeling bark combined with the presence of latex indicates a species of corkwood.
- Whereas it is relatively easy to recognize the corkwoods as a genus, species identification is often difficult, especially in the present group with trifoliolate leaves. Identification is complic-ated by the fact that there are still species in this group that have not been formally named.

- Latex flow is particularly strong in some cork-woods from the arid western parts of our region. In *Commiphora oblanceolata* (swakopmund corkwood; swakopmund-kanniedood), *C. cervifolia* (antler-leaf cork wood; spoeg-boom) and *C. gracilifrondosa* (karee corkwood; kareekanniedood), for example, latex may squirt several centimetres from broken twigs and leaves, so special care should be taken not to get any of this very irritating liquid into the eyes.
- Corkwood flowers are small and inconspicuous, with the sexes separate and usually on different plants. The flowers are not very useful for field identification.

# 29. Coraltree group

Leaflets may be stalked or sessile, entire or toothed. Stipules are sometimes very small and may easily be overlooked; a scar is left after shedding. The icon depicts alternate leaves, the prevailing state in the group, but opposite leaves do occur in one species. Short, spiny outgrowths (prickles) are found on the stems and leaves of some coraltrees.

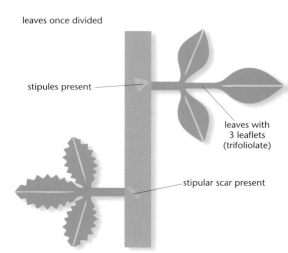

leaves once divided

stipules present

leaves with 3 leaflets (trifoliolate)

stipular scar present

latex absent

## Capparaceae
### Caper family; Kapperfamilie

In this family, the ovary is borne on an elongated stalk (gynophore), which is clearly visible at the fruiting stage, when a scar left by the perianth and stamens (see arrows in photograph of *Maerua cafra*, below left) demarcates the true flower stalk from the gynophore.

### *Maerua cafra*
**Spiderbush (SA)**
**Bushcherry (Z)**
**Witbos**

Evergreen shrub or small tree; occurring in a variety of vegetation types, often in rocky places. Leaflets usually 3, rarely 4 or 5, leathery to almost succulent (coastal forms), each ending in a hair-like tip. Flowers in terminal clusters, large, comprising 30–45 spreading, white stamens. Fruit oval, pendulous, pale green with dark green longitudinal lines.

Arrows indicate where flower stalk and gynophore meet

*Maerua cafra*: flowers

# Cunoniaceae

**Wild-alder family; Wilde-elsfamilie**

A mainly southern hemisphere family, poorly represented in our area with only two native species. Recognized by opposite, imparipinnate or trifoliolate leaves with serrate leaflets and well-developed stipules. The leaflet teeth have a glandular tip.

### *Platylophus trifoliatus*
White alder
Witels

Small to large evergreen tree; occurring in forest, often along streams. The only tree species in our region with trifoliolate, opposite leaves with toothed margins. Flowers borne in many-flowered heads or panicles, small, white. Fruit a capsule, about 10 mm long, dark brown, tipped with the persistent styles.

*Platylophus trifoliatus:* flowers

# Fabaceae

**Pea family; Ertjiefamilie**

One of three families characterized by a pod (legume) as fruit type. Stipules always present, although deciduous in some species. Easily recognized by the butterfly-like flower type with the petals differentiated into a large standard at the back, two wings on the sides (very small in coraltrees) and a boat-shaped keel that conceals the stamens and ovary in front.

### *Erythrina humeana*
Dwarf coraltree
Kleinkoraalboom

Shrub to small deciduous tree, often multistemmed; occurring in coastal grassland and bushveld. Branchlets and leaves armed with short prickles. Flowers in late summer or autumn; most other coral trees are spring-flowering.

*Erythrina humeana:* flowers

## Notes

- Diagnostic for coraltrees is the presence of two protruding glands (stipels) at the point where the terminal leaflet attaches to the rachis, and where the basal pair of leaflets attaches to the petiole.
- Coraltrees are legumes, and their characteristic pods are deeply constricted between the seed.

- Seeds are bright orange to red, with a usually black (rarely white) spot at the point of attachment.
- The showy red flowers in coraltrees produce copious amounts of nectar and are adapted for pollination by sunbirds.

### *Erythrina lysistemon*
Coraltree (SA)
Sacred coraltree (Z)
Koraalboom

Small to medium-sized deciduous tree; occurring in bushveld and coastal bush. A spectacular tree when mass-flowering before the appearance of new leaves in spring. Standard petal folded lengthwise and conceals the stamens, unlike in the closely related *Erythrina caffra* [cape coraltree; Kaapse koraalboom] where it curves backward to expose the stamens.

*Erythrina lysistemon:* fruit

---

**What to look for:** *Erythrina* species

- Season of flowering.
- Presence and distribution of prickles.
- Size of leaves.
- Hairiness of leaves.
- Shape of calyx lobes.
- Position of standard petal and exposure of stamens.

*Erythrina lysistemon:* flowers

# Vitaceae
## Grape family; Druiwefamilie

Typical for the grape family, the tendrils and inflorescences are often borne opposite leaves, and not in their axils as would be expected. This seemingly odd arrangement is due to their derivation from a laterally displaced growing tip of the shoot and not from axillary buds (so-called sympodial growth; see p41).

### *Rhoicissus tridentata*
Bushmans-grape
Boesmansdruif

Scrambling shrub or small bushy tree with tendrils; occurring in wooded grassland and bushveld, often in rocky places. Leaflets nearly stalkless, lateral ones usually asymmetrical; margin toothed to almost entire. Flowers in leaf-opposed heads, small, greenish yellow. Fruit a berry, spherical, ripening through red to black.

*Rhoicissus tridentata:* flowers

*Erythrina lysistemon:* tree

# 30. White-ironwood group

When a tree with trifoliolate leaves is encountered, first check for latex (Group 28, p132), and then check for stipules (Group 29, p134); if both are absent, carefully check for secretory cavities (see p29).

For purposes of group recognition, in trifoliolate leaves the presence of latex and stipules overrides, in order of importance, the presence of secretory cavities. Hence the present group includes all those trees that lack stipules and latex, but contain secretory cavities.

The presence of secretory cavities in this group is usually indicated by a strong citrus-like smell when a leaf is crushed. In nearly all members of the group the leaves are alternate, but opposite leaves do occur in one species. Leaflets may be variously stalked or sessile and the margins are always entire, yet sometimes wavy (undulate).

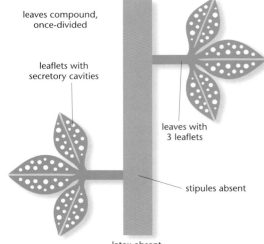

leaves compound, once-divided

leaflets with secretory cavities

leaves with 3 leaflets

stipules absent

latex absent

## Rutaceae
### Citrus family; Sitrusfamilie

Native trees with trifoliolate leaves that lack stipules but contain secretory cavities invariably belong to the citrus family; this also applies to palmately compound leaves with more than three leaflets (all alien). If stipules are present though, the tree most probably belongs to the Fabaceae [pea family; ertjiefamilie], here placed in Group 29 (p134).

### Teclea natalensis
Natal cherry-orange
Natalkersielemoen

Small to medium-sized evergreen forest tree with separate male and female plants. Leaves alternate. Leaflets leathery, distinctly stalked with tapering tips and tend to droop. Flowers small, yellowish green and borne in branched axillary or terminal heads or panicles. Fruit oval, about 10 mm long. Ripe fruit resembles miniature oranges, being yellow to orange and gland-dotted. Easily confused with *Oricia bachmannii* (twinberry; tweelingbessie), which has mainly opposite or sub-opposite leaves.

*Teclea natalensis:* flowers

## *Vepris lanceolata*
White-ironwood
Witysterhout

Small to large evergreen tree with an erect trunk and wide, rounded crown. It occurs mainly in forest and riverine bush. Leaflets are stalkless with tapering apices and conspicuously wavy margins. Flowers are small, greenish yellow and borne in branched terminal heads, male and female ones on separate plants. The fruit is a small berry (about 5 mm in diameter), black and gland-dotted when ripe.

*Vepris lanceolata:* fruit

## *Vepris reflexa*
Bushveld white-ironwood
Bosveldwitysterhout

Shrub or small tree, multistemmed or with a short trunk; occurring in hot, arid bushveld, often on rocky hillsides or along rivers. Leaflets are shortly stalked and the blade is more or less folded upwards along the midrib; they also tend to droop. Unlike in the previous species (white-ironwood), the leaflet margins are not conspicuously undulate. Flowers are small, greenish yellow, the male and female ones borne on different plants. The fruit is a small berry (about 12 mm in diameter), orange-red and gland-dotted when ripe.

*Vepris reflexa:* flowers

## Notes

- All trees in this group belong to the citrus family.
- On account of the very similar trifoliolate leaves, this group is easily confused with members of the genus *Rhus* (karees and wild-currants; karee-en taaibosse) of Group 31 (see p140).
- Whereas crushed fresh leaves of the present group have a distinct citrus-like smell, *Rhus* leaves are also aromatic, but with a 'resinous' or turpentine-like smell, which is difficult to describe, although in some species it has been associated with the smell of sour green apples. The scent in *Rhus* does not originate from secretory cavities (as in members of the citrus family) but from the resin ('latex') contained in special ducts that permeate the plants. Practise on any species of *Rhus* to become familiar with the smell. See Group 31 for more on how to recognize a *Rhus*.
- White ironwoods are susceptible to pests and diseases, especially when planted in gardens. The leaves are often deformed and yellowish because of damage caused by psyllids (family Psyllidae), small winged insects resembling winged aphids. Immature insects are disc-like, sedentary and feed on the lower leaf surface. Their presence is indicated by galls that are dome-shaped on the upper surface of the leaf and pit-like from below.

# 31. Karee group

This group contains those trees with trifoliolate leaves (divided into three leaflets) but without special attributes such as stipules, secretory cavities or, seemingly, latex. In nearly all local members the leaves are alternate and possession of three leaflets is very consistent. Leaflets may be variously stalked or sessile and the margins entire or variously toothed. Spinescent twigs are sometimes present.

**Note:** Local members of Anacardiaceae with trifoliolate leaves have ducts that contain watery or cloudy latex, best detected at the base of a freshly picked leaf during active growth. They rightly belong in Group 28 (see p132), but in these species latex flow is difficult to detect in older leaves or drought-stressed plants. For practical reasons, karee and wild-currant trees are treated here as if they are without latex. If an unknown tree with trifoliolate leaves and latex is encountered, look under Group 28; if not found there, search the present group.

leaves compound, once divided

leaflets without secretory cavities

leaves with three leaflets

stipules absent

latex absent (if present, flow often inconspicuous or inconsistent; see Note)

## Anacardiaceae
### Mango family; Mangofamilie

*Rhus* [karees and wild-currants; karees en taaibosse] contribute the bulk of the species in this group. Crushed leaves have a characteristic resinous or turpentine-like smell (see Notes under Group 30, p138) and the branchlets usually have many prominent brownish lenticels. The small flowers, male and female on separate plants, are very similar among species. Fruit characters, however, are diagnostic. Often confused with species of *Allophylus* (see p141).

> ### What to look for: *Rhus* species
> - Habit: climber, suffrutex, shrub or tree.
> - Presence of spinescent branchlets.
> - Leaflet size, shape and colour.
> - Whether leaflet margins are entire or toothed.
> - Hairiness of leaves.
> - Fruit size, colour and hairiness.
> - Shape of fruit, especially whether spheroidal or compressed.

### *Rhus lancea*
**Karee**

Small to medium-sized evergreen tree with rough dark brown to blackish bark; occurs in many different habitats. Leaflets are narrowly lanceolate, sessile, dark olive-green and hairless with entire margins. They are often covered by a shiny exudate, particularly when young. The fruit is spheroidal and slightly compressed, hairless and pale yellowish brown when ripe.

*Rhus lancea:* flowers

### Rhus pyroides var. *pyroides*
**Common wild-currant (SA)**
**Firethorn rhus (N, Z)**
**Taaibos**

Multistemmed deciduous shrub or small tree; occurring in a wide range of habitats. Branchlets densely hairy and often spinescent. Leaflets are obovate, usually hairy and the margins entire or irregularly toothed. The fruit is spheroidal, hairless and ripens through dull yellow to yellowish brown.

*Rhus pyroides* var. *pyroides*: fruit

# Sapindaceae
## Litchi family; Lietsjiefamilie

Trifoliolate members of *Allophylus* [false-currants; valstaaibosse] differ from *Rhus* in that the plants do not contain resin ('latex'); crushed leaves therefore lack a resinous smell. Branchlets are without prominent brownish lenticels and the leaflets often have hairtuft-domatia in the axils of the principal side veins. Flowers have 4 sepals/petals and are produced in spike-like racemes, whereas in *Rhus* they have 5 sepals/petals and are in loose, branching panicles. Fruits are round, crimson or purplish black.

### Allophylus natalensis
**Dune false-currant**
**Duinevalstaaibos**

Shrub or small tree associated with coastal dune forest and bush. Leaflets are shortly stalked, narrowly elliptic, almost hairless, stiff and leathery with the margins shallowly toothed. The fruit is round, about 7 mm in diameter, and bright red.

*Allophylus natalensis*: fruit

## Notes

- If a tree with opposite, trifoliolate leaves can't be found among members of this group it may be a *Vitex* (fingerleaf trees; vingerblaarbome), most of which are classified in Group 40 (see p162).
- *Rhus* is the largest genus in the group – with about 50 species considered as trees. It is essential to be able to recognize at least the genus as species identification often requires good familiarity with the group.
- Species delimitation in the false-currants in our region is unsatisfactory and the classification of the genus is in need of study.

☠ **CAUTION** *Smodingium argutum* (agonybush; pynbos) resembles a *Rhus* but the fruit is a flattened nut encircled by a reddish, papery wing. It should be handled with care as some people are highly allergic to the plant and contact may result in painful blisters on the skin. If a tree is suspected to be this species, use the black-spot test to check. Place a fresh petiole in a folded sheet of white paper. Use a stone to thoroughly crush the petiole between the folds of paper. Dispose of the plant material. If the leaf is from the agonybush, the sap (latex) absorbed by the paper should turn brown within 15 minutes and black within 24 hours.

# 32. Sausagetree group

This is an easy group to recognize, as the emphasis is on the arrangement of the pinnately compound leaves, namely opposite or whorled. Note that 'arrangement' here refers to the leaves, not the leaflets. Leaflet arrangement is irrelevant for defining this group as it includes all types of pinnately compound leaves, provided they have an opposite or whorled attachment to the stem. Leaves in this group are usually not clustered (as is often the case in alternately arranged leaves) and the opposite or whorled arrangement tends to be quite obvious.

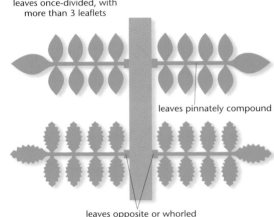

leaves once-divided, with more than 3 leaflets

leaves pinnately compound

leaves opposite or whorled

The icon depicts opposite, imparipinnate leaves, which are the common states. Rarely, the leaves are whorled or paripinnate. Whorled and opposite arrangements are closely related and, at times, many species with whorled leaves produce a few opposite ones. Leaflet margins can be entire or toothed.

## Bignoniaceae
### Jacaranda family; Jakarandafamilie
Members of this family make up the bulk of the species in the group and are characterized by large, showy, irregular flowers and elongated, pod-like fruit that usually split open to release flat, winged seeds. The fruits are not true pods, but capsules, because they are partitioned longitudinally by a wall (septum) into two chambers; true pods (legumes) are 1-chambered.

### *Kigelia africana*
Sausagetree
Worsboom

Medium to large tree with a rounded crown; occurring in bushveld. Leaflets hard, leathery; margin wavy, toothed in young plants. An unusual member of the family in that it has 3-whorled, rather than opposite leaves and large, fleshy, indehiscent fruit, rather than narrow, dry, capsular ones. The dark maroon flowers are pollinated by bats.

*Kigelia africana*: fruit (left) and flowers (right)

## *Tecomaria capensis*
**Cape-honeysuckle**
**Kaapse kanferfoelie**

Many-stemmed shrub or, rarely, a small tree; occurring in valley bushveld, bushveld and along forest margins. Leaflets 2–5 pairs plus a terminal one; small hairtuft-domatia present in axils of principal side veins below; margin scalloped or toothed. Flowers attractive, orange in the wild form, pollinated by sunbirds. The species is a popular garden plant and cultivars with flowers ranging from yellow through various shades of pink to dark red are available in the horticultural trade.

*Tecomaria capensis:* flowers          *Tecomaria capensis:* fruit

## *Stereospermum kunthianum*
**Pink-jacaranda**
**Pienkjakaranda**

Small to medium-sized deciduous tree with a rounded crown; occurring in woodland, usually in rocky places or on termitaria. Leaflets 4 pairs plus a terminal one, stiff and brittle; petiole up to 70 mm long. Flowers pale pink with reddish streaks, produced before the leaves in large, showy panicles. Fruit a capsule, long and narrow, pendulous, reddish brown, splitting into 2 valves.

*Stereospermum kunthianum:* flowers

## Notes

- *Ptaeroxylon obliquum* (sneezewood; nieshout) is the only tree with opposite, paripinnate leaves in southern Africa. Rather than establishing a 'group' just for this one species, it has been retained in the present group. In the key to the groups (see p58), leaf arrangement takes priority over the type of pinnately compound leaf, hence this species ends up as the only paripinnate tree in the present, predominantly imparipinnate, group.

- *Fagaropsis angolensis* (fagaropsis) is the only tree with opposite leaves and secretory cavities in southern Africa. It is found in the eastern highlands of Zimbabwe and adjacent parts of Mozambique.
- Many garden creepers with large, showy flowers belong to the jacaranda family (Bignoniaceae). Although the jacaranda has bipinnately compound leaves (Group 43, p168), native members of the family have only pinnately compound, trifoliolate or simple leaves.

# Cunoniaceae

## Wild-alder family; Wilde-elsfamilie

At present poorly represented by only two species native to our region. Probably an ancient group with intriguing biogeographical patterns in the southern hemisphere; only one species of *Cunonia* occurs in southern Africa, all the others (16) on the Pacific Ocean island of New Caledonia, east of Australia.

### *Cunonia capensis*

Red-alder
Rooi-els

Shrub to tall evergreen tree; occurring in forest and associated vegetation, usually in marshy places and along streams. Unmistakable, with terminal buds of growing shoots covered by two large, tightly appressed, spoon-shaped stipules (see p34). Young stems and petioles often reddish. Leaflet margins sharply toothed. Fruit a small, 2-horned capsule.

*Cunonia capensis:* flowers

# Oleaceae

## Olive family; Olyffamilie

A family with opposite, simple or pinnately compound leaves with entire margins and no stipules. Flowers regular, with 4 or 5 (rarely 6) fused petals and, very characteristically, only 2 stamens.

### *Schrebera alata*

Wild-jasmine (SA, N)
Wingleaf woodenpear (Z)
Wildejasmyn

Small tree; occurring in bushveld and forest. Leaflets 1 or 2 pairs plus a terminal one; rachis and petiole distinctly winged. Flowers white, often flushed with pink; petals 6, an unusual number for dicots, most of which are characterized by 4 or 5 petals, or multiples thereof. Fruit a woody capsule, somewhat wedge-shaped, dehiscent.

*Schrebera alata:* flowers

*Schrebera alata:* fruit

# Ptaeroxylaceae

## Sneezewood family; Nieshoutfamilie

A small family with a single species in our region. Closely related to the citrus family (Rutaceae) with which it is sometimes united but, unlike the former, it lacks secretory cavities in the leaves.

### *Ptaeroxylon obliquum*

Sneezewood
Nieshout

Deciduous or evergreen shrub or small to large tree; occurring in bushveld or forest. Canopy very variable, upright or rounded. Leaves opposite, paripinnate; leaflets 3–7 pairs, with the base markedly asymmetric. Flowers in axillary clusters, small, yellowish, male and female ones on different trees. Fruit a capsule, splitting into 2 valves; seeds winged.

*Ptaeroxylon obliquum:* male flowers

*Ptaeroxylon obliquum:* female flowers

*Ptaeroxylon obliquum:* fruit (dehisced)

*Ptaeroxylon obliquum:* tree

# 33. Boerbean group

Paripinnate leaves not only end in a pair of leaflets, but the other leaflets are usually also arranged in pairs. This pattern may result in the leaf being mistaken for a stem with pairs of opposite leaves. The arrangement of the actual leaves in this group is always alternate. If leaves are arranged in tufts it is difficult to establish leaf arrangement. As a general rule, take such leaves as being alternate. Note the position of the axillary bud (or side shoot if it has sprouted) to establish where the actual leaf is attached to the stem. In this group there is a pair of stipules at the point where the leaf stalk is attached to the stem. The stipules can be very small (orange triangle) and, if deciduous, a scar (orange rectangle) would be left; if necessary use a hand lens. Leaflets in this group always have entire margins.

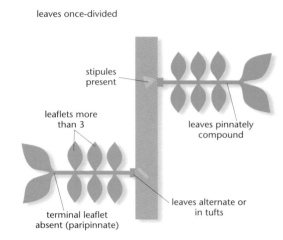

leaves once-divided

stipules present

leaflets more than 3

leaves pinnately compound

terminal leaflet absent (paripinnate)

leaves alternate or in tufts

## Caesalpiniaceae
### Flamboyant family; Flambojantfamilie

One of three families characterized by a pod (legume) as fruit type – the other two being the Mimosaceae and Fabaceae. An important family in our region, particularly well-represented in the woodlands of south-central Africa; many species found there belong to the present group.

### *Afzelia quanzensis*
Pod-mahogany
Chamfute (Z)
Peulmahonie
Mwanda (N)

Medium to large deciduous tree with a spreading crown; occurring in hot bushveld, usually on deep sand. Leaflets are hairless, glossy dark-green with a wavy margin. Flowers with 4 sepals and a single, stalked, pinkish red petal. The pods are very characteristic. They are large, flat, woody and dehisce to reveal up to 10 blackish seeds embedded in a white pith, each seed partly enveloped by a scarlet to orange aril at one end.

*Afzelia quanzensis:* flowers and fruit

## *Brachystegia spiciformis*
**Musasa**
**Msasa**

Medium to large deciduous tree with a somewhat layered crown. Flush of new leaves in spring very attractive in shades of bronze, pink and red. It occurs in woodlands and is one of the dominant trees in large parts of south-central Africa (miombo woodlands). Leaflets with base markedly asymmetrical, usually in 4 pairs with the terminal pair the largest. Two small stipellar expansions occur below each pair of leaflets. Pods hairless with a broad flat ridge along one of the margins.

*Brachystegia spiciformis:* flowers

## *Cassia abbreviata*
**Longtail cassia**
**Sambokpeul**

Small to medium-sized bushveld tree. Leaflets 5–20 pairs per leaf, thinly textured, with tips rounded. Flowers are bright yellow; produced in large, loose sprays with the appearance of new leaves in spring. The pods are pendulous, cylindrical, up to 900 mm long and remain on the tree for a long time.

*Cassia abbreviata:* flowers

## *Schotia brachypetala*
**Weeping boerbean (SA)**
**Weeping schotia (Z)**
**Huilboerboon**

Medium-sized, semi-deciduous tree with a densely branched crown; occurring in bushveld, often along rivers. Leaflets 4–7 pairs per leaf with the upper pair the largest. Flowers produced in clusters, mainly on old wood, deep red or scarlet with abundant nectar (see p58). Pods woody with hard margin along upper edge that persists after dehiscence of the valves. Seeds pale brown with a yellow basal aril.

*Schotia brachypetala:* fruit

## Notes

- Most trees classified in this group belong to the flamboyant family. The other family represented is the related Fabaceae (pea family; ertjiefamilie) which contributes only the genus *Sesbania* (riverbeans; rivierboontjies).
- Always check that what might appear to be a paripinnate leaf is not a imparipinnate one which has lost its terminal leaflet due to damage by, for example, strong winds or insects.

- A diagnostic feature of many legumes is the presence of a conspicuous thickening (pulvinus) at the base of each petiole and leaflet stalk. Through hydrostatic changes (changes in the water pressure inside cells), these structures regulate leaf and leaflet orientation, including the so-called sleep movements that occur in legumes when the leaflets fold together at night and open during the day.

# 34. Soapberry group

This group is essentially similar to the previous one (Group 33, see p146), except that stipules are absent. What is said under Group 33 about paripinnate leaves and their arrangement is also applicable here. The leaflets are sometimes sub-opposite, resulting in the terminal pair being slightly asymmetrically positioned.

An outstanding feature of this group is that the rachis (axis) of the leaf often ends in what appears to be a short aborted extension between the terminal pair of leaflets. This appendage resembles an inactive terminal growing tip and may create the false impression that the rachis is a stem with opposite pairs of leaves, a mistake that is often made. Pay particular attention to the point where the petiole is attached to the stem to confirm the lack of stipules or a stipular scar. As indicated by the icon, leaflet margins may be entire or toothed.

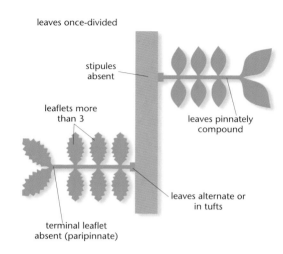

leaves once-divided

stipules absent

leaflets more than 3

leaves pinnately compound

terminal leaflet absent (paripinnate)

leaves alternate or in tufts

## Meliaceae
### Mahogany family; Mahoniefamilie

The leaves of *Entandrophragma* [wooden-bananas; wildemahonies] can be confused with those of the litchi family in that they often have a pronounced aborted rachis tip. Most members of the mahogany family in our region have imparipinnate or simple leaves.

### *Entandrophragma caudatum*
**Mountain mahogany**
**Caprivi wooden-banana (N)**
**Bergmahonie**

Large deciduous tree with a long and straight bole; occurring in dry, hot bushveld, often on rocky hill slopes or in deep Kalahari sand. Leaflets 5–8 pairs, each tapering from near the base to a sharp, bristle-like tip. Flowers are small, inconspicuous and pale-green. The fruit is very characteristic, a cigar-shaped woody capsule up to 200 mm long. It splits into 5 valves which curve back from a central column, the whole resembling a partly peeled banana. The seeds have a large wing on one side.

*Entrandrophragma caudatum:* fruit, dehisced example on left

## Khaya anthotheca

**Red-mahogany**
**Rooimahonie**

Large to very large evergreen tree occurring in forest and riverine fringe forest. Leaflets 2–7 pairs per leaf, dark glossy green above with the tips abruptly and shortly pointed. Flowers are white and inconspicuous. The fruit is a characteristic round, woody capsule, 30–50 mm in diameter. It splits into 4 or 5 valves to release the winged seeds.

*Khaya anthotheca:* flowers

# Sapindaceae

## Litchi family; Lietsjiefamilie

An easily recognized family on account of its paripinnate leaves, lack of stipules and aborted rachis tip between the terminal pair of leaflets.

## Deinbollia oblongifolia

**Dune soapberry**
**Duineseepbessie**

Slender, erect shrub or small tree, usually sparsely branched with an upright habit. It occurs in coastal dune forest and associated bushveld. Leaves large, up to 500 mm long, congested in terminal clusters. Leaflets 5–10 pairs per leaf, hard-textured with an entire margin. Flowers are white to cream and borne in dense, many flowered axillary racemes. They attract a great diversity of insects. Fruit an oval to round berry of about 10 mm in diameter, pale yellow, produced in dense clusters.

*Deinbollia oblongifolia:* fruit

### Notes

- Most trees classified in this group belong to the litchi family.
- *Ptaeroxylon obliquum* (sneezewood; nieshout) is the only native tree in southern Africa with opposite, paripinnate leaves. Rather than establish a 'group' for just one species, it has been placed in Group 32 (see p142).
- As with the previous group (see p146), ensure that what appears to be a paripinnate leaf is not an imparipinnate one which has lost its terminal leaflet due to damage by, for example,

strong winds or insects. Also keep in mind that if leaflets are sub-opposite rather than opposite, the terminal pair may be positioned slightly asymmetrically, resulting in the paripinnate state being less obvious.
- The largest native tree in southern Africa is probably an ancient red-mahogany located in the Chirinda Forest east of Chipinge, Zimbabwe. It is about 65 m high with a girth of almost 16 m at breast height. Although still alive, large portions of it have died, probably of old age.

# 35. Peppertree group

A small and easily recognizable group. Latex flow tends to be consistent and is usually readily detected. Note that the leaflet margins should be toothed or lobed (sinuate). Sometimes a tree with more than three leaflets per leaf may produce a few trifoliolate ones. The general rule is to use the predominant compound state on mature growth for group recognition purposes. Stipules are absent, but this knowledge is not required for group identification.

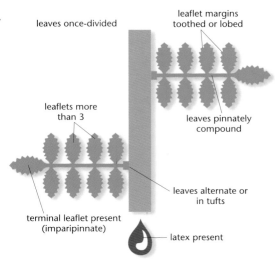

leaves once-divided

leaflet margins toothed or lobed

leaves pinnately compound

leaflets more than 3

leaves alternate or in tufts

terminal leaflet present (imparipinnate)

latex present

## Anacardiaceae
### Mango family; Mangofamilie

Most native members of this family with pinnately compound leaves have leaflets with entire margins (see Group 37; Notes, p155). Latex (resin) flow tends to be unpredictable – the introduced peppertree with its abundant whitish, sticky latex being a notable exception.

### Schinus molle
**Peppertree**
**Peperboom**

Medium to large evergreen tree with drooping branches and foliage. Leaflets up to 18 pairs plus a terminal one. They have entire or usually toothed margins and smell strongly of pepper when crushed. Flowers small, white and produced in drooping clusters. This is followed by globose, pinkish red, single-seeded drupes about 5 mm in diameter; they have a peppery taste when dry.

A native of South America, once widely planted for ornament and shade in particularly the arid parts of South Africa, it is now considered an alien invader and further cultivation is discouraged.

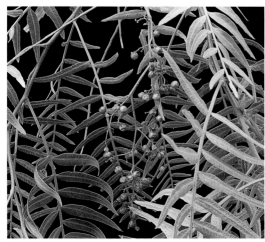

*Schinus molle:* fruit

## Notes

- Native trees of this group are not very familiar to the public, especially under their common names. Hence the choice of the introduced peppertree, which is widely known, to name the group.
- Most native trees in this group belong to the genus *Commiphora* (corkwoods; kanniedoodbome).
- Young plants or sucker shoots of *Sclerocarya birrea* subsp. *caffra* (marula; maroela;

omungongo (N)), a member of the mango family, usually have leaflets with distinctly toothed leaf margins (see p18). Latex flow in the actively growing shoots is often strong, making it a logical fit into the present group. However, the mature growth of the marula has leaflets with entire margins, so the species is treated as part of Group 37 (see p154).

# Burseraceae
### Corkwood family; Kanniedoodfamilie

Represented in our region only by *Commiphora* (corkwoods; kanniedoodbome). This is an exceptionally diverse genus as far as leaf morphology is concerned, resulting in the species being scattered among several groups. A good field characteristic for many, but not all, members of *Commiphora* is that the bark tends to peel in papery pieces (see p39). All corkwoods have fleshy drupes that dehisce to reveal a blackish stone partly surrounded by a red or sometimes bright yellow appendage (pseudo-aril, see p52).

## *Commiphora harveyi*
### Copper-stem corkwood
### Koperstam-kanniedood

Small to medium-sized deciduous tree of coastal forest and valley bushveld, often found in rocky places. Easily identified by its bark which is greenish, smooth and usually peels in large bronze or reddish brown papery flakes (see p39). Flowers are small and inconspicuous, with male and female on different trees. The fruit is a subglobose red drupe containing a blackish stone enveloped by a red or bright yellow pseudo-aril.

*Commiphora harveyi:* fruit

## *Commiphora marlothii*
### Paperbark corkwood
### Papierbaskanniedood

Small to medium-sized tree of warm arid bushveld, usually found on rocky hills and mountain slopes. Trunk often thickset with a smooth green bark that peels in large, yellowish, papery pieces. Leaflets 3–5 pairs per leaf plus a terminal one, densely and softly hairy. The subglobose drupes are hairy and green or reddish when they dehisce to release a single black stone partly enveloped by a yellow pseudo-aril.

*Commiphora marlothii:* flowers

*Commiphora marlothii:* bark

# 36. Knobwood group

An easily recognizable group, similar to Group 35 (see p150) but without latex. Note that the leaflet margins should be toothed or lobed (sinuate). Sometimes a tree with more than three leaflets per leaf may produce a few trifoliolate ones. The general rule is to use the predominant compound state of mature growth for group recognition purposes.

leaves once-divided

leaflet margins toothed or lobed

stipules absent

leaflets more than 3

leaves pinnately compound

leaves alternate or in tufts

terminal leaflet present (imparipinnate)

latex absent

If the leaves are arranged in tufts, it is usually difficult to establish leaf arrangement. As a general rule, take such leaves as being alternate. Stipules, spines and secretory cavities may be present or absent, but this knowledge is not required for group identification and these are therefore not depicted by the icon.

## Apiaceae
### Carrot family; Geelwortelfamilie

A predominantly herbaceous family with about ten tree species in our region. The base of the petiole forms a short sheath around the stem (see p42) and the crushed leaves have a strong, often carrot-like smell. Flowers are borne in simple or compound umbels.

### *Steganotaenia araliacea*
Carrot-tree (SA)
Popgun-tree (Z)
Geelwortelboom

Small, slender deciduous tree with the bark grey-green and peeling in small papery flakes (reminiscent of a corkwood). Grows in hot, dry bushveld, usually in rocky places. Leaves fresh to yellowish green and crowded near ends of branches. Leaflet margins conspicuously and jaggedly toothed with tip tapering to a fine point. Flowers are borne in compound spherical umbels, usually before the new leaves.

*Steganotaenia araliacea*: flowers

---

### Notes

- Very few native trees have attractive autumn colours. Perhaps the most striking one is *Kirkia wilmsii* (mountain seringa; bergsering), which turns reddish to bright scarlet in autumn, making the trees easy to spot from a distance in their otherwise drab bushveld surroundings (see p58).

- The spines on the leaves and stems of the knobwoods, referred to as prickles or emergences, develop from the epidermis and subepidermal tissue of the leaf or stem and are not modified stipules, stems or leaves as is usually the case with spines (see p35). A good example of epidermal prickles is the cultivated rose.

# Rutaceae

## Citrus family; Sitrusfamilie

The citrus family is an important contributor of trees to this group. As a rule, trifoliolate or pinnately compound leaves with secretory cavities, but no stipules, belong to this family. Leaves have a strong citrus scent when crushed. (The icon for the group is slightly misleading in that it does not show secretory cavities.)

### Zanthoxylum davyi

**Forest knobwood**

**Bosknophout**

Medium to large forest tree, often a constituent of the forest canopy. Bark with conspicuous thorn-tipped knobs. Leaflets with secretory cavities confined mainly to the margin and with two tiny, sack-shaped domatia at the base. Petiole and rachis often with scattered prickles. When ripe the reddish-brown fruit splits open to reveal a shiny black seed.

*Zanthoxylum davyi*: fruit

*Zanthoxylum davyi*: bark

# Kirkiaceae

## White-seringa family; Witseringfamilie

A small family represented by three species of *Kirkia* (white-seringas; witseringbome] in our region. Previously these were usually included in the Simaroubaceae [tree-of-heaven family; hemelboomfamilie]. Leaves of the white seringas are crowded at the ends of branches; their arrangement is alternate.

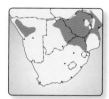

### Kirkia acuminata

**White-seringa (SA)**

**Common kirkia (N)**

**Kirkia (Z)**

**Witsering**

Medium to large deciduous tree with tall erect trunk and spreading rounded crown. It grows in bushveld, often on rocky hills and mountain slopes. Leaflets 6–9 pairs per leaf plus a terminal one, sharply tapering at the tip and slightly oblique at the base. Fruit a capsule that separates into four one-seeded segments, each attached by a strip of tissue to the top of the central column.

*Kirkia acuminata*: flowers

# 37. Marula group

This can be a problematic group to identify because of the inconsistent flow of latex (resin) in members of the Anacardiaceae [mango family; mangofamilie]. In this family, latex is often difficult to detect or seemingly absent in mature growth and drought-stressed plants. The presence of latex is sometimes only detected as stickiness when the broken end of a petiole is touched. Always look for young leaves on actively growing stems, especially sucker/coppice shoots, to test for latex (but see under Notes). Leaflet margins in this group are always more or less entire in mature growth.

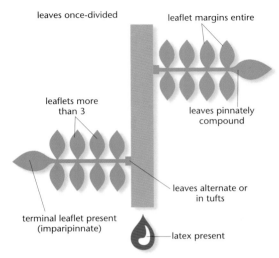

Sometimes a tree with mainly more than three leaflets per leaf may produce a few trifoliolate ones. The general rule is to use the predominant compound state on mature growth for group recognition purposes. If leaves are crowded towards the ends of branches or borne in tufts, it is often difficult to establish leaf arrangement. As a general rule, take such leaves as being alternate. Spines are rare in this group, but this knowledge is not required for group identification.

## Anacardiaceae
### Mango family; Mangofamilie

Anatomically the family is characterized by resin ducts and all members should, theoretically, contain what is here generally referred to as latex. This liquid (responsible for the resinous taste of the fruit peel in the mango and marula) is usually watery or cloudy, rather than white. As already pointed out, it is sometimes difficult to detect due to inconsistent flow. Species have separate male and female trees.

### *Loxostylis alata*
Tarwood
Teerhout

Small to medium-sized evergreen tree; occurring along forest margins and on outcrops of sandstone and quartzite. Leaflets sessile, hairless; rachis markedly winged (see p47). Flowers in dense terminal inflorescences, male and female on separate plants; petals small, white; sepals enlarging in fruit, becoming petal-like and bright-pink to red. Fruit small, dry, enclosed by the persistent sepals.

*Loxostylis alata:* fruit

## *Harpephyllum caffrum*
**Wild-plum**
**Wildepruim**

Medium to large evergreen forest tree, often recognized from a distance by the odd red leaf in the canopy. Leaves crowded towards the ends of rather thick branchlets, often in attractive rosette-like clusters. The leaflets are sickle-shaped with the base markedly asymmetric. Flowers are small, white and inconspicuous. The edible fruit is oval, fleshy and bright red when ripe (see p157).

*Harpephyllum caffrum:* flowers

## *Lannea discolor*
**Live-long**
**Dikbas**

Small to medium-sized deciduous tree; occurring in bushveld, often on rocky ridges. Branches thick, sturdy, with a dense layer of white velvety hairs. Leaflets 3–5 pairs plus a terminal one, dark green above, velvety whitish grey below. Flowers are small, creamy yellow, produced in spike-like inflorescences before the new leaves in spring. The fruit is fleshy, ovoid, reddish to purple-black when ripe and tipped by four minute style remnants. Fruit is edible but the hard skin is discarded.

*Lannea discolor:* flowers

## Notes

- Despite the inconsistent flow of latex, the inclusion of trees with imparipinnate leaves of the mango family in the present group is still considered useful as it assists in distinguishing them from the often very similar-looking trees of the Meliaceae family (mahogany family; mahoniefamilie), which always lack latex (see Group 38, p158).
- In the marula, juvenile growth and coppice shoots can have leaflets with distinctly toothed margins. Not only are these stages easy to come by, but latex is more readily detected in such material. This combination of characters will lead to Group 35 (see p150). However, the marula is here grouped according to the mature stage, when the leaflets are entire-margined.
- The latex of the mango family may cause skin irritations. Contact with *Trichoscypha ulugurensis* (allergytree, agonytree; pynboom) causes a severe reaction in sensitive people, similar to that of *Smodingium argutum* (agonybush; pynbos). In our region, the former species is confined to evergreen forest in the Eastern Highlands of Zimbabwe and adjacent Mozambique. See Note under Group 31 (p141) for how to test for the toxin.
- *Cordyla africana* (wild-mango; wildemango) was provisionally assigned to this group in Van Wyk & Van Wyk (1997), but it has subsequently been established that latex (resin) flow in the species is seen mainly in the rind of the fruit and not when a leaf is picked. It is therefore best placed in Group 38.

## *Sclerocarya birrea* subsp. *caffra*
Marula
Maroela
Omungongo (N)

Medium to large deciduous tree with an erect trunk and spreading, rounded crown. Widespread in bush-veld and woodland. Leaflets dark green above, bluish green below, margin entire, but toothed in young plants and coppice shoots (see p18). Flowers small, yellowish tinged with pink, produced in spike-like inflorescences before the new leaves. The fleshy fruits are oval with a hard stone. The popular edible fruit falls from the tree whilst still green and then ripens to yellow while on the ground.

*S. birrea* subsp. *caffra:* flowers, male (left) and female

# Burseraceae
## Corkwood family; Kanniedoodfamilie

Several species of *Commiphora* [corkwoods; kanniedoodbome] with imparipinnate leaves occur in our region. Here we include those that have the leaflet margins entire. Corkwoods are not only very diverse in leaf morphology, but also in bark features. Bark that peels in papery flakes is common in the group, but there are also other patterns, such as the one described below.

## *Commiphora multijuga*
Purplestem corkwood
Persstamkanniedood
Omuzumba (N)

Small deciduous tree with a rounded canopy and graceful, pale green, drooping foliage. Common in the semi-desert parts of northwestern Namibia (Kaokoveld), usually on rocky hills. Bark smooth and not peeling, purplish grey to dark grey. Leaflets elliptic to round, abruptly pointed at both ends, hairless. Flowers small and inconspicuous. The fleshy fruits are subglobose and split open to reveal a blackish stone partly covered by a red appendage (pseudo-aril).

*Commiphora multijuga:* fruit

> ☠ **Warning:** Latex in the purplestem corkwood is under considerable pressure and may squirt up to 10 cm high from broken twigs. It is extremely painful if it gets into the eyes.

*Commiphora multijuga* is found in the Kaokoveld of northwestern Namibia and adjacent arid parts of Angola

Fruit of *Harpephyllum caffrum* is edible, and bright red when ripe

# 38. Kiaat group

A large and easily recognizable group. Leaflet margins are always more or less entire. If leaves are crowded towards the ends of branches or borne in tufts, it is often difficult to establish leaf arrangement. As a general rule, take such leaves as being alternate.

Stipules are common in this group, but this knowledge is not required for group identification, hence these structures are not depicted by the icon. Secretory cavities and spines are rarely present.

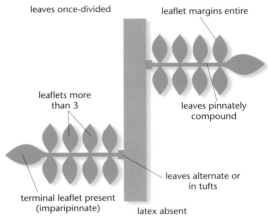

leaves once-divided

leaflet margins entire

leaflets more than 3

leaves pinnately compound

terminal leaflet present (imparipinnate)

leaves alternate or in tufts

latex absent

## Fabaceae
### Pea family; Ertjiefamilie

The bulk of trees in this group belong to this family, one of three families with a pod (legume) as fruit types and one that is well-represented among native trees. In addition to pods, the family has leaves with stipules and the flowers have a characteristic shape (see Notes).

### *Bolusanthus speciosus*
**Tree-wisteria**
**Vanwykshout**

Small deciduous tree with upright crown and drooping foliage, usually multistemmed; occurring in bushveld, often on calcareous soils. Leaflets lanceolate with narrowly tapering tips and a markedly asymmetric base, greyish green with silvery hairs above. Flowers borne in attractive hanging racemes, pale blue to violet.

*Bolusanthus speciosus:* flowers

### *Pterocarpus angolensis*
**Kiaat**
**Bloodwood (Z)**
**Mukwa (N, Z)**

Medium to large deciduous tree with an open spreading crown. Grows in bushveld and woodland, often on deep sandy soil or rocky hillsides. Leaflets 11–25 pairs plus a terminal one, hairless with tip ending in a narrow bristle-tipped point and the base rounded; side veins prominent above, more or less parallel. Flowers orange-yellow. The distinctive circular pods consist of a central seed case densely covered with coarse bristles, and surrounded by a broad, thin, wavy wing.

*Pterocarpus angolensis:* fruit

# Meliaceae

### Mahogany family; Mahoniefamilie

Many large imposing trees in our region are members of this family. Stipules are lacking and the leaves resemble those in some Anacardiaceae [mango family; mangofamilie]. The latter, however, always have latex (resin) ducts and, although latex flow is sometimes difficult to detect, they are here found under Group 37 (see p154). All members of the mahogany family in the present group have separate male and female plants; flowers in the two sexes are very similar though.

### *Ekebergia capensis*

**Cape-ash (SA)**
**Dogplum (Z)**
**Essenhout**

*Ekebergia capensis:* fruit

Medium-sized to large deciduous tree usually associated with forest. Branchlets usually hairless with whitish lenticels. Leaflets with the base asymmetrical. Flowers small, white, inconspicuous. Fruit subglobose, fleshy, pink to bright red when ripe. Some forms are very similar to *Harpephyllum caffrum* [wild-plum; wildepruim], but the latter exudes watery latex, or have the base of the broken-off petiole somewhat sticky when latex flow is weak (see Group 37, p154).

## Notes

- As a general rule, trees with imparipinnate leaves and conventional stipules – common in the present group – probably belong to the pea family (Fabaceae/Papilionaceae), which is easily recognized by the characteristic butterfly-like flower type (see p49): the petals are unequal, with the uppermost (standard or banner) being the largest, the two side ones small and stalked (wings), and the two basal ones united into a boat-shaped structure (keel).
- Conspicuous intrapetiolar stipules are diagnostic for the genus *Bersama* (white-ashes; witessenhoute). This type of stipule occurs between the petiole and the stem, across the leaf axil (p34).
- If the leaves are finely divided and dotted with blackish or whitish secretory cavities, then the tree is a *Psoralea* (fountainbushes; fonteinbosse) of the pea family.

- If the fruit is a dehiscent capsule with the seed partly or completely enveloped by a fleshy yellow, red or orange aril, and the leaves lack stipules, then the tree belongs to the mahogany family, but if stipules are present then it is a *Bersama* of the Melianthaceae.
- *Cordyla africana* (wild-mango; wildemango), an unusual member of the Fabaceae (pea family; ertjiefamilie), is included in this group. Formerly it was usually classified in the Caesalpiniaceae (flamboyant family; flambojantfamilie), another legume family. Instead of a pod, *Cordyla africana* has a large (40–80 x 30–60 mm), oval, orange-yellow fleshy fruit reminiscent of a mango (hence the common names). As with the marula it ripens on the ground. The species is also unusual for not having the typical butterfly-like flower of the pea family and for having leaflets with secretory cavities.

# 39. Baobab group

A small, easily recognizable group. The more than three leaflets all arise from a single point at the tip of the petiole and radiate outward like the fingers of an open hand. Occasionally only three leaflets may be present, but such leaves will always be in the minority. Leaflets may be stalked or sessile and their margins entire or toothed. Pay attention to leaf arrangement, which should be alternate.

Stipules and latex may be present, but this knowledge is not required for group identification, hence it is not depicted by the icon. Secretory cavities and spines are absent among native trees of the group.

Palmately compound leaves that are often twice divided in complex patterns are found in *Cussonia* [cabbagetrees; kiepersolbome], most of which have a distinctive growth form and have been placed in Group 2 (see p70).

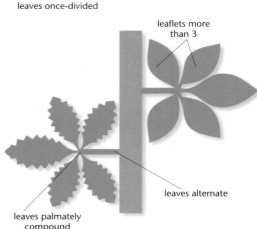

leaves once-divided

leaflets more than 3

leaves alternate

leaves palmately compound

## Araliaceae
### Cabbagetree family; Kiepersolfamilie

Closely related to the carrot family [Apiaceae], crushed leaves in this family often have a carrot-like smell. Although the flowers may be arranged in complex inflorescences, the umbel-pattern (see p49) is usually present in one form or another. The fleshy fruit develops from an inferior ovary and is tipped by the remains of the calyx.

### *Schefflera umbellifera*
**False-cabbagetree**
**Valskiepersol**

Medium to large evergreen tree with tall trunk and rounded crown; occurring in and around forest. Leaflets 3–5, glossy dark-green above; margins entire or toothed in the upper half and distinctly wavy. Flowers small, cream to white and borne in large branched inflorescences near the ends of branches.

*Schefflera umbellifera*: fruit

# Bombacaceae

### Baobab family; Kremetartfamilie

Small family with only two native trees in our region, the best known being the baobab. Palmately compound leaves with stipules are characteristic for the family, many of the species have thick, bottle- or barrel-shaped trunks. Madagascar, with eight species, is the centre of baobab diversity.

### *Adansonia digitata*

**Baobab**

**Kremetart**

An unmistakable tree because of its swollen trunk; with its distinctive growth form it could just as well qualify for inclusion in Group 2 (see p70). Mature plants have leaves with 3–9 leaflets, but seedlings and juvenile plants are quite different in having simple leaves (see p18).

Flowers are large, pendulous, white and only last for about a day. The fruit is ovoid to elliptic with a hard, woody shell densely covered with yellowish grey hair.

*Adansonia digitata:* fruit

# Sterculiaceae

### Cacao family; Kakaofamilie

Most native members of the family have simple leaves, but these are often lobed and 3- or more-veined from the base. Only two species have palmately compound leaves with stipules. The family is closely related to the baobab family.

### *Sterculia murex*

**Lowveld star-chestnut**

**Laeveldsterkastaiing**

Medium-sized deciduous tree found on rocky ridges in bush-veld. Leaflets 5–9, soft-textured and hairy. Flowers yellowish brown, produced in abundance before or with the new leaves in spring. The fruit is unmistakable and comprises 1–5 palmately arranged fruit chambers (carpels), each covered with spiny protuberances. Typically for members of the genus, the seeds are embedded between irritating hairs.

*Sterculia murex:* flowers

## Notes

- The presence of latex indicates a member of the Euphorbiaceae (euphorbia family; naboom-familie) or Moraceae (fig family; vyfamilie). Stipules are small in the former, large in the latter. The presence of large glands, often dark-coloured, at the junction of the leaflets and petiole, or on the petiole, is diagnostic for the euphorbia family.

- Because of their distinctive growth form and large palmately or bipalmately compound leaves, most species of *Cussonia* (cabbagetrees; kiepersolbome) are placed in Group 2 (see p70). However, some smaller shrubby species, with a tendency to scramble, key out to the present group. An inflorescence of spikes grouped in an umbel (p49) indicates a cabbagetree.

# 40. Fingerleaf group

An easy group to recognize. The leaflets all arise from a single point at the tip of the petiole and radiate outward like the fingers of an open hand. It is common in this group for the number of leaflets to vary between three and five, rarely seven, even on the same branch. More than three should, however, be the dominant state. The terminal leaflet is often the largest with the adjacent ones smaller and the two lower ones in some cases much smaller than the rest. Leaflets may be stalked or sessile and their margins entire or toothed. Pay attention to leaf arrangement, which should be opposite, rarely 3-whorled. Stipules, latex and secretory cavities are always absent.

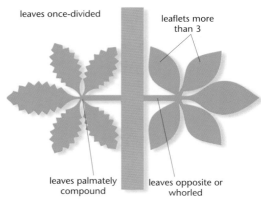

leaves once-divided

leaflets more than 3

leaves palmately compound

leaves opposite or whorled

## Lamiaceae
### Sage family; Saliefamilie

All trees in this group belong to *Vitex* [fingerleaf trees; vingerblaarbome], a genus with several native species. Formerly the genus was classified in the Verbenaceae. Crushed leaves of all the species are more or less pleasantly scented and the young twigs of some species have a spongy pith. Fruit type is very useful for species identification. It is either a fleshy drupe or a dry nut with an enlarged, plate-like, persistent calyx at the base.

### *Vitex doniana*
**Prune fingerleaf**
**Blinkvingerblaar**

Medium-sized deciduous tree of forest margins and associated riverine vegetation and woodland. Leaflets 5, shortly stalked, thick and leathery with rounded tips, hairless and glossy. Fruit fleshy, purplish black when ripe, up to 30 mm in diameter, edible, with the taste of prunes. The calyx is persistent and remains on the tree after the fruit has fallen.

*Vitex doniana:* fruit

## Vitex pooara
**Pooraberry**
**Poerabessie**

*Vitex pooara:* fruit

Shrub or small deciduous tree; occurring in bushveld on rocky hillsides, usually in sandy soil. Leaflets 3–5 per leaf, sessile, dull yellowish green, hairy. Fruit fleshy, round or ellipsoid, black, edible but rather unpleasantly scented (said to be reminiscent of bedbugs!).

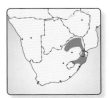

## Vitex rehmannii
**Pipestem tree**
**Pypsteelboom**

*Vitex rehmannii:* fruit

Shrub or small deciduous tree with drooping branchlets and leaves, associated with bushveld, often in rocky places or on deep sandy soil. Leaflets 3–5 per leaf, shortly stalked, long and narrow, more or less hairless, pleasantly scented when crushed. Fruit a dry nut enclosed by the persistent, papery, bell-shaped calyx.

## Vitex zeyheri
**Silver pipestem tree**
**Vaalpypsteelboom**

*Vitex zeyheri:* flowers

Shrub or small deciduous tree with silvery grey foliage; occurring in bushveld. Leaflets 3–5 per leaf, shortly stalked, grey-green with upper surface velvety with whitish hairs, pleasantly scented when crushed. Fruit a dry nut subtended by an enlarged, persistent papery bell-shaped calyx.

---

### What to look for: *Vitex* species

- Number and shape of leaflets.
- Size of leaflets.
- Length of leaflet stalks.
- Leaflet margins entire or toothed.
- Prominence of leaflet venation: indented, plane (flush with leaf surface) or raised.
- Hairiness of leaflets.
- Colour of leaflets.
- Fruit type: fleshy drupe or dry nut.

### Notes

- Fingerleaf trees with trifoliolate leaves will key out to Group 31 (see p140) although they differ from other trees in that group by their opposite leaves and lack of stipules.
- Fingerleaf trees all have small, rather similar bell-shaped flowers. These are two-lipped and white, mauve or blue, often with darker purplish markings. Whereas genus identification is easy, species identification can be difficult, especially in the absence of fruit.

# 41. Hook thorn group

The bipinnately compound leaves are easy to recognize. They are alternately arranged or in tufts. Check carefully for the presence of spines and whether they are hooked or straight. Should both types be present, which is rare, the species should be treated in the present group.

Although the icon depicts hooked spines in pairs at each node, the spines can occur in threes at a node, or be scattered irregularly as single spines (prickles) along the length of the internodes.

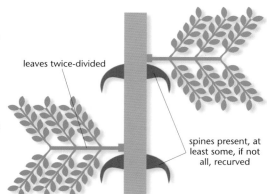

leaves twice-divided

spines present, at least some, if not all, recurved

## Mimosaceae
### Thorn tree family; Doringboomfamilie

All species in this group are legumes and most belong to the thorn tree family. Group 41 consists mainly of those thorn trees with at least some hooked (recurved) spines. This feature is often associated with flowers that are borne in elongated spikes, but exceptions do occur, for example, globose heads are found in *Acacia mellifera* and *Acacia tortilis*.

**What to look for:** *Acacia* species

- Presence of both hooked and straight spines on the same tree.
- Number of spines at a node.
- Presence of spines along internodes.
- Presence of spines on raised knobs on older stems and/or trunks.
- Presence and position of glands on leaf.
- Size and hairiness of leaflets.
- Shape, size and colour of pods.

### *Acacia ataxacantha*
Flamethorn (N, SA)
Flamepod acacia (Z)
Vlamdoring

Shrub or small tree with a tendency to become scandent (to climb); occurring in bushveld, forest margins and riverine bush. Flowers cream, borne in elongated spikes towards tips of branches. Pods, thin, flat, reddish to purplish brown, hence the common names. Spines scattered along the branches (also on internodes) frequently render dense stands of this scandent scrub essentially impenetrable.

*Acacia ataxacantha:* fruit

### Acacia caffra
**Common hook thorn**
**Tynwald hook thorn (Z)**
**Wag-'n-bietjiedoring**

Small to medium-sized deciduous tree with drooping foliage; occurring in bushveld and grassland. Spines in pairs below the nodes, but in older trees they are often poorly developed and sometimes absent. Flowers in elongated, often drooping spikes, cream, fading to yellowish. Pods flat, pale brown to reddish brown, straight, dehiscent.

*Acacia caffra:* flowers

### Acacia mellifera
subsp. *detinens*
**Black thorn**
**Swarthaak**

Shrub or small tree with rounded or spreading flat growth. Very spiny with well-developed blackish thorns in pairs at each node. Leaflets relatively large (3.5–22 x 2–16 mm). Unlike many other hooked thorn acacias, it has globose flower heads; flowers cream or rarely pink. Pods flat, papery, dehiscent.

*Acacia mellifera* subsp. *detinens:* fruit

### Acacia tortilis
subsp. *heteracantha*
**Umbrella thorn**
**Haak-en-steek**

A flattened and spreading or umbrella-shaped crown allows mature trees of this species to be identified from a distance (see title page). Unusual in having pairs of short, hooked spines as well as long, straight ones on the same plant. Leaflets very small (0.5–4 x 0.5–1 mm). Flowers borne in globose heads, white. Pods spirally twisted.

*Acacia tortilis* subsp. *heteracantha:* flowers

## Notes

- In many *Acacia* species the spines become smaller as the tree grows taller. In older trees, spines are often poorly developed and are not consistently present at each node. It is advisable to check a number of stems before a tree is declared spineless (which would then lead to Group 43, see p168).
- In many hook thorn acacias with spike-like inflorescences, spines are not modified stipules, as their paired position at nodes would suggest (compare Group 42, p166), but epidermal outgrowths (technically 'prickles'). This explains why, in some species, they occur in threes or are scattered along the internodes.
- *Acacia senegal* (three-hook thorn; driehaak-doring) is the only thorn tree in our region with the spines arranged in threes at the nodes.

# 42. Sweet thorn group

The bipinnately compound leaves are alternately arranged or in tufts. Check carefully for the presence of spines and whether they are hooked or straight. Only trees with consistently straight spines are placed in the present group. Although the icon depicts straight spines in pairs at each node, the group also includes trees with straight spines arranged singly. When paired, the spines are often white, positioned at the base of a leaf and are therefore strictly confined to the nodes on the stems. Solitary spines are positioned axillary or at the tips of shoots. They are the same colour as the branchlets and often bear leaves.

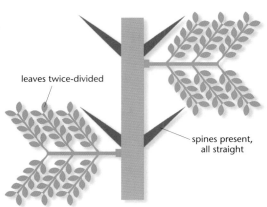

leaves twice-divided

spines present, all straight

## Mimosaceae

**Thorn tree family; Doringboomfamilie**

All species in this group belong to the thorn tree family. They are made up mainly of those species of *Acacia* [thorn trees; doringbome] with straight spines. In thorn trees, this type of spine is usually associated with flowers that are borne in globose heads. This group of thorn trees is well represented in our region.

**What to look for:** *Acacia* species

- Bark texture and colour.
- Hairiness of young twigs.
- Size, shape and number of leaflets.
- Presence and position of glands on leaf.
- Flowering time.
- Colour of inflorescences.
- Hairiness of leaflets.
- Shape, size and colour of pods.
- Whether pods are dotted with glands or not.

### *Acacia erioloba*
**Camel thorn**
**Kameeldoring**

Medium to large tree with a rounded or umbrella-shaped crown. Usually associated with deep sandy soils. Common along water courses in arid areas. Spines paired, white or reddish, often swollen and fused together at the base. Inflorescences globose, bright golden-yellow. Pods very distinctive, large, velvety, grey, thick and semi-woody, indehiscent.

*Acacia erioloba:* fruit

## Acacia karroo
**Sweet thorn**
**Soetdoring**

Acacia karroo: flowers

Shrub to medium-sized tree with a rounded crown. Widespread and common in a wide range of vegetation types. Spines paired, slender, white, usually larger and more conspicuous on young plants and coppice shoots. Inflorescences globose, bright yellow. Pods flat, brown, hairless, slightly sickle-shaped, dehiscent.

## Dichrostachys cinerea
**Sicklebush**
**Sekelbos**
**Omutjete (N)**

Dichrostachys cinerea: flowers

Shrub or small tree with rather untidy crown, often flat-topped. Very common in bushveld, often proliferating in overgrazed areas. Spines not paired, represent spinescent branchlets, often leaf-bearing. Inflorescences attractive bicoloured pendulous spikes, the basal portion with mauve or pink sterile flowers, the upper part with yellow fertile flowers. Pods of each inflorescence twisted and curled into globose bunches, indehiscent.

## Faidherbia albida
**Anatree (N, SA)**
**Albida (Z)**
**Anaboom**

Faidherbia albida: flowers

Only member of the genus, confined to Africa; easily mistaken for an *Acacia*. Medium to large tree with a wide, rounded crown in mature plants; occurring in bushveld, often on alluvial floodplains or along river banks. Branchlets often somewhat zigzag. Spines paired, small (up to 20 mm long), whitish. Flowers in elongated spikes, pale cream. Pods flat, pale orange-brown or reddish brown, hairless, distinctly curled into a circular coil or variously twisted.

## Notes

- In thorn trees with paired, straight spines, the spines represent modified stipules, thus explaining their paired arrangement and fixed position at the base of leaves. Spines in many hook thorn acacias with spike-like inflorescences are not modified stipules, but epidermal outgrowths – technically 'prickles'. (See Group 41, p164.)
- Solitary spines, as in the sicklebush, are spinescent stems. They develop from side shoots or stems when the growing tip ceases to elongate and changes into a spine. This explains why these spines often bear leaves (see p35).

- In many species of *Acacia* the spines become smaller as a tree grows taller. In older trees they are often poorly developed and not consistently present at each node. It is advisable to check a number of stems before declaring a tree spineless (which would lead to Group 43, p168).
- In arid parts of our region *Prosopis glandulosa* (glandular mesquite; suidwesdoring), an invader species from North and Central America, is often mistaken for an *Acacia*. However, it has only one pair of pinnae, each with 7–18 pairs of leaflets.

# 43. False-thorn group

This group has bipinnately compound leaves, as in thorn trees, but spines are always absent. The leaves are alternately arranged or in tufts, rarely opposite. Bipinnately compound leaves are easy to recognize when the leaflets are very small ('feathery' leaves). Some species in this group have large leaflets and their bipinnate state is not immediately obvious. Check carefully for the presence or absence of spines (see Notes below).

Although not depicted by the icon, stipules are very common in this group. Leaflet margins are entire, rarely toothed.

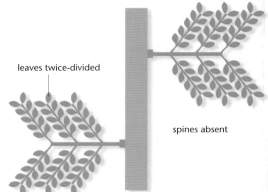

leaves twice-divided

spines absent

## Caesalpiniaceae
### Flamboyant family; Flambojantfamilie

One of the three legume (pod-bearing) families. Usually with paripinnate leaves, a few native members of this family do, however, have bipinnately compound leaves. As is the case with legumes, stipules are present.

### *Burkea africana*
**Wild-syringa (SA)**
**Burkea (N, Z)**
**Omutundungu (N), Mukarati (Z)**
**Wildesering**

Attractive medium-sized tree with an erect trunk and somewhat flattened and spreading crown. Common in bushveld, usually on deep sandy soil. Tips of branchlets with velvety, reddish brown hairs. Leaflets quite large, so bipinnate state of leaves is easily overlooked. Short-lived small, cream flowers, produced in drooping spikes with the new leaves. Pods flat, elliptic, wing-like, brown, single-seeded and indehiscent.

*Burkea africana:* flowers

### Notes

- Presence of conventional stipules in thorn tree-like trees may serve as confirmation of lack of spines. In the sweet thorn group (Group 42, see p166) the paired spines represent modified stipules.
- Young branchlets often form spine-tipped side shoots in *Albizia anthelmintica* (wormbark falsethorn (SA), worm-cure albizia (N, Z); wurmbasvalsdoring).
- Australian species of *Acacia* (wattles; wattels) lack stipular or other spines and vegetatively

- bear some resemblance in leaf morphology to false-thorns. A number of introduced wattles are naturalized in our region.
- In this group, one of the trees with opposite leaves is *Jacaranda mimosifolia* (jacaranda; jakaranda), a South American species widely cultivated for ornament and now naturalized in many parts of southern Africa.
- If leaflet margins are toothed, the tree is most probably *Melia azedarach* (seringa; maksering), an invader species from Asia.

## Peltophorum africanum
**African-wattle**
**Huilboom**
**Muparara (N)**

Small to medium-sized tree with a dense crown; occurring in bushveld, usually on sandy soil. Branchlets densely covered with fine, rust-brown hairs. Leaves feathery with lower surface of leaflets densely hairy. Flowers with petals yellow and crinkled, produced in attractive erect terminal racemes. Pods flat, winged, with fine velvety hairs.

*Peltophorum africanum:* flowers

# Mimosaceae
## Thorn tree family; Doringboomfamilie

Among the legumes, bipinnately compound leaves are usually associated with the thorn tree family, to which many trees in the present group belong. Best represented is *Albizia* [false-thorns; valsdorings], a genus superficially resembling thorn trees, but without the paired spines of the latter; instead they all have conventional stipules. Flowers in this family tend to have colourful stamens, rather than colourful petals.

### What to look for: *Albizia* species

- Bark texture.
- Number of pinnae per leaf.
- Leaflet shape: oblong, or more or less rectangular.
- Size of leaflets.
- Hairiness of leaflets.
- Colour of lower and upper leaflet surfaces.
- Presence and position of nectary glands on the leaves.
- Presence or absence of staminal tube in the flowers.

## Albizia adianthifolia
**Flatcrown (SA)**
**Roughbark flatcrown (Z)**
**Roughbark munjerenje (Z)**
**Platkroon**

Medium to large tree with a flattened and spreading crown; occurring in forest and associated woodland. Branchlets with velvety brown or greyish hairs. Leaflets more or less rectangular, dark-green above, yellowish or brownish and hairy below. Flowers in half-spherical heads, whitish, with long (up to 55 mm) staminal tubes. Pods flat, pale brown, hairy, swollen over each seed, dehiscent.

*Albizia adianthifolia:* flowers

## Albizia tanganyicensis
**Paperbark false-thorn (SA)**
**Paperbark albizia (Z)**
**Papierbasvalsdoring**
**Omupepe (N)**

Small to medium-sized tree; occurring in bushveld and woodland, often in rocky places. Bark very distinctive, smooth, creamy white, peeling in large reddish or yellowish papery pieces (reminiscent of a *Commiphora*). Leaflets large, up to 45 x 25 mm, base asymmetric. Flowers in large globose heads, white fading to cream, without long staminal tubes, usually produced before or with the new leaves in spring. Pods flat, dark-brown, indehiscent.

*Albizia tanganyicensis:* flowers

# Guide to tree families

This book arranges trees into 43 groups. The same groups are used in the authors' *Field Guide to Trees of Southern Africa* (see p179) which features more than 1 000 tree species native to our region. At present only one book, *Keith Coates Palgrave Trees of Southern Africa*, covers all southern African trees. While the latter book provides many excellent keys, it follows a system in which the trees are arranged according to **family**. By contrast, *How to Identify Trees in Southern Africa* uses a **group** approach to narrow down the number of families to which an unknown tree may belong.

In the list below, each group includes those families that have one or more members in the particular group. In some instances, only specific genera or species within a family should be looked at and these are given in brackets. Families that are particularly well represented in any group are labelled 'many' while those that are poorly represented are marked 'few'. If the details of a specific tree cannot be found in *Field Guide to Trees of Southern Africa*, check in *Palgrave's Trees of Southern Africa* or any other good tree book under the families or genera applicable to the group.

**Important:** The classification of flowering plants is still being refined, and family definitions and the family placement of genera are adjusted from time to time as new knowledge becomes available. In the list of tree families below, a conservative approach has been followed in that traditional generic placements of southern African trees are used as a point of departure. However, botanists are not always in agreement as to the demarcation of some flowering plant families, so different practices and philosophies prevail. Moreover, ongoing attempts to refine the definition of angiosperm families in the light of new molecular data have resulted in some controversial family delimitations that are not yet widely accepted. Hence, where applicable, alternative family placements are indicated.

**Key:**
*   = Local representatives in the particular group are all alien species.
/   = Alternative family placements, or family names used in different tree books.
[ ] = Alternative family placements hitherto rarely used in local tree books.

## 1. Succulent group
Agavaceae *
Apocynaceae
Asphodelaceae/Liliaceae/Aloaceae (many)
Asteraceae/Compositae (few)
Bombacaceae/[Malvaceae] (baobab, *Adansonia digitata*)
Burseraceae (few)
Cactaceae *
Crassulaceae
Euphorbiaceae (many)
Lamiaceae/Labiatae (*Tetradenia*)
Mesembryanthemaceae (*Stoeberia*)
Moringaceae
Passifloraceae (*Adenia*)
Pedaliaceae
Portulacaceae/[Didiereaceae]
Vitaceae

## 2. Palm group
Araliaceae (many)
Arecaceae/Palmae (many)
Bombacaceae/[Malvaceae] (baobab, *Adansonia digitata*)
Cyatheaceae
Cycadaceae
Dracaenaceae/[Convallariaceae]/formerly under Agavaceae
Musaceae
Pandanaceae
Poaceae/Gramineae (bamboos)
Strelitziaceae (many)
Welwitschiaceae
Zamiaceae (many)

## 3. Cedar group
Apiaceae/Umbelliferae (*Anginon*)
Asteraceae/Compositae (*Stoebe; Metalasia*)
Bruniaceae (*Raspalia*)

Burseraceae (few)
Caesalpiniaceae/Leguminosae/Fabaceae:
　Caesalpinioideae (*Parkinsonia*)
Casuarinaceae *
Capparaceae (*Cadaba aphylla*)
Chenopodiaceae (*Salsola*)
Cupressaceae (many)
Ericaceae
Papilionaceae/Leguminosae/Fabaceae:
　Papilionoideae (*Psoralea*)
Pinaceae *
Podocarpaceae
Polygalaceae (*Nylandtia*)
Portulacaceae/[Didiereaceae]
Proteaceae *
Rhamnaceae (*Phylica*)
Rubiaceae (*Anthospermum*)
Rosaceae (*Cliffortia*)
Tamaricaceae
Thymelaeaceae (*Passerina*)

## 4. Fig group
Moraceae

## 5. Milkplum group
Anacardiaceae (many)
Apocynaceae (*Adenium*)
Burseraceae
Euphorbiaceae (many)
Sapotaceae (many)
Urticaceae

## 6. Tamboti group
Anacardiaceae
Burseraceae
Euphorbiaceae (many)

## 7. Silver-oak group
Annonaceae (*Sphaerocoryne*; *Monanthotaxis*)
Asteraceae/Compositae (many)
Chrysobalanaceae
Dipterocarpaceae
Erythroxylaceae (*Erythroxylum delagoense*)
Euphorbiaceae (*Clutia*; *Croton*; if latex does
　not flow)
Flacourtiaceae/[Achariaceae]/[Kiggelariaceae:
　*Kiggelaria*]
Hamamelidaceae
Lauraceae (*Cryptocarya*)
Rhamnaceae (*Phylica*)

Rosaceae *
Salicaceae
Solanaceae
Tiliaceae/[Malvaceae] (*Heritiera*; also others if
　three veins from base overlooked)

## 8. Spikethorn group
Annonaceae (*Artabotrys*)
Bignoniaceae (*Rhigozum*)
Capparaceae (*Boscia foetida*)
Celastraceae (many)
Combretaceae (*Terminalia*)
Ebenaceae (*Diospyros simii*; *D. sinensis*)
Flacourtiaceae/[Salicaceae]
Nyctaginaceae
Olacaceae
Pedaliaceae
Rhamnaceae (*Colubrina*; *Rhamnus*)
Solanaceae (*Lycium*)
Ulmaceae/Celtidaceae (*Chaetacme*)

## 9. Wild-plane group
Aquifoliaceae (*Ilex*, juvenile leaves)
Asteraceae/Compositae
Boraginaceae
Celastraceae (many)
Ericaceae (*Vaccinium*)
Escalloniaceae (*Choristylis*)
Euphorbiaceae
Flacourtiaceae/[Achariaceae]/[Aphloiaceae:
　*Aphloia*]/[Kiggelariaceae: *Kiggelaria*, *Rawsonia*]
　/Salicaceae
Myricaceae
Myrsinaceae/[Maesaceae: *Maesa*]
Ochnaceae (many)
Passifloraceae (*Paropsia*)
Proteaceae (*Leucospermum*)
Rhamnaceae
Rosaceae
Salicaceae
Sapindaceae
Turneraceae (*Turnera oculata*)
Violaceae

## 10. Common group
Annonaceae
Apiaceae/Umbelliferae (*Heteromorpha*)
Aquifoliaceae (*Ilex*, mature leaves)
Canellaceae
Capparaceae (many)

Celastraceae
Chenopodiaceae (*Atriplex*) *
Chrysobalanaceae (*Maranthes*)
Combretaceae (*Combretum*, few, especially
  creepers; *Lumnitzera; Pteleopsis*, young
  growth; *Terminalia*)
Dichapetalaceae (*Tapura*)
Dipterocarpaceae
Ebenaceae (many)
Erythroxylaceae
Escalloniaceae/Brexiaceae/[Celastraceae]
  (*Brexia*)
Euphorbiaceae/[Phyllanthaceae]/
  [Putranjivaceae; *Drypetes*]
Fabaceae/Leguminosae/Fabaceae:
  Papilionoideae
Flacourtiaceae/[Achariaceae]/[Aphloiaceae:
  *Aphloia*]/[Kiggelariaceae: *Xylotheca*]/
  [Salicaceae: *Casearia*]
Heteropyxidaceae/[Myrtaceae]
  (secretory cavities: *Heteropyxis*)
Icacinaceae
Lauraceae
Lecythidaceae
Linaceae/formerly under Hugoniaceae
  (*Hugonia*)
Malpighiaceae
Meliaceae
Mimosaceae/Leguminosae/Fabaceae:
  Mimosoideae (*Acacia*) *
Montiniaceae
Myricaceae
Myrsinaceae
Myrtaceae (e.g. *Eucalyptus*, mature leaves) *
Ochnaceae
Olacaceae
Opiliaceae (*Opilia campestris*)
Podocarpaceae
Polygalaceae
Proteaceae (many)
Rhamnaceae (*Colubrina*)
Santalaceae
Sapindaceae
Solanaceae (mainly aliens)
Sterculiaceae/[Malvaceae]
Thymelaeaceae

**11. Raisin bush group**
Alangiaceae/[Cornaceae] (*Alangium chinense*)
Araliaceae
Boraginaceae
Dracaenaceae/[Convallariaceae]/formerly
  under Agavaceae
Euphorbiaceae
Flacourtiaceae/[Salicaceae]
Greyiaceae/Melianthaceae (*Greyia*)
Hernandiaceae
Lauraceae
Malvaceae (many)
Mimosaceae/Leguminosae/Fabaceae:
  Mimosoideae (*Acacia*) *
Passifloraceae (*Adenia*)
Piperaceae
Poaceae/Gramineae (bamboos)
Rhamnaceae
Rosaceae (*Cliffortia grandifolia*)
Sterculiaceae/[Malvaceae] (many)
Tiliaceae/[Malvaceae] (many)
Ulmaceae/Celtidaceae
Urticaceae
Vitaceae (*Rhoicissus tomentosa*)

**12. Monkey-orange group**
Asteraceae/Compositae (*Distephanus angulifolius*)
Loganiaceae/Strychnaceae (*Strychnos*, many)
Melastomataceae/Memecylaceae (few)

**13. Sagewood group**
Buddlejaceae/[Stilbaceae]/formerly under
  Loganiaceae (*Buddleja*, many)
Euphorbiaceae/[Picrodendraceae] (*Androstachys
  johnsonii*)

**14. Turkeyberry group**
Rubiaceae

**15. Bridesbush group**
Rubiaceae (*Pavetta*, many; *Psychotria*, few)

**16. Wild-medlar group**
Rubiaceae

**17. False-gardenia group**
Icacinaceae
Loganiaceae/Gentianaceae (*Anthocleista*)
Rhizophoraceae
Rubiaceae

**18. Onionwood group**
Celastraceae (*Catha; Lydenburgia*)
Cornaceae/Curtisiaceae (*Curtisia*)
Icacinaceae
Rhamnaceae (*Lasiodiscus*)
Rhizophoraceae

**19. Spoonwood group**
Acanthaceae
Asteraceae/Compositae
Buddlejaceae/[Scrophulariaceae]; formerly
    under Loganiaceae (*Nuxia*)
Celastraceae
Flacourtiaceae [Salicaceae]
Lamiaceae/Labiatae/some genera formerly
    under Verbenaceae
Monimiaceae/formerly under Trimeniaceae
Scrophulariaceae/[Stilbaceae: *Halleria*]
Verbenaceae

**20. Numnum group**
Apocynaceae

**21. Poisonbush group**
Apocynaceae (many)
Asclepiadaceae/Apocynaceae (*Calotropis procera,*
    *Fockea*)
Clusiaceae/Guttiferae (many)
Euphorbiaceae (*Excoecaria madagascariensis*)

**22. Waterberry group**
Myrtaceae (many)
Rutaceae (few)

**23. Bushwillow group**
Acanthaceae
Avicenniaceae/Verbenaceae (*Avicennia*)
Buddlejaceae/[Scrophulariaceae: *Gomphostigma*]
Buxaceae
Celastraceae
Clusiaceae/Guttiferae/[Hypericaceae: *Hypericum*]
Combretaceae (many, especially *Combretum*)
Cornaceae (*Cornus (=Afrocrania) volkensii*)
Ebenaceae
Euphorbiaceae (*Mallotus oppositifolius*)
Hamamelidaceae
Lauraceae (*Dahlgrenodendron natalensis*)
Lythraceae
Melastomataceae/Memecylaceae
Nyctaginaceae (*Pisonia aculeata*)

Oleaceae (many)
Oliniaceae
Rhamnaceae
Rhynchocalycaceae/formerly under Lythraceae
    (*Rhynchocalyx lawsonioides*)
Salvadoraceae
Santalaceae
Scrophulariaceae/[Stilbaceae: *Anastrabe*]
Sonneratiaceae (*Sonneratia alba*)
Thymelaeaceae

**24. Quininetree group**
Anacardiaceae
Apocynaceae
Clusiaceae/Guttiferae

**25. Wild-almond group**
Buddlejaceae/[Stilbaceae]/ formerly under
    Loganiaceae (*Nuxia*)
Combretaceae (*Combretum adenogonium*)
Euphorbiaceae/[Picrodendraceae: *Hyaenanche*]
Lamiaceae/Labiatae/some genera formerly
    under Verbenaceae
Proteaceae
Rhizophoraceae
Rubiaceae
Scrophulariaceae/[Stilbaceae: *Bowkeria,*
    *Ixianthes retzioides*]

**26. Bauhinia group**
Caesalpiniaceae/Leguminosae/Fabaceae:
    Caesalpinioideae

**27. Mopane group**
Balanitaceae/Zygophyllaceae (*Balanites*)
Caesalpiniaceae/Leguminosae/Fabaceae:
    Caesalpinioideae
Meliaceae (*Xylocarpus granatum*)
Sapindaceae (*Lepisanthes (=Aphania) senegalensis*)

**28. Corkwood group**
Burseraceae

**29. Coraltree group**
Bignoniaceae
Capparaceae
Cunoniaceae
Fabaceae/Leguminosae/Fabaceae:
    Papilionoideae (many)
Vitaceae

## 30. White-ironwood group
Rutaceae

## 31. Karee group
Anacardiaceae (many)
Apiaceae/Umbelliferae (*Polemannia*)
Bignoniaceae (*Rhigozum*)
Lamiaceae/Labiatae/formerly under
    Verbenaceae (*Vitex*, few)
Sapindaceae

## 32. Sausagetree group
Bignoniaceae (many)
Connaraceae (*Cnestis*)
Cunoniaceae
Oleaceae
Ptaeroxylaceae/[Rutaceae: *Ptaeroxylon*]
Rutaceae

## 33. Boerbean group
Caesalpiniaceae/Leguminosae/Fabaceae:
    Caesalpinioideae
Fabaceae/Leguminosae/Fabaceae:
    Papilionoideae (*Aeschynomene*; *Sesbania*)

## 34. Soapberry group
Meliaceae
Sapindaceae

## 35. Peppertree group
Anacardiaceae (*Schinus*) *
Burseraceae

## 36. Knobwood group
Apiaceae/Umbelliferae
Kirkiaceae/formerly under Simaroubaceae
Melianthaceae
Proteaceae (*Grevillea*) *
Rosaceae
Rutaceae
Simaroubaceae/[Ptaeroxylaceae]/[Rutaceae]
    (*Harrisonia*)

## 37. Marula group
Anacardiaceae
Burseraceae

## 38. Kiaat group
Apiaceae/Umbelliferae
Araliaceae
Caesalpiniaceae/Leguminosae/Fabaceae:
    Caesalpinioideae
Connaraceae (*Cnestis*; *Rourea*)
Fabaceae/Leguminosae/Fabaceae:
    Papilionoideae (many)
Meliaceae (many)
Melianthaceae
Sapindaceae
Zygophyllaceae (*Neoluederitzia sericeocarpa*)

## 39. Baobab group
Anacardiaceae (*Rhus montana*)
Araliaceae
Bombacaceae/[Malvaceae]
Capparaceae
Cecropiaceae/[Urticaceae]/formerly
    under Moraceae
Euphorbiaceae
Passifloraceae (*Adenia*)
Sterculiaceae/[Malvaceae]

## 40. Fingerleaf group
Lamiaceae/Labiatae/formerly under
    Verbenaceae (*Vitex*)

## 41. Hook thorn group
Caesalpiniaceae/Leguminosae/Fabaceae:
    Caesalpinioideae
Mimosaceae/Leguminosae/Fabaceae:
    Mimosoideae (many)

## 42. Sweet thorn group
Mimosaceae/Leguminosae/Fabaceae:
    Mimosoideae

## 43. False-thorn group
Bignoniaceae (*Jacaranda mimosifolia*) *
Caesalpiniaceae/Leguminosae/Fabaceae:
    Caesalpinioideae
Meliaceae (*Melia azedarach*) *
Mimosaceae/Leguminosae/Fabaceae:
    Mimosoideae (many)
Moringaceae
Sapindaceae (*Macphersonia hildebrandtii*)

# Glossary

This glossary covers descriptive terms commonly encountered in tree identification literature. More information on some of the terms is supplied in Part 1. Numbers placed within square brackets refer to pages containing information and/or illustrations. Synonyms are supplied for some terms, and are given in parenthesis at the end of the definition.

**alien** a plant introduced from elsewhere and now more or less naturalized (= exotic). Compare **native, naturalized**.

**alternate** applied to leaves placed singly at different heights on a stem [26]. Compare **opposite, whorl**.

**anther** the part of the **stamen** containing the pollen; usually borne on a slender stalk (filament) [48, 49].

**anthesis** the opening of the flower bud.

**apex, apical** the tip of an organ (plural: apices).

**appressed** lying close to or pressed flat against a surface, as the hairs on certain leaves.

**aril** a fleshy outer covering or appendage that encloses the seed or part thereof, and usually develops from its stalk; often brightly coloured [51, 52].

**armed** bearing thorns, spines, or prickles [35].

**axil** the upper angle between the leaf and the stem on which it is carried [11, 24]; **axillary** in, or arising from, an axil.

**axis** the main stem of a plant, or inflorescence, on which other organs are borne.

**bacterial nodule** a swelling or knob containing bacteria [30]; found in leaves or roots.

**berry** a many-seeded fleshy fruit with a soft outer portion and the seeds embedded in the fleshy or pulpy tissue (e.g. the tomato) [50]. Compare **drupe**.

**bifoliolate, 2-foliolate** with two leaflets [25].

**bilobed** divided into two lobes [24].

**bipinnate, bipinnately compound** when the first divisions (pinnae or leaflets) of a leaf are further divided, i.e. with leaflets (pinnules) borne on branches of the rachis [24] (= twice pinnate). Compare **pinnate**.

**blade** the flat, expanded part of a leaf [24] (= lamina).

**bloom** 1. the flower, or process of flowering. 2. a thin layer of white waxy powder on some leaves and fruit [27].

**bole** the main stem or trunk of a tree (= trunk).

**bract** a usually small, leaf-like structure, in the axil of which arises a flower or a branch of an inflorescence [49].

**bracteate** having bracts.

**branchlet** a twig or small branch.

**calyx** collective term for all the sepals of a flower; the outer whorl of most flowers; usually green [48].

**capitate** head-like, or in a head-shaped cluster, as in the flowers in some species of *Acacia* [49].

**capsule** a dry fruit produced by an ovary comprising two or more united carpels and usually opening by slits or pores. Compare **pod**.

**carpel** one of the leaf-derived, usually ovule-bearing units of a pistil or ovary; sometimes free, but usually united to form a compound pistil or ovary. The number of carpels in a compound pistil is generally difficult to establish, but often equals the number of chambers or stigmatic lobes per pistil.

**chamber** the cavity of an ovary which contains the ovules [48] (= locule).

**cladode, cladophyll** a leaf-like structure formed by a modified stem, as in the genus *Opuntia* (prickly pears).

**clasping** used for leaf bases that partly or completely enclose the stem [41, 42].

**compound** consisting of several parts; e.g. a compound leaf has two or more separate leaflets [24, 25].

**cone** a rounded or elongate structure comprising, on a central axis, many overlapping bracts which bear pollen, spores or seed; characteristic of many gymnosperms.

**congested** crowded

**coppice, coppicing** vegetative shoots at the base of the stem; sprouts arising from a stump.

**cordate** heart-shaped, with a notch at the base [43].

**corolla** collective term for petals of a flower; usually coloured [48].

**crenate** with rounded teeth along the margin [32]; often described as toothed (= scalloped).

**cyathium** a flower-like inflorescence characteristic of the genus *Euphorbia*; it consists of a central 3-chambered ovary (equivalent to a female flower) surrounded by groups of single stamens (each equivalent to a male flower), all grouped together within petal-like bracts and glands.

**deciduous** shedding leaves at the end of the growing season. Compare **evergreen**.

**dehiscent** opening, as in anthers or fruit.

**dichotomous** branched or forked into two more or less equal divisions.

**disc (disk)** 1. the fleshy outgrowth developed from the receptacle at the base of the ovary or from the stamens surrounding the ovary, usually in the form of a ring, cushion, or of separate gland-like parts; often secreting nectar. 2. the central part of the head-like inflorescence of the Asteraceae.

**domatia** small structures in the forks of the midrib and the main lateral veins. They take two main forms, either conspicuous tufts of hairs or small pits. Domatia are formed by the plant to act as shelter for mites, who in return assist with cleaning the leaf surface and protect against damage by plant-eating mites [45] (singular: **domatium**).

**drip-tip** a long, gradually tapering tip of a leaf [43] (= attenuate).

**drooping** bending or hanging downwards, but not quite pendulous. Compare **pendulous**.

**drupe** a fleshy, indehiscent fruit with one or more seeds, each of which is surrounded by a hard stony layer formed by the inner part of the ovary wall (e.g. stone fruit such as olives, peaches) [50]. Compare **berry, stone**.

**ellipsoid** a solid body elliptic in its long section and circular in cross-section.

**elliptic** oval and narrowed to rounded ends, widest at or about the middle [43].

**entire** with an even and continuous margin; lacking teeth, lobes or indentations [32] (= smooth). Compare **toothed**.

**epiphyte** a plant that grows on another plant but is not parasitic on it; usually with its roots not in the ground. Compare **parasite**.

**even-pinnate** see **paripinnate**.

**evergreen** retaining green leaves throughout the year, even in winter. Compare **deciduous**.

**exfoliate** to peel off in thin flakes, as occurs in the bark of certain shrubs and trees.

**exserted** projecting beyond the surrounding parts, as stamens protrude from a corolla; not included.

**extrafloral nectaries** nectar-secreting glands located outside the flower, as in leaves [44].

**felted** closely matted with intertwined hairs [27].

**filament** the thread-like stalk of the stamen bearing the anther [48].

**flower** the structure concerned with sexual reproduction in flowering plants [48, 49]. Compare **perianth**.

**foliolate** pertaining to, or having leaflets; usually used in compound words, such as bifoliolate or trifoliolate [24, 25].

**free** not joined to each other or to any other organ (e.g. petals to petals, or stamens to petals). Compare **united**.

**fruit** the ripened ovary (pistil) and its attached parts; the seed-containing structure [50]. Compare **seed**.

**gall** a localized abnormal plant growth induced by a fungus, insect or other foreign agent.

**glabrous** smooth; hairless.

**gland** an appendage or protuberance which secretes sticky, oily or sugary liquid; found on the surface of, or within, an organ (e.g. leaf, stem or flower) [44].

**gland-dotted** small translucent or coloured dots when viewed against the light, usually said of leaves with secretory cavities within its tissues [29] (= pellucid gland-dotted; glandular-punctate). Compare **secretory cavities**.

**glandular hairs** terminated by minute glands, often sticky to the touch.

**globose** spherical, rounded.

**glutinous** gluey; sticky; gummy; covered with a sticky exudate.

**gregarious** growing in groups or colonies.

**heart-shaped** see **cordate**.

**hemiparasite** a parasitic plant which contains chlorophyll and is partly self-sustaining, as in the Santalaceae. Holoparasites lack chlorophyll and are entirely dependent on the host for nourishment (not among native trees). Compare **epiphyte, parasite**.

**herb** a plant which does not develop persistent woody tissue above ground and either dies at the end of the growing season or overwinters by means of underground organs (e.g. rhizomes, bulbs, corms).

**herbaceous** like a herb; non-woody, soft and leafy, with a stem that dies back to the ground each year.

**imparipinnate** a pinnately compound leaf with an odd number of leaflets, and with a single terminal leaflet [24] (= odd-pinnate). Compare **paripinnate, bipinnate**.

**indehiscent** remaining closed and not opening when ripe or mature.

**indigenous** see **native**.

**inflorescence** any arrangement of more than one flower; the flowering portion of a plant, e.g. head, spike, panicle, cyathium, raceme [49].

**interpetiolar** between the leaf stalks, as an interpetiolar stipule that extends from the base of one leaf stalk across the stem to the base of the stalk of the opposite leaf (e.g. in many Rubiaceae) [33, 34]. Compare **intrapetiolar**.

**intersecondary veins** the veins in a leaf blade that interconnect the main lateral veins.

**intramarginal vein** a vein of constant thickness (much thinner than the midrib) just inside the margin of the leaf blade, from the base to the apex [28]. Lateral veins run from the midrib to the intramarginal vein.

**intrapetiolar** between the petiole and the stem, as an intrapetiolar stipule that extends across the axil of the leaf (e.g. in members of the Melianthaceae) [33, 34]. Compare **interpetiolar**.

**involucral bracts** one or more whorls of bracts or leafy structures (often sepal-like) surrounding the base of an umbel or flower head [49], notably in the Asteraceae (= phyllaries).

**irregular** flowers that can be divided into two equal halves (mirror images) along only one plane, i.e. corolla lobes unequal [49] (= zygomorphic). Compare **regular**.

**keel (petals)** the two loosely united lower petals of the flowers of the Fabaceae [49] (= carina). Compare **standard, wing**.

**lamina** see **blade**.

**lanceolate** with the shape of a lance or spear; much longer than broad, tapering to the tip from a broad base, with the widest point below the middle [43] (lance-shaped).

**lateral** borne on or at the side.

**latex** in this book used loosely for any copious liquid exudate, whether watery (clear), cloudy, milky or any other colour [36, 37].

**lax** loose; with parts open and spreading, not compact.

**leaf** an aerial outgrowth from a stem, numbers of which make up a plant's foliage. Characterized by an axillary bud. It typically consists of a stalk (petiole) and a flattened blade (lamina), and is the principal food manufacturing (photosynthetic) organ of a green plant [10, 11].

**leaflet** the individual division of a compound leaf which is usually leaf-like, with a stalk of its own, but lacks an axillary bud in the axil with the rachis [24, 25] (= pinna, pinnule).

**lenticel** a slightly raised, somewhat corky, often lens-shaped area on the surface of a young stem. Facilitates gaseous exchange between plant tissues and the atmosphere [40, 41].

**linear** resembling a line; long and narrow, with more or less parallel sides [43]. Compare **oblong**.

**lobe** a part or a segment of an organ (e.g. leaf, petal) deeply divided from the rest of the organ but not separated; segments usually rounded.

**locule** see **chamber**.

**mangrove** generally applied to several groups of highly specialized tropical trees that grow in mud and silt, especially in tidal estuaries and lagoons. Many mangroves are characterized by aerial 'breathing roots'.

**mesic** moist, especially in reference to habitats or environments.

**midrib** the central or largest vein or rib of a leaf or other organ.

**monopodial** (of growth) with a mode of stem extension growth by the apical (terminal) bud producing many lateral organs successively [11]. Compare **sympodial**.

**mucro** a short, sharp, abrupt point, usually at the tip of a leaf or other organ [43].

**native** a plant occurring naturally in an area and not introduced from elsewhere (= indigenous). Compare **alien, naturalized**.

**naturalized** a plant introduced from a foreign area (an alien) which has become established and is reproducing successfully in the new area. Compare **alien, native**.

**nectar** the sugary liquid produced by flowers or other floral parts on which insects and birds feed; **nectary** any structure which produces nectar, such as glands or special hairs.

**notched** with a small V-shaped cut or indentation at the apex; usually referring to leaves [43] (= emarginate).

**nut** a dry, single-seeded and indehiscent fruit with a hard outer covering, as in acorns, walnuts; **nutlet** a small nut.

**obconic(al)** conical or cone-shaped, with the attachment at the narrow end.

**ob-** prefix meaning opposite, inverse or against.

**obcordate** inversely cordate (heart-shaped), with the attachment at the narrow end; sometimes refers to any leaf with a deeply notched apex.

**oblanceolate** inversely lanceolate (lance-shaped), with the attachment at the narrow end [43].

**oblong** an elongated but relatively wide shape, longer than broad with nearly parallel sides [43] (= strap-shaped). Compare **linear**.

**obovate** inversely egg-shaped; with the broadest end towards the tip [43]. Compare **ovate**.

**obtriangular** inversely triangular; with the broadest end towards the tip.

**odd-pinnate** see **imparipinnate**.

**opposite** of two organs (e.g. leaves) arising at the same level on opposite sides of the stem [26]; also used for organs that arise opposite each other or when the one arises at the base of another, as a stamen opposite a petal or sepal. Compare **alternate, whorl**.

**oval** broadly elliptic, the width more than half the length [43].

**ovary** the hollow basal portion of a pistil which contains the ovules within one or more chambers and which produces the fruit if pollination and fertilization take place [48, 49].

**ovate** (of flat surfaces) egg-shaped in outline; attached at the broad end [43]. Compare **ovoid**.

**ovoid** egg-shaped (applied to three-dimensional structures). Compare **ovate**.

**ovule** minute roundish structure(s) within the chamber of the ovary. Contains the egg cell and after fertilization develops into the seed [48, 49].

**palmate** with three or more parts arising from a single point, radiating outward like the fingers of an open hand; as in palmately compound leaves [25, 28] or palmate venation.

**panicle** an inflorescence with an axis that can continue to grow and does not end in a flower (i.e. the axis is indeterminate) and many branches, each of which bears two or more flowers; often loosely applied to any complex, branched inflorescence [49].

**parasite** a plant which obtains its food from another living plant (the host) to which it is attached. Compare **hemiparasite**.

**paripinnate** a pinnately compound leaf with an even number of leaflets and terminated by a pair of leaflets [24, 25] (even-pinnate). Compare **imparipinnate, bipinnate**.

**pedicel** the stalk of an individual flower.

**peltate** shield-shaped; a flat structure borne on a stalk attached to the lower surface rather than to the base or margin (like the handle of an umbrella); usually used to describe leaves.

**pendulous** hanging downward (= pendant). Compare **drooping**.

**perennial** living for three or more years.

**perianth** the outer sterile whorls of a flower, made up of sepals or petals or both [48].

**persistent** remaining attached; not falling off.

**petal** one of the units of the inner whorl(s) of sterile appendages in flowers that together are called the corolla; often brightly coloured [48].

**petiolate** leaves possessing a stalk (petiole).

**petiole** the leaf stalk [24].

**petiolule** stalk of a leaflet of a compound leaf [25].

**phyllode** an expanded, leaflike petiole lacking a true leaf blade [42]. Used to describe the 'leaves' of some Australian acacias.

**pinna** 1. the primary division of a pinnate leaf (= leaflet). 2. the first series of branches within a bipinnate leaf which bears the pinnules [24, 25].

**pinnate, pinnately compound** when a compound leaf has its leaflets arranged in two rows along an extension (the rachis) of the leaf stalk [24]. Compare **imparipinnate, paripinnate, bipinnate**.

**plane** with a flat surface.

**pod** a general term applied to any dry and many-seeded dehiscent fruit, formed from one unit or carpel. In this book usually applied to a legume which is the product of a single pistil (carpel) and usually splits open along one or both the two opposite sutures or seams (characteristic of many Mimosaceae, Caesalpiniaceae and Fabaceae). Compare **capsule**.

**prickle** a small, sharp-pointed outgrowth of the epidermis or bark [35].

**pseudo-aril** a false aril. Used for the fleshy, often brightly coloured, covering of the stone in the Burseraceae, which develops from the fruit wall and not the stalk of a seed as in a typical aril [52].

**raceme** an inflorescence in which the flowers are borne consecutively along a single (unbranched) axis, the lowest on the axis being the oldest [49]. Each flower has a stalk. Compare **spike**.

**rachis (rhachis)** 1. the axis of a compound leaf [24, 25]; 2. the axis of an inflorescence.

**rank** a vertical row; leaves arranged in two ranks are in two vertical rows when viewed from the tip of the shoot [26].

**receptacle** the uppermost part of a flower stalk on which the floral parts are borne [48, 50].

**regular** radially symmetrical, as in a flower that can be divided into two identical halves (mirror images) along more than one plane, i.e. the corolla lobes are equal. Compare **irregular**.

**rosette** a dense radiating cluster of leaves (or other organs), usually at or near the ends of shoots.

**scalloped** the margin notched with rounded or broad and blunt teeth or projections [32] (= crenate, crenulate). Compare **toothed**.

**scandent** climbing.

**secondary pollen presentation** a method of pollen presentation common in members of the Rubiaceae. Whilst still in bud, the anthers open and deposit the pollen on a slightly swollen and sticky portion of the style just below the terminal stigma.

By the time the flowers open the anthers are shrivelled and the pollen is presented to would-be pollinators on the often long, protruding styles.

**secretory cavities** roundish cavities within the leaf blade that contain secretions such as resin, mucilage and oil [29]. Compare **gland-dotted**.

**seed** the ripened ovule containing an embryo [51, 52]. Compare **fruit**.

**sepal** one of the outer set of usually green organs of a flower which normally encloses the other floral parts in the bud; collectively called the calyx [48].

**sessile** attached directly, without a supporting stalk, as a leaf without a petiole (= stalkless).

**shrub** a perennial woody plant with usually two or more stems arising from or near the ground; differs from a tree in that it is smaller and does not possess a trunk or bole. Compare **tree**.

**silky** having a covering of soft, appressed, fine hairs (= sericeous).

**simple** leaf with only a single blade [24]; the opposite of a compound leaf.

**sinuate** used to describe structures such as leaf margins with a number of regular curved indentations or small lobes [32]. Compare **wavy** (= undulate).

**smooth** see entire.

**solitary** (of flowers) occurring singly in each axil.

**spathulate** like a spatula in shape, with a rounded blade gradually tapering to the base.

**spike** an inflorescence with stalkless flowers arranged along an elongated, unbranched axis [49]. Compare **raceme**.

**spine** a hard, straight and sharply pointed structure, often long and narrow. Usually a modified leaf or stipule [35, 36]. Compare **thorn**.

**spinescent** ending in a spine or very sharp hard point, as in a spinescent shoot (= thorn) [35].

**spray** a slender shoot or branch with its leaves, flowers or fruit.

**spreading** having a gradual outward direction.

**stamen** one of a flower's male reproductive organs, usually made up of a narrow stalk (filament), and an anther in which the pollen is produced [48].

**standard** large upper petal of a flower in Fabaceae [49] (= banner, vexillium). Compare **keel, wing**.

**stellate** star-shaped, as in hairs with several to many branches radiating from the base [31].

**stem** the main axis of the plant or a branch of the main axis that produces leaves and buds at the nodes [11]. Usually above ground, but sometimes modified and underground (e.g. rhizomes).

**sterile** lacking functional sex organs; a sterile flower produces neither pollen nor functional ovules.

**stigma** the part of the pistil on which pollen grains germinate, normally situated on top of the style and covered with a sticky secretion [48].

**stipel** the equivalent of stipules but found on compound leaves near the point of attachment of leaflet stalks (plural: stipellae).

**stipule** small scale- or leaf-like appendages at the base of the leaf stalk in some plants; generally found in pairs on each side of the stem at the junction of the leaf stalk and stem. Frequently fall off early in life, leaving scars on the stem. Best seen on young actively growing shoots [33].

**stone** hard, seed-containing pit of a drupe (e.g. the so-called 'seed' of a peach or olive) [50]. Compare **drupe**.

**style** a more or less elongated projection of the ovary which bears the stigma [48].

**sub-opposite** nearly opposite [26].

**subcapitate** a nearly globose head of densely clustered flowers.

**subtend** to be below and close to, as a bract may subtend a flower.

**succulent** plant with fleshy and juicy organs (leaves, stems) which contain reserves of water.

**sympodial** (of growth) without a single persisting growing point; changing direction by frequent replacement of the growing apex (apical bud) by a lateral growing point (axillary bud) below it [41]. Compare **monopodial**.

**taxon** any taxonomic unit into which living organisms are classified, such as order, family, or species (plural: taxa). Taxonomy, **taxonomic** science of the classification of organisms.

**tendril** a slender, usually coiling part of the leaf or stem that supports the stem; a climbing organ [41].

**terminal** at the tip (= apical, or distal end). Compare **ultimate**.

**thicket** vegetation type characterized by thickly growing shrubs, sometimes very thorny or with many succulents. Common in river valleys along the east coast.

**thorn** 1. a curved spine. 2. a sharply pointed branch. Often used synonymously with spine [35, 36]. Compare **spine**.

**throat** the opening or orifice of a tubular or funnel-shaped corolla.

**toothed** used in a generalized sense to refer to leaf margins which are toothed in various ways, e.g. dentate (coarse sharp teeth perpendicular to the margin), serrate (sharp, forward-pointing teeth) and crenate (shallow, rounded teeth) [32]. Compare **entire**.

**trifoliolate, 3-foliolate** referring to a compound leaf with three leaflets [25].

**tree** a perennial woody plant with a single (usually) main stem and a distinct upper crown [12, 13]. Compare **shrub**.

**trunk** main stem of a tree below the branches (= bole) [12].

**ultimate** used in this book to refer to the highest degree of branching in woody plants.

**umbel** umbrella-shaped inflorescence in which the stalks of the flowers all arise from the top of the main stem [49].

**unarmed** lacking spines, thorns, or prickles.

**undulate** with a wavy margin [32] (= wavy).

**united** joined together (= fused). Compare **free**.

**venation** the pattern of veining on a leaf [28].

**wavy** used to describe margins of leaves which are wavy (not flat), but not indented as in sinuate margins [32] (= undulate). Compare **sinuate**.

**white-felted** closely matted with a felt-like layer of white, intertwined hairs [27].

**whorl** 1. the arrangement of three or more leaves or flowers at the same node of the axis so as to form an encircling ring [26] (= verticill). Compare **alternate, opposite, rosette**. 2. more than two of any other organs (e.g. sepals, petals, stamens) arising at the same level.

**wing** 1. any thin, flat extension of an organ, as in winged fruit or seed. 2. each of the two side (lateral) petals of a Fabaceae flower [49] (= ala, alae). Compare **keel, standard**.

# References

Much of the information in this book supplements *Field Guide to Trees of Southern Africa*, by Braam van Wyk and Piet van Wyk (1997), see below for more information.

Baluska, F., Mancuso, S. & Volkman, D. (eds). 2006. *Communication in Plants: Neuronal Aspects of Plant Life*. Springer, Berlin.

Bell, A.D. 1991. *Plant Form: An Illustrated Guide to Flowering Plant Morphology*. Oxford University Press, Oxford.

Coates Palgrave, M, 1996. *Key to the Trees of Zimbabwe*, 1st ed. Modern Press, Gweru, Zimbabwe.

Coates Palgrave, M, 2005. *Keith Coates Palgrave Trees of Southern Africa*, 3rd ed., 2nd imp. Struik Publishers, Cape Town.

Collins, M.W., Hunt, D.G. & Atherton, M.A. (eds). 2004. *Optimisation Mechanics in Nature*. WIT Press, Southampton.

Curtis, B. & Mannheimer, C. 2005. *Tree Atlas of Namibia*. National Botanical Research Institute, Windhoek.

Hallé, F. 2002. *In Praise of Plants*. Timber Press, Portland.

Jeffrey, C. 1982. *An Introduction to Plant Taxonomy*, 2nd ed. Cambridge University Press, Cambridge.

Kellert, S.R. & Wilson, E.O. 1993. *The Biophilia Hypothesis*. Shearwater Books, Washington D.C.

Pooley, E. 1994. *The Complete Field Guide to Trees of Natal, Zululand and Transkei*, 1st ed., 2nd imp. Natal Flora Publications Trust, Durban.

Reyneke, W.F., Coetzer, L.A. & Grobbelaar, N. 1987. *Plantkunde: Morfologie en Sitologie*, 2nd ed. Butterworth, Durban.

Schmidt, E., Lötter, M. & McCleland, W. 2002. *Trees and Shrubs of Mpumalanga and Kruger National Park*. Jacana, Johannesburg.

Simpson, M.G. 2006. *Plant Systematics*. Elsevier Academic Press, Amsterdam.

Tinbergen, N. 1951. *The Study of Instinct*. Clarendon Press, Oxford.

Van der Schijff, H.P. (ed.) 1985. *Algemene Plantkunde*, 5th ed. J.L. van Schaik, Pretoria.

Van Wyk, A.E. & Smith, G.F. 2001. *Regions of Floristic Endemism in Southern Africa: A review with emphasis on Succulents*. Umdaus Press, Hatfield, Pretoria.

Van Wyk, B. [A.E.] & Van Wyk, P. 1997. *Field Guide to Trees of Southern Africa*. Struik Publishers, Cape Town.

Van Wyk, B. [A.E], Van Wyk, P. & Van Wyk, B-E. 2000. *Photographic Guide to Trees of Southern Africa*. Briza Publications, Pretoria.

# Acknowledgements

We are indebted to many people and institutions who, over the years, have helped us with our work on trees. A special word of thanks to Elsa van Wyk and Emmarentia van Wyk for assistance with the preparation of the manuscript of this book, and Jaco van Wyk for contributing the diagrams, line drawings and icons. We gratefully acknowledge the contribution of Meg Coates Palgrave toward the preparation of the tree distribution maps and for her permission, as co-copyright holder, to use them in this book. Thanks are due to Alan Hall, Laboratory for Microscopy and Microanalysis, University of Pretoria, for the use of photographic facilities, and Johan Hurter, Lowveld National Botanical Garden, Nelspruit, for his hospitality and assistance during visits to the garden.

Numerous field workers have generously shared with us their knowledge on tree identification in southern Africa and we sincerely thank them all; in particular, we would like to acknowledge the guidance and support received from Daan Botha, Tony Abbott, Marie Jordaan, Meg Coates Palgrave and the late Mr. Hugh Nicholson. We would also like to thank the University of Pretoria for financial and institutional support. Piet van Wyk gratefully acknowledges the substantial financial and other support received from the Mazda Wildlife Fund, Total SA, Agfa and Persetel (now part of the Business Connection group) during his extensive travels throughout southern Africa to photograph trees.

At Struik Publishers we are much indebted to Pippa Parker for commissioning the manuscript, and to the rest of the team involved in the book's production, particularly Gill Gordon for her skilful editing of the text and Robin Cox for the pleasing design and layout.

# Index

Main species entries in **bold**; photographs and illustrations in *italics*.

CANDY KITTENS

# CANDY KITTENS

## JAMIE LAING

### MITCHELL BEAZLEY

An Hachette UK Company
www.hachette.co.uk

First published in 2013 by Mitchell Beazley, an imprint
of Octopus Publishing Group Ltd, Endeavour House,
189 Shaftesbury Avenue, London, WC2 8JY.
www.octopusbooks.co.uk

A CIP catalogue record for this book is available from the British Library.

ISBN: 978 1 84533 830 5

Colour reproduction in Italy
Printed and bound by Castelli Bolis, Cenate Sotto (Bg), Italy

Neither the authors nor the publishers take any responsibility for any injury or damage
resulting from the use of techniques shown or described in this book.

Standard level spoon measurements are used in all recipes
1 tablespoon = 15ml
1 teaspoon = 5ml

Ovens should be preheated to the specified temperature. If using a fan-assisted oven,
follow the manufacturer's instructions for adjusting the time and temperature. Grills
should also be preheated.

This book includes dishes made with nuts and nut derivatives. It is advisable for those with
known allergic reactions to nuts and nut derivatives and those who may be potentially
vulnerable to these allergies, such as pregnant and nursing mothers, invalids, the elderly,
babies and children, to avoid dishes made with nuts and nut oils. It is also prudent to
check the labels of prepared ingredients for the possible inclusion of nut derivatives.

The Department of Health advises that eggs should not be consumed raw. This book
contains some dishes made with raw or lightly cooked eggs. It is prudent for more
vulnerable people, such as pregnant and nursing mothers, invalids, the elderly, babies
and young children, to avoid uncooked or lightly cooked dishes made with eggs.

When using lustre dust or glitter in the recipes in this book, ensure you use a product
that is labelled 'edible'. Glitters and dusts described as 'non-toxic' are not the same as
products labelled 'edible' and should not be eaten.

# CONTENTS

# *Introduction*
# JAMIE LAING

**WHAT'UP GUYS! IT'S ME, JAMIE, AND THE BOOK YOU HAVE IN YOUR HANDS IS THE VERY FIRST FROM CANDY KITTENS. OUR TEAM AT CANDY KITTENS HQ HAVE BEEN WORKING AT THIS FOR A LONG TIME AND I'M DELIGHTED THAT WE NOW GET TO SHARE MY SUPER-SWEET WORLD OF TREATS WITH YOU.**

I have crammed this book full of my favourite candy-inspired recipes and top tips for hosting the perfect Candy Kittens PARDY! For as long as I can remember I have been in love with all things sweet. While other boys dreamt of becoming footballers (I wasn't bad at that either!) I dreamt of one day owning my own sweet factory. Was it possible that I could one day become a real-life Willy Wonka? I think a lot of people thought I was mad, but that wasn't going to stop me.

During the summer after finishing school, I travelled to America with friends. I was completely mesmerized by the huge candy stores and couldn't believe there was nothing like this in London. Rows upon rows of the most amazing sweets I had ever seen. All my friends call me the little boi and, at that time, I was literally like a kid in a sweet shop.

After returning home I went off to university to study drama, but I continued to travel to America at every chance I got to indulge my sweet tooth. When I left university I knew I didn't want to follow in the footsteps of my friends and older brother and take a job in the City. I knew exactly what I wanted to do and so Candy Kittens began.

It took a lot of hard work to get to where we are today but I have been lucky enough to work with some amazing people along the way. Although we have come a long way since I dreamt up the name, I still feel like we are at the very beginning. We have so many more brilliant ideas in store; I am as excited about Candy Kittens now as I have ever been. My dreams have come true and Candy Kittens has become a beautiful reality.

This book allows you to share in my SW3ET DREAMS. There is a whole list of scrumptious recipes that we have developed using the delicious flavours from our Candy Kittens range. You can create the Candy Kittens taste with your favourite bois and kittens in the comfort of your own home. Or maybe you'll use our cookery tips to help you prepare the perfect Candy Kittens gift.

Why not start your journeys through my Sweets Dreams chapter with one of my personal favourites - Sparkling Blackcurrant Marshmallows and Salted Caramel Sweets. Just pop a handful of the sweets into a cool jar and decorate however you like. These sweet treats will make the perfect gift for your best guys and girls!

As most of you will know, I live and grew up in Chelsea. I'm probably biased - well, actually definitely - but I think Chelsea is one of the most beautiful parts of London. The grand white townhouses that line the streets are famous all over the world! When we started to put together this book I wanted to include Chelsea, which is of course the birthplace of Candy Kittens. After a great deal of thinking we created the Gingerbread Chelsea Townhouse! It's one of the more tricky recipes in the book, but the results are brilliant. If you're not up to making that, why not try the Trillionaire's Shortbread?

If you're hosting your very own Candy Kittens PARDY, make sure there are plenty of Kitten Cakes on offer. For a more sophisticated twist on your event, I'd recommend the truly divine Eton Mess Cupcakes, just try not to make as much mess as me! To wash those cakes down, check out my Rhubarb and Custard Milkshakes, just one of the great recipes in our ultimate list of fruity Pardy Drinks.

Throughout the book you'll also find tips from my Candy Kittens. Find out just how to host your perfect Candy Kitten PARDY with advice on what to wear, plan a day out on the King's Road and learn the Candy Kittens lingo.

## SW3ET DREAMS
*Jamie*

# Augmented Reality App

## SCAN THE PAGES TO GET EXCLUSIVE VIDEO MESSAGES FROM ME!

Got an iPhone or Android phone? Then download the free Layar app and scan the pages in the book to see if you can hunt out my favourite recipe!

There's a message from me when you find it. I was spoilt for choice, so you may find a few cheeky extra videos in there, too.

# Equipment basics

MAKING SWEETS IS A LOT OF FUN AND NEEDN'T BE COMPLICATED. HERE ARE A FEW GADGETS THAT ARE PRETTY MUCH ESSENTIAL, OR THAT WILL AT LEAST MAKE YOUR LIFE MUCH SIMPLER AND YOUR SW3ET MAKING MORE CONSISTENT.

**Piping bags** are good for decorating cakes and biscuits and for piping French macarons. Use a large piping bag, or a pack of disposable piping bags, with interchangeable piping nozzles of different shapes and sizes.

**Biscuit cutters** will help you cut out biscuits and cookies in clean shapes and rounds.

**A silicone baking mat** will provide a heatproof, nonstick surface to cook on and may be washed and used time and again. They are particularly useful for making perfect French macarons, as they create a completely flat surface on a baking sheet.

**At least one heavy-based saucepan** will really help when making sweets and candies, as it will heat ingredients through evenly and thoroughly. Using thin, cheap pans often results in hotspots and burning.

**A silicone spatula** won't melt at high temperatures, is easy to clean and is very useful for folding, beating and cleaning every last scrap of mixture out of a bowl.

**Hand-held electric beaters or a freestanding mixer** are practically essential for beating and whisking egg whites and batters (e.g. meringues, marshmallows and cakes). A balloon whisk is fine for smaller jobs, but won't cut the mustard when it comes to whipping marshmallows for 10 minutes straight.

**A sugar thermometer** is the most important bit of kit you'll need to invest in when making sweets. Sugar syrup has different properties at different temperatures, which in turn affect the texture of your finished sweets, i.e. whether they are soft or hard or brittle or chewy. Make sure the bulb at the base of the thermometer is submerged in your boiling mixture.

Though not nearly as accurate as a thermometer, it is possible to keep an eye on the stages as your sweet mixture cooks by scooping a tiny bit out with a spoon and dropping it into a glass of very cold water. Fish the mixture out and examine the texture. The chart on the opposite page will guide you.

**BEFORE YOU PARDY, A WORD OF CAUTION: BOILING SUGAR SYRUPS AND TOFFEES CAN CAUSE EXTREMELY BAD BURNS. PLEASE USE OVEN GLOVES AND TAKE CARE WHEN MAKING YOUR SWEETS AND CANDY.**

| NAME | TEMPERATURE | DESCRIPTION |
|---|---|---|
| Thread | 110 to 112°C | Forms thin threads in water and drips from a spoon. |
| Soft ball | 112 to 116°C | Forms a soft ball in water. Squashes completely when pressed. |
| Firm ball | 118 to 120°C | Forms a sticky ball in water. May be flattened when pressed firmly. |
| Hard ball | 121 to 130°C | Forms a firm ball in water, holding its shape when pressed. |
| Soft crack | 132 to 143°C | Forms pliable threads in water. |
| Hard crack | 146 to 154°C | Shatters and breaks when pressed or moulded. |
| Caramel | Above 155°C | Sugar syrup turns golden and eventually burns as the temperature increases. |

# SW3ET DREAMS

# Sparkling blackcurrant marshmallows

Every Candy Kitten's must-have sweet. They look amazing, taste amazing and are totally easy to make. Store in cute jars or team with hot chocolate (see page 122).

## MAKES 18 SHAPED MARSHMALLOWS OR 40 SMALL CUBES

sunflower oil, for brushing
500g caster sugar
250ml water
8 gelatine leaves
120ml blackcurrant cordial
60g egg whites
2 tsp vanilla extract
100g icing sugar
100g cornflower
2-3 tbsp edible glitter

Line a 20x30cm baking tin or other container with clingfilm, overlapping the sheets to make a smooth lining. Brush with oil, making sure to get into all the corners.

Place the caster sugar and water in a medium saucepan over a low heat and stir occasionally until the sugar has completely dissolved. Turn up the heat, bring to the boil, stirring occasionally, and bubble until it reaches 122°C (hard ball stage) on a sugar thermometer (see page 11).

Meanwhile, place the gelatine in a small bowl with plenty of cold water and set aside for 5 minutes to soften. Once the syrup has reached 122°C, remove the pan from the heat, squeeze the excess water from the softened gelatine with your hands and stir into the sugar syrup with the blackcurrant cordial.

Use an electric whisk to whisk the egg whites until soft peaks form. Continue whisking while you trickle the blackcurrant mixture into the bowl. Add the vanilla extract and continue to whisk on high speed for about 7 minutes until the mixture is cool and thick. Quickly spoon the marshmallow mixture into the prepared tin, smoothing the top with a spatula before it begins to set. Leave to set at room temperature.

Combine the icing sugar and cornflour in a bowl and sift half the mixture evenly over a work surface. Turn the sheet of marshmallow out on top and sift a little more of the icing sugar mixture over the top. Dip a biscuit cutter in the remaining icing sugar mixture and stamp out shaped marshmallows, or simply cut into small cubes using a sharp knife. Shake off excess icing sugar mixture and dust with edible glitter. Store in an airtight container in a cool place for up to a week.

# Sherbet dip-dabs

If you can find ovenproof lolly moulds, use them to make neatly shaped lollies to dip into the little bags of sherbet. Otherwise, follow the instructions to make freeform lollies in jewel-like colours.

## MAKES 9

1 tsp bicarbonate of soda
1 tsp citric acid
165g icing sugar, sifted
1 tsp cream of tartar
food colouring gels (optional)
24 hard boiled sweets, in 2 or 3 different colours
9 small paper bags
9 heatproof lolly sticks

To make the sherbet, grind the bicarbonate of soda and citric acid to a fine powder in a pestle and mortar. Place in a bowl with the icing sugar and cream of tartar and use a hand whisk to mix well.

If you want to colour the sherbet, divide it into 2 or 3 bowls and add a few drops of food colouring to each bowl. Whizz the contents of each bowl in a mini food processor until evenly coloured. Pass through a sieve to remove any small lumps of colour, then divide the sherbet between 9 small paper bags.

To make the lollies, preheat the oven to 160°C, fan 140°C, gas mark 3, and line a baking sheet with nonstick baking paper. Place the boiled sweets in a plastic bag and crush with a rolling pin, keeping the colours separate.

Space 9 heatproof lolly sticks out on the lined baking sheet and sprinkle a scant 3 tsp crushed sweets on to one end of each, forming a mound. Carefully slide the baking sheet into the oven and bake for 4–5 minutes until the sweets have melted, keeping a close eye on them to prevent burning. Leave to cool on the baking sheet for at least 20 minutes before releasing. Serve the lollies with the bags of sherbet for dipping. Store the sherbet and lollies separately in airtight containers for up to 2 weeks.

# White chocolate, raspberry and Candy Kittens bark

Dried cherries or other chopped dried fruit would make a good substitute for the freeze-dried raspberries coating this edible bark. You could also add nuts instead of the rock or candy canes, and substitute milk or dark chocolate for the white.

### MAKES 5-8 BAGS

500g white chocolate, chopped
large handful of freeze-dried raspberries
80g Candy Kittens rock or 6 candy canes, roughly crushed
5-8 cellophane bags
twine or ribbon

Line a large baking sheet with nonstick baking paper. Melt the chocolate in a heatproof bowl set over a saucepan of gently simmering water, making sure the water does not touch the bowl.

Pour the melted chocolate on to the lined baking sheet and spread it out with a spatula or spoon to about 1cm thick. It doesn't matter if the edges are ragged. Scatter with the freeze-dried raspberries, crushing a few as you go, and the crushed rock or candy canes. Set aside in a cool place to harden for at least 3 hours.

Break the bark into shards and divide between 5–8 cellophane bags. Tie the tops with twine or ribbon and store in a cool place for up to 10 days.

# PARDY PREP

**NO MATTER WHAT THE OCCASION, EVERY KITTEN LOVES TO PARDY, SO WHY NOT HOST YOUR VERY OWN? TO MAKE SURE THAT YOUR PARDY IS ONE TO REMEMBER, FOLLOW OUR CANDY KITTEN TIPS AND PLAN WELL IN ADVANCE.**

Begin your pardy planning by creating the perfect guest list with all your favourite bois and girls. You want to make sure everyone has a super-fun time, so no pardy poopers allowed! Once you've compiled your exclusive list, get creative by making your very own invitations and hand deliver them for a more personal touch.

Every kitten's pardy needs a sweet and stylish food selection - choose your favourites from this book. Take the time to display your Candy Kittens treats to look inviting - presentation is the key, so get creative and think up some unusual ways to serve your food. Kittens on Sticks (see pages 44-47), Eton Mess Cupcakes (see pages 52-53) and White Chocolate, Raspberry and Candy Kittens Bark (see pages 20-21) are just a few of Jamie's pardy favourites.

To complete your pardy scene, prepare the perfect playlist. Whether you choose a selection of fun current hits or cool classics, ensure your playlist is upbeat and easy to pardy to. Kitten dancing is a must!

# Coconut ices

The freeze-dried raspberries in the pink layers are optional, but they add a real flavour kick. You can find them in health food shops, online and in some supermarkets.

## MAKES ABOUT 24

400g icing sugar, sifted
380g sweetened condensed milk
340g unsweetened desiccated coconut
pink food colouring gel
2 tbsp crushed or powdered freeze-dried raspberries (optional)
1 tsp vanilla extract

Line a 20cm square baking tin or other container with nonstick baking paper. Place the icing sugar and condensed milk in a bowl and mix well. Stir in the coconut, then spoon about half the mixture into a second bowl. Colour one bowl of mixture with a few drops of pink food colouring and stir in the freeze-dried raspberries, if using. Stir the vanilla extract into the other bowl.

Spoon half the pink mixture into the lined tin, flattening out evenly. Cover with the white mixture, again pressing down firmly. Finish with an even layer of the remaining pink mixture. Press the whole lot down firmly and leave to set for about 2 hours. Cut into squares and store in an airtight container in the refrigerator for up to 2–3 weeks.

# Sour watermelon jelly diamonds

Don't worry if the watermelon jelly doesn't set straight away: it will take 12 hours for the mixture to settle and set firmly, so you'll need to start this recipe at least a day ahead.

## MAKES ABOUT 35

20 gelatine leaves
1kg watermelon
450g caster sugar
250ml liquid pectin
3 tsp citric acid
4 tbsp granulated sugar (optional)

Line a 20cm square baking tin or other container with clingfilm, overlapping the sheets to make a smooth lining. Place the gelatine in a small bowl with plenty of cold water and set aside to soften.

Remove the skin and as many seeds as possible from the watermelon, then whizz in a blender or food processor to a smooth juice. Pass through a sieve and measure out 550ml of the juice.

Place the measured juice in a large saucepan with the caster sugar. Heat gently until the sugar has dissolved, then add the pectin and citric acid, bring to the boil and simmer for 8–10 minutes until thick and syrupy. Squeeze the excess water from the softened gelatine with your hands and add to the pan. Stir for a few seconds until the gelatine has dissolved, then remove from the heat and pour the liquid through a sieve into a jug. Pour into the lined tin and set aside in a cool place for at least 12 hours to set the jelly firmly.

Slice the set jelly into diamond shapes with a sharp knife dipped in hot water. Roll the jellies in granulated sugar, if liked. Store uncoated jellies in an airtight container in the refrigerator for up to 2 weeks. Once coated with sugar, eat within 1–2 hours.

# Salted caramel sweets

Add neon ribbon and wrapping paper to make these melt-in-your-mouth sweets a BEAUT gift for all your friends.

## MAKES ABOUT 50

.........................................................................

sunflower oil, for brushing
450g caster sugar
320g golden syrup
480ml double cream
75g butter, cubed
1 tsp vanilla extract
1/2 tsp salt
sea salt flakes, for sprinkling
cellophane and ribbon, for wrapping

.........................................................................

Line a 20cm square baking tin or other container with nonstick baking paper and brush with oil.

Place the sugar, golden syrup, cream and butter in a large, heavy-based saucepan over a low heat and stir occasionally until the sugar has completely dissolved. Turn up the heat, bring to the boil, stirring occasionally, and bubble until the mixture reaches 121°C (hard ball stage) on a sugar thermometer (see page 11).

Remove the pan from the heat, add the vanilla extract and salt and pour the caramel into the prepared tin. Leave to set completely in a cool place for at least 6 hours before slicing into small cubes or bars.

Sprinkle a flake or two of sea salt on to each sweet before wrapping in pieces of cellophane and tying the ends with ribbon. Store in an airtight container for up to 2 weeks.

# JAMIE'S LINGO

### PARDY
Jamie loves nothing more than going out with his bois and his kittens to PARDY!

### WHAA
A fun way to describe something or someone Jamie would find super cute.

### YEA BOI!
Jamie's signature phrase. You will always hear Jamie say this when he answers his phone.

### BEAUT
Jamie's favourite way to describe something he loves. A great way to describe all your delicious PARDY treats.

### SW3ET DREAMS
The Candy Kittens tag line; SW3ET DREAMS incorporates the Chelsea postcode SW3.

# Popping candy popcorn clusters

**This twist on popcorn is a complete PARDY in your mouth. Order in the films and add a bit of fizz to a great night in.**

## MAKES ABOUT 15

40 toffee sweets, wrappers removed
3 tablespoons water
⅛ tsp salt
4 tablespoons sunflower oil
150g popping corn
4 tbsp popping candy

Melt the toffees with the water in a heavy-based saucepan over a low heat, stirring gently to form a sauce. Add the salt.

Place the oil in a large saucepan with a lid over a medium-high heat. Add the corn and swirl the pan to coat the kernels with oil. Cover, turn down the heat and wait for the kernels to pop. Once the popping has slowed, remove the pan from the heat but keep the lid on.

Tip the hot popcorn into a large bowl, leaving any kernels that have not popped in the bottom of the pan. Pour the toffee mixture over the popcorn, add the popping candy and quickly mix with a spoon. Press the corn into balls a little bigger than a golf ball and then pile into popcorn boxes or tubs, or arrange on a plate. Eat warm or cold. Store in an airtight container for up to 2 days.

# Chocolate toffee popcorn

Here at Candy Kitten Head Office we think there's no such thing as too much chocolate. Go all out with this tasty, crunchy mash up.

## SERVES 3-4

3 tbsp sunflower oil
100g popping corn
50g butter
50g light soft brown sugar
3 tbsp golden syrup
¼ tsp salt
100g plain dark or milk chocolate, chopped

Place the oil in a large saucepan with a lid over a medium-high heat. Add the corn and swirl the pan to coat the kernels with oil. Cover, turn down the heat and wait for the kernels to pop. Once the popping has slowed, remove the pan from the heat but keep the lid on.

In a separate saucepan, melt the butter, sugar, golden syrup and salt over a medium heat. Bring to the boil and bubble for 1–2 minutes.

Meanwhile, melt the chocolate in a heatproof bowl set over a saucepan of gently simmering water, making sure the water does not touch the bowl.

Tip the hot popcorn into a large bowl, leaving any kernels that have not popped in the bottom of the pan. Pour the toffee mixture over the popcorn and quickly mix with a spoon.

Spread the popcorn out on a tray and use a spoon to drizzle thin streams of melted chocolate in a crisscross pattern over the corn. Serve straight away or leave to cool and harden. Store in an airtight container for up to 2 days.

# Butterscotch toffee apples

YEA BOI! You're never too old to enjoy toffee apples. Try these with cinnamon sticks for something a little different.

### MAKES 8

.....................................................................................................

sunflower oil, for brushing
8 crisp apples
8 clean short sticks or cinnamon sticks
360g light soft brown sugar
100ml water
40g butter
2¹/₂ tbsp golden syrup
2 tsp white wine vinegar

.....................................................................................................

Line a baking sheet with nonstick baking paper and brush with oil. Scrub the apples in hot water to remove the wax coating, then insert a clean short stick or cinnamon stick firmly into the stalk end of each apple.

Place the sugar and water in a medium saucepan over a low heat and stir occasionally until the sugar has completely dissolved. Turn up the heat, then add the butter, golden syrup and vinegar, swirl the pan (don't stir) and bring to the boil. Boil steadily for 15–20 minutes until the mixture reaches 138°C (soft crack stage) on a sugar thermometer (see page 11).

Working quickly, hold an apple by the stick and dip it in the caramel, swirling to coat completely. Transfer to the lined baking sheet and leave to set while you dip the remaining apples. Leave the toffee apples in a cool place to set for 20 minutes. Serve immediately, or wrap in cellophane and store in a cool place for up to 2 days.

# Marshmallow fluff

This delicious fluff can be served with little spoons as a naughty dessert, or with biscuits for dipping as a sweet treat. You can even spread it on toast!

## SERVES 2-4

......................................................................

165g granulated sugar
165g golden syrup
¼ tsp salt
60ml water
2 large egg whites, at room temperature
¼ tsp cream of tartar
1½ tsp vanilla extract
food colouring gel (optional)

......................................................................

Place the sugar, golden syrup, salt and water in a medium saucepan over a low heat and stir occasionally until the sugar has completely dissolved. Turn up the heat, bring to the boil, stirring occasionally, and bubble until the mixture reaches 115°C (soft ball stage) on a sugar thermometer (see page 11).

Meanwhile, use an electric whisk to whisk the egg whites and cream of tartar until soft peaks form. When the syrup has reached 115°C, continue whisking the egg whites on low speed while you trickle the syrup into the bowl until it has all been incorporated. Add the vanilla extract and continue to whisk on high speed for about 7 minutes until the mixture is cool and thick.

Stir in a few drops of food colouring, if liked, to colour the fluff, then serve immediately or store in small jars with lids in the refrigerator for up to 2 weeks.

# Chocolate-dipped honeycomb bites

Perfect for sleepovers! Gather round, choose your favourite chocolate and get dipping with these crunchy bites. SW3ET DREAMS!

## MAKES ABOUT 25

300g caster sugar
150g golden syrup
¼ tsp cream of tartar
75ml water
1½ tsp bicarbonate of soda
100g white chocolate, chopped
100g milk chocolate, chopped
100g plain dark chocolate, chopped

Line a 20cm square tin with nonstick baking paper. Place the sugar, golden syrup, cream of tartar and water in a medium saucepan over a low heat and stir occasionally until the sugar has completely dissolved. Turn up the heat, bring to the boil, swirling the pan occasionally (don't stir), and bubble until the mixture reaches 154°C (hard crack stage) on a sugar thermometer (see page 11). Meanwhile, run about 5cm of cold water into the sink, and crush the bicarbonate of soda with the back of a spoon to remove any lumps.

Place the pan in the sink (the water should reach partway up the sides) and immediately whisk in the bicarbonate of soda, scraping right down to the base. The toffee will foam up straight away. Carefully pour it into the lined tin and leave to cool for at least an hour, then smash or cut the honeycomb into pieces.

Melt the 3 chocolates separately in 3 heatproof bowls set over a saucepan of gently simmering water, making sure the water does not touch the bowls. Half or fully dip the honeycomb pieces in the melted chocolate, waiting for the excess to drip back into the bowl, then transfer to a wire rack. Put a little of each melted chocolate into separate plastic food bags, snip off a tiny corner of each bag and use to drizzle the honeycomb pieces with chocolate of a contrasting colour. Leave to set in a cool place for at least 30 minutes. Store in an airtight container in a cool place for up to 5 days.

# KITTEN CAKES

# Kittens on sticks

These cute kitty cake-pops are fiddly to make but well worth the effort.
Candy melts, cake pop sticks and sugar decorations are easy to find online,
or in specialist cake-decorating shops.

## MAKES ABOUT 20

150g butter, cubed, plus extra for greasing
150g plain dark chocolate
95ml water
65g self-raising flour
65g plain flour
pinch of bicarbonate of soda
150g light soft brown sugar
150g golden caster sugar
20g cocoa powder
2 eggs
60ml buttermilk
800g candy melts, in a number of different colours
black edible food pen
small sugar decorations
small tube of ready-made icing
20 cake pop sticks
large block of polystyrene
ribbon

### Chocolate icing
200g icing sugar
15g cocoa powder
50g butter, melted
1 tsp vanilla extract
2-4 tbsp milk

Preheat the oven to 160°C, fan 140°C, gas mark 3, grease a deep 23cm round cake tin and line the base and sides with nonstick baking paper. Place the butter, chocolate and water in a small saucepan over a very low heat until melted. Set aside to cool slightly.

Combine the flours, bicarbonate of soda, sugars and cocoa in a large mixing bowl. Whisk the eggs and the buttermilk together in a separate bowl until smooth. Add the chocolate mixture and egg mixture to the flour mixture and stir with a wooden spoon to form a smooth batter. Pour into the tin, smooth the top and bake for about 50 minutes until well risen and a skewer inserted into the centre comes out clean. Turn out on to a wire rack, peel the paper away and leave to cool completely.

Meanwhile, make the icing. Sift the icing sugar and cocoa into a mixing bowl. Pour in the melted butter and vanilla extract and then mix with a wooden spoon, adding enough milk to reach a light, fluffy consistency. Cover with clingfilm and set aside at room temperature until needed.

Chop the cooled cake into rough chunks, then blitz to fine crumbs in a food processor. Add the crumbs to the chocolate icing and mix thoroughly. Divide the mixture into 30g portions. Roll each into an even ball between your palms. Use the remaining mixture to make 2 pointed ears for each cat and smooth them firmly into place. Spread the kitties out on baking sheets lined with nonstick baking paper and freeze for 1 hour to firm up.

Melt the candy melts in a heatproof bowl set over a saucepan of gently simmering water, making sure the water does not touch the bowl, stirring occasionally until smooth. Dip the end of a cake pop stick into the liquid and insert about halfway into the base of a cat's head. Repeat with the remaining sticks and heads and return to the freezer for about 15 minutes to set.

If the candy melts in the bowl harden in the meantime, reheat in the same way as before to melt. Holding a cake pop by the stick, dip it into the liquid candy melts, turning to coat generously. Gently tap the stick on the side of the bowl, with your chosen 'face' side upwards, so the candy runs off evenly to form a smooth surface. Wait until any drips have subsided, then firmly plant the stick into a large block

of polystyrene. Repeat with the remaining cats and leave to set for 1 hour. Any leftover candy melts can be allowed to harden, then melted and reused in another recipe.

Use a black edible food pen to draw pupils on small round or almond-shaped sugar decorations to make eyes, and stick them in place with the tube of icing. Add mouths using small sugar hearts or other shapes and then use the edible food pen to draw on whiskers. Finally, tie ribbon in a bow around each stick. Store in a cool, dry place for up to 3–4 days.

# Jam tart pops

The Queen of Hearts is back in Chelsea. And this time she's brought a contemporary twist to her famous tarts.

## MAKES ABOUT 12

375g ready-made all-butter shortcrust pastry
120g jam, such as strawberry, cherry, blueberry or peach
1 egg yolk
1 tbsp milk
12 heatproof lolly sticks
whipped cream, to serve

Line 2 large baking sheets with nonstick baking paper. Roll out half the pastry between 2 sheets of nonstick baking paper to 4mm thick. Use a 6cm biscuit cutter to stamp out 12 rounds for the tart backs. Arrange on the lined sheets. Press a lolly stick on to each, overlapping the pastry by at least 2cm, then chill.

Roll out the remaining pastry and stamp out 12 more rounds for the fronts of the tarts. Stamp out heart or star shapes from some fronts to make windows. Use a 5cm cutter to cut the centres out of the remaining fronts to leave a thin ring of pastry. Chill all the fronts and pastry trimmings for at least 20 minutes.

Spoon a heaped teaspoon of jam on to each tart back, covering the stick but leaving a 5mm border all round the edge. Mix the egg yolk and milk and use to brush the borders. Arrange the pastry fronts with windows on to the backs, pressing gently but firmly all round the edges to seal, especially around the sticks. To make a lattice pattern, cut some thin strips from the pastry trimmings, weave them over and under each other on the tarts and trim the edges. Lay the pastry rings on top and press gently but firmly into place to seal.

Brush the fronts of the tarts with the egg yolk mixture and chill for another 20 minutes. Meanwhile, preheat the oven to 180°C, fan 160°C, gas mark 4.

Bake for about 20 minutes until golden brown. Cool completely on the sheets. Serve with whipped cream for dipping. Best eaten immediately, but can be stored in an airtight container in the refrigerator for up to 3 days. Refresh in the oven preheated as before for 5–7 minutes and cool on the sheets.

# THE PERFECT OUTFIT

**THE SCENE IS SET AND YOUR FRIENDS ARE GETTING EXCITED WAITING FOR A CANDY KITTENS PARDY TO REMEMBER. NOW ALL THAT'S LEFT IS TO MAKE SURE THAT YOU'RE LOOKING BEAUT!**

In summer you could make an impression with a playful summer dress teamed with a pair of simple sandals. Alternatively, go for a more laid-back look with a stylish skirt or shorts and an elegant summery top. If going for more of a winter wonderland theme, try to create a memorable look with the perfect seasonal colours. Deep reds and fabulous festive shades are a great way to invent a show-stopping outfit. Add some sparkle with pretty sequins or statement accessories.

Follow the Kittens' top five outfit essentials and you can't go wrong:

**Sequined clutch** - The perfect way to bring any outfit alive

**Statement heels** - Just make sure you're able to pardy in them!

**Classic black dress** - Simple, elegant and essential for any occasion

**Beautiful bling** - Jewels to give your look an element of class

**Cute cami** - Be it a bold bright or classy black look, team your cami with a pair of skinnies for simple and stylish glamour!

If you're still struggling to decide on your PARDY outfit, just remember that Jamie loves a girl with fun, fabulous and individual style, so just be yourself!

# Eton Mess cupcakes

If you can't find freeze-dried strawberries to decorate the cupcakes, use slices of fresh strawberry, but add them at the very last minute to prevent the juice running.

## MAKES 12

110g butter, softened
110g caster sugar
2 eggs, lightly beaten
1 tsp vanilla extract
110g self-raising flour
1-2 tbsp milk, at room temperature
20g freeze-dried strawberries, sliced
2 small ready-made meringues nests, crumbled
4 tbsp ready-made strawberry or raspberry syrup

### Strawberry compote
400g strawberries, hulled and quartered
150g caster sugar

### Icing
3 egg whites
200g caster sugar
225g unsalted butter, softened
1½ tsp vanilla extract

To make the compote, place the strawberries and sugar in a saucepan and simmer over a medium heat, stirring often, for 5–10 minutes until the mixture is bubbling and jammy. Set aside to cool.

Preheat the oven to 180°C, fan 160°C, gas mark 4, and line a 12-hole muffin tin with paper cases. To make the cakes, beat the butter and sugar together in a large mixing bowl using a wooden spoon for 5 minutes until very light and fluffy. Beat in the eggs, half at a time, beating very well between each addition, then add the vanilla extract. Add the flour and milk and combine with a spatula to make a smooth batter.

Divide the batter between the paper cases; they should be just over half full. Bake for 10–15 minutes until golden brown and springy on top. Cool in the tin for a few minutes, then turn out on to a wire rack to cool completely.

To make the icing, place the egg whites and sugar in a heatproof bowl, mix well and set over a saucepan of gently simmering water, making sure the water does not touch the bowl. Heat until the mixture reaches 60°C on a sugar thermometer, or feels hot to the touch. Remove from the heat and immediately use an electric whisk to whisk the egg white mixture at high speed for 5–10 minutes until stiff peaks form. Continue whisking at medium speed, adding the butter teaspoonful by teaspoonful, until it has all been incorporated. If the mixture begins to separate, keep beating until it comes back together. Whisk in the vanilla extract, then transfer the mixture to a piping bag fitted with a 1cm round nozzle.

Use a small knife to cut a round hole in the centre of each cake, about 2cm across and 3cm deep, reserving the 'plugs'. Drop a little compote into each hole, then replace the plugs to seal. Pipe the icing generously on the cakes and top with freeze-dried strawberry slices, crumbled meringue and a drizzle of syrup.
    Store in an airtight container for up to 2 days.

# Candy Kittens cupcakes

A Candy Kitten should have their own sense of style. Express yourself with a whole spread of cupcakes in your favourite colours. You could use an edible writing pen to make signature Candy Kitten cupcakes with our logo drawn on a chocolate button or get creative with your own lingo. Let me know how they turn out!

**MAKES ABOUT 12**

125g butter, softened
125g caster sugar
2 large eggs, lightly beaten
1 tsp vanilla extract
125g self-raising flour
2 tbsp milk, at room temperature
12 white chocolate buttons

**Buttercream icing**
200g butter, softened
400g icing sugar, sifted
3 tbsp milk, at room temperature
food colouring gels

Preheat the oven to 180°C, fan 160°C, gas mark 4, and line a 12-hole muffin tin with paper cases. Beat the butter and sugar together in a large mixing bowl using a wooden spoon for 5 minutes until very light and fluffy. Beat in the eggs, half at a time, beating very well between each addition, then add the vanilla extract. Add the flour and milk and combine with a spatula to make a smooth batter.

Divide the batter between the paper cases; they should be just over half full. Bake for 10–15 minutes until golden brown and springy on top. Cool in the tin for a few minutes, then turn out on to a wire rack to cool completely.

To make the icing, beat the butter in a large mixing bowl until really light. Add the icing sugar and beat very slowly until it has all been incorporated. Add the milk and beat vigorously until smooth. Divide the icing into a number of small bowls and beat a different food colouring into each.

Use a palette knife to spread and swirl a thick cap of icing on to each cupcake. Finish by pressing a chocolate button on to the centre of each cake. Store in an airtight container for up to 2 days.

# Jam doughnut muffins

These tempting vanilla muffins are filled with oozing jam and rolled in cinnamon sugar for extra crunch. Best served warm.

## MAKES 12

.....................................................

300g plain flour
1 tbsp baking powder
200g caster sugar
pinch of salt
2 eggs
125ml sunflower oil, plus extra for greasing
2 tsp vanilla extract
120ml vanilla yogurt
12 tsp strawberry or cherry jam
125g granulated sugar
1½ tsp ground cinnamon
100g unsalted butter, melted

.....................................................

Preheat the oven to 190°C, fan 170°C, gas mark 5, and grease a 12-hole muffin tin. Sift the flour and baking powder into a large mixing bowl and stir in the caster sugar and salt. In a separate mixing bowl, whisk the eggs and oil together, then whisk in the vanilla extract and yogurt.

Add the wet ingredients to the dry ingredients and mix quickly to just combine everything. Don't worry about a few lumps, and don't overmix or the muffins will be tough.

Drop a heaped teaspoonful of batter into each hole in the muffin tin, add a teaspoonful of jam on top and then cover with the remaining batter. Bake for 15–17 minutes until golden brown, well risen and springy when lightly touched. Meanwhile, mix the granulated sugar and cinnamon together in a wide, shallow bowl.

When the muffins have been out of the oven for 5 minutes, carefully tip them out of the tin, brush all over with the melted butter and then roll in the cinnamon sugar to coat. Allow to cool for another 10 minutes before serving, as the jam will be hot. Best served warm, but can be stored in an airtight container for up to 2 days.

# Peanut Rice Krispies squares

**These snacks are so simple to make that you can spend all your time eating peanut butter out of the jar. We all do that, right?**

## MAKES ABOUT 16

. . . . . . . . . . . . . . . . . . . . . . . . . . . . . . . . . . . . . . . . . . . . . . . . . . . . . . . . . . . . . . . . . . . . . . . . .

75g butter
250g mini marshmallows
150g crunchy or smooth peanut butter
1¹/₂ tsp vanilla extract
130g Rice Krispies

. . . . . . . . . . . . . . . . . . . . . . . . . . . . . . . . . . . . . . . . . . . . . . . . . . . . . . . . . . . . . . . . . . . . . . . . .

Line a 20x30cm baking tin or other container with nonstick baking paper.

Melt the butter in a large saucepan over a low heat. Add 200g of the mini marshmallows and stir until melted. Remove from the heat and stir in the peanut butter and vanilla extract until smooth.

Add the Rice Krispies and remaining marshmallows and mix well. Quickly pour into the lined tin and press into an even layer, using a piece of baking paper to protect your hands from the heat. Leave to set for at least 2 hours before cutting into squares. Store in an airtight container for up to 5 days.

# ... *try these extra flavours*

Instead of Rice Krispies, try Coco Pops for a chocolate fix or Cheerios for extra colour.

...................................................................................

Not keen on peanuts? Skip the peanut butter and add a different nut butter of your choice.

...................................................................................

For special occasions, add your choice of sprinkles to the top of the mixture before leaving it to set.

...................................................................................

Try substituting chocolate spread for peanut butter, and adding a handful of chocolate chips at the same time as the Rice Krispies.

...................................................................................

Squares just too... square? Use a shaped cookie cutter to create shapes of your choice from the cooled, set mixture.

# Strawberry-vanilla rainbow cake

With its six layers, this spectacular cake is a lot of fun to make, but it does take time. The sponges can be made a day ahead if kept well wrapped in clingfilm; the icing can be made up to four days ahead and should be stored in the refrigerator.

## SERVES 20

450g butter, softened, plus extra for greasing
450g caster sugar
8 large eggs
4 tsp vanilla extract
450g self-raising flour
4 tsp baking powder
red or pink food colouring gel
400g good-quality strawberry jam
600g strawberries, hulled and sliced, plus a few left whole to decorate

### Vanilla cream cheese icing
250g unsalted butter, softened
600g cream cheese, at room temperature
2 tsp vanilla extract
450g icing sugar, sifted

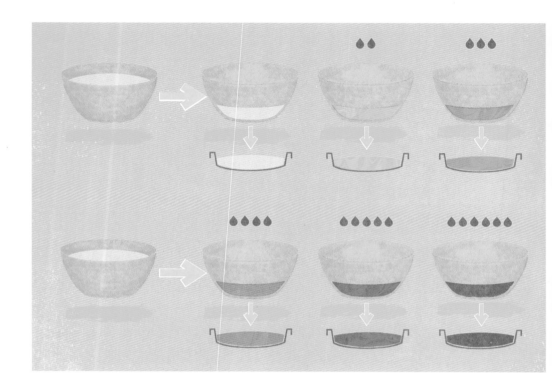

Preheat the oven to 180°C, fan 160°C, gas mark 4, and grease and line 3 sandwich tins, 19cm across.

Make and bake the sponge in 2 batches. Beat half the butter and half the caster sugar in a large mixing bowl using a wooden spoon for 5 minutes until very light and fluffy. Beat in half the eggs, one at a time, beating very well between each addition, then add half the vanilla extract. Add half the flour and half the baking powder and combine with a spatula to make a thick batter.

Scrape one-third of the cake batter into one of the prepared tins, leave one-third in the bowl and transfer the remaining third to a second bowl. Add 1–2 drops of food colouring to one bowl of batter and

3–4 drops to the second bowl. Mix both batters well and scrape into the 2 remaining prepared tins.

Bake on the middle oven shelf for 20 minutes until risen and springy when lightly pressed. Turn out, peel the paper away and leave to cool completely on wire racks.

Make a second batch of cake batter in the same way, then divide the batter between 3 bowls and colour each batch successively darker, finishing with a really strong colour. Bake and cool the cakes as before.

To make the icing, beat the butter and cream cheese in a food processor using the paddle attachment for about 4 minutes, scraping down the sides from time to time. Add the vanilla extract, then turn the

speed down very low and add the icing sugar, a little at a time, until it has all been incorporated. Turn the speed up for the last few seconds to give it a good whip. Transfer to a bowl, cover and chill to firm up.

To assemble the cake, place the most deeply coloured cake, flat-side up, on a serving plate and then tuck strips of baking paper under the edges to prevent the icing from getting on the plate. Spread the cake with a layer of icing, followed by a layer of jam, leaving a 2cm border around the edges of the jam. Scatter with a few sliced strawberries and top with the next-darkest cake, flat-side up, as before. Repeat this filling and stacking until you have used all the cakes, leaving the top of the top cake plain.

Spread a thin layer of icing over the top and down the sides of the cake with a palette knife, to catch any crumbs and stray jam. Leave to set for 10 minutes.

Then use the palette knife to sweep the remaining icing all over the cake, taking your time to create a smooth finish. Carefully remove the paper strips at the base and top the cake with a few whole strawberries. Keep in a cool place for up to 3–4 hours until ready to serve.

# YEA BOI! BISCUITS

# Candy Kittens jammy dodgers

These biscuits are very easy to make, but take a bit of time, simply because the dough has to be chilled to help the biscuits keep their shape when baked. But they're worth it just for their cute kitten jam filling shape.

## MAKES ABOUT 16, PLUS TRIMMINGS

175g unsalted butter, softened
200g golden caster sugar
2 large eggs
1 tsp vanilla extract
425g plain flour, plus extra for dusting
1 tsp baking powder
3/4 tsp salt
7 tbsp seedless raspberry or strawberry jam
icing sugar, for dusting

Beat the butter and sugar together in a large mixing bowl using a wooden spoon until pale. Beat in the eggs and vanilla extract. Sift the flour, baking powder and salt into a separate mixing bowl. Add to the butter and egg mixture and mix gently to make a soft dough. Divide the dough into quarters, then form into 4 flat discs, wrap in clingfilm and chill in the refrigerator for 30 minutes–1 hour.

Line 2 large baking sheets with nonstick baking paper. Roll out the dough, one portion at a time and keeping the other portions in the refrigerator until needed, on a generously floured work surface to 5mm thick. Use a 7.5cm biscuit cutter to cut out about 32 rounds, dipping the cutter in flour to prevent sticking. Transfer the biscuits to the lined baking sheets with a palette knife, spacing them well apart.

Use a 6cm biscuit cutter to stamp circles out of the centres of half the biscuits, then use a small sharp knife to cut out cat ears. Transfer the cut-out trimmings to a baking sheet to be baked too. Chill in the refrigerator for 10 minutes to prevent the biscuits spreading in the oven. Meanwhile, preheat the oven to 180°C, fan 160°C, gas mark 4.

Bake the biscuits for 8–10 minutes until lightly golden. Leave to cool on the baking sheets for a few minutes, then transfer to wire racks to cool completely.

Spread each biscuit base with jam, making sure most of it is in the centre with just a thin covering at the edges. Gently press the cat biscuits on top and dust with a little icing sugar. Store the filled biscuits in an airtight container in a cool place for up to 4 days.

# Gingerbread Chelsea townhouse

OMG! This is a complete show-stopper. Who thought decorating windows and doors could be so much fun? We've drawn a handy template on the following page to help you assemble this fancy house fit for SW3.

## MAKES 1 LARGE HOUSE

750g plain flour, plus extra for dusting
1 tsp baking powder
2 tsp ground ginger
1 tsp ground mixed spice
250g butter
½ tsp salt
150g light soft brown sugar
320g black treacle or golden syrup
500g instant royal icing sugar
3½-4 tablespoons water

### To decorate
tubes of ready-made icing in different colours
edible pearl lustre powder (optional)
edible glitter (optional)
small sweets and sugar decorations, such as milk bottles and flowers
yellow food colouring gel

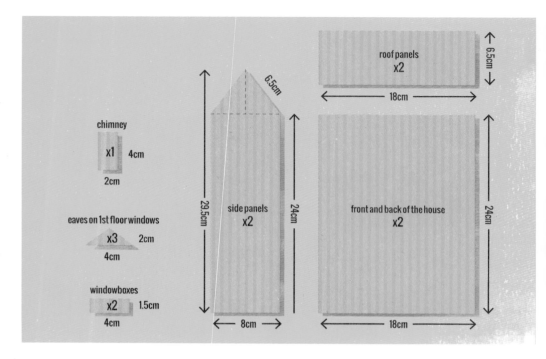

roof panels
x2

↕ 6.5cm

← 18cm →

chimney

x1  4cm

2cm

6.5cm

29.5cm

24cm

side panels
x2

front and back of the house
x2

24cm

eaves on 1st floor windows

x3  2cm

4cm

windowboxes

x2  1.5cm

4cm

← 8cm →

← 18cm →

Start by making templates for the pieces of the house out of thin card, following the illustrations above.

Preheat the oven to 180°C, fan 160°C, gas mark 4, and line 2 or 3 large baking sheets with nonstick baking paper. Sift the flour, baking powder, ginger and mixed spice into a large mixing bowl. Melt the butter with the salt, brown sugar and black treacle or golden syrup in a heavy-based saucepan over a low heat. Stir until smooth, then pour over the dry ingredients and mix vigorously with a wooden spoon until a dough forms.

Roll out the dough on a lightly floured work surface to about 1cm thick. Using a sharp knife, cut around the templates to create 2 roof panels, 2 gable ends, 2 rectangles for the front and back panels, 1 chimney, 2 window boxes and 3 triangles for the window eaves. If liked, stamp out 2 small trees using biscuit cutters.

Transfer all the pieces to the baking sheets, well spaced apart (working in 2 batches if the pieces won't all fit on your baking sheets). Use a sharp knife to cut a door out of the front panel, turn it over and place on one of the baking sheets. Bake for 12–15 minutes until the pieces are turning darker around the edges. Leave to cool on the baking sheets for 5 minutes before transferring to wire racks to cool completely.

Meanwhile, make the icing. Sift the royal icing sugar into a large mixing bowl and add enough of the water to form a thick paste. Use an electric whisk to whisk the mixture for about 8 minutes until stiff peaks form. Transfer half the mixture to a piping bag fitted with a small round or fluted nozzle. Lay a piece of clingfilm directly over the surface of the remaining royal icing to prevent it drying out.

Use the icing as glue to stick the 2 gable ends of the house to the back panel in a U-shape, working on the serving board or plate. If necessary, use unopened food cans to hold the panels upright and together for a few minutes until the icing dries.

Meanwhile, lay the front panel on the work surface and decorate it using the tubes of icing to pipe the window outlines and other features, following the photograph on page xx as a guide. Use a soft brush to dust the house with edible pearl lustre powder and use edible glitter to make the windows shine, if liked. The house can be as tasteful or as colourful as you wish.

Next, using the royal icing as glue again, stick in place the window boxes below the ground floor windows, the eaves above the first floor windows and the 2 trees, then decorate them with the tubes of icing. Add the final touches with milk bottles and sugar flowers, then leave to harden.

When the decoration has dried on the front panel, pipe royal icing up the 2 sides and press into place on the house. Hold in place for a minute or so and then leave to dry for a few minutes before continuing. Pipe royal icing along the top edges of all 4 walls, then stick the roof panels in place and the chimney on one side. Stick the front door in place, leaving it slightly ajar. Again, leave to dry for a few minutes before proceeding.

Colour the remaining royal icing in the bowl with a little yellow food colouring, then transfer to a new piping bag fitted with a star-shaped nozzle. Use to pipe waves or loops of icing over the roof and down the corners of the building to look like tiles, then leave to dry. Store in a cool place for up to 2 days.

# Candy glass biscuits

These biscuits look AMAZING when they catch the light. Choose brightly coloured ribbon and hang in the windows of your PARDY venue for a decorative treat.

## MAKES ABOUT 16

85g butter, softened
100g caster sugar
1 large egg
1 tsp vanilla extract
210g plain flour, plus extra for dusting
1/2 tsp baking powder
1/4 tsp salt
100g hard boiled sweets, in a number of different colours
ribbon or twine, for hanging

Beat the butter and sugar together in a large mixing bowl using a wooden spoon until pale. Beat in the egg and vanilla extract. Sift the flour, baking powder and salt into a separate mixing bowl, then add to the butter and egg mixture and mix gently to make a soft dough. Form into a flat disc, wrap in clingfilm and chill in the refrigerator for 30 minutes–1 hour.

Line 2 large baking sheets with nonstick baking paper. Roll out the dough on a generously floured work surface to 5mm thick. Use shaped biscuit cutters about 6cm across to cut out biscuits, dipping the cutters in flour to prevent sticking. Transfer the biscuits to the lined baking sheets with a palette knife, spacing them well apart. Use a screw-top bottle lid to stamp circles out of the centres of the biscuits. Chill in the refrigerator for 10 minutes to prevent the biscuits spreading in the oven. Meanwhile, preheat the oven to 180°C, fan 160°C, gas mark 4.

Bake the biscuits for 6 minutes until not quite cooked. Meanwhile, place the boiled sweets in a plastic bag and crush with a rolling pin, keeping the colours separate. Remove the biscuits from the oven and fill the holes with crushed sweets. Return to the oven and cook for another 2–3 minutes until the sweets have melted and the biscuits are lightly golden.

While the biscuits are still hot, use a round lolly stick or skewer to make a small hole in each. Leave to cool on the baking sheets. When cold, carefully thread with ribbon or twine and hang where the light will shine through them. Store in an airtight container for up to 5 days.

# GET THE LOOK

### KEY KITTEN STYLES TO MAKE YOU LOOK AS WHAA! AS POSSIBLE.

### CLASSIC KITTEN

Every perfect pardy face begins with a flawless base. A liquid or cream foundation is a great way to hide any blemishes and tired eyes, with a pink blush or bronzer to brighten your natural skin tone. Whichever look you choose, it's always good to finish with striking black lashes, kitten style. Finally, go for a simple up hairdo such as a cute pony and a French manicure for a clean polished finish.

### CHIC KITTEN

Start with the classic make-up base. Add flirty eyeliner flicks to the eyes and rouge the lips. For super chic hair you could try a top knot or ballerina bun. Update a French manicure with bright, eye-catching shades for your nail tips.

### PLAYFUL KITTEN

Follow the make-up as above, but use shimmer or glitter-based eye shadows and leave your hair in relaxed waves. Channel a pretty, girly feel with subtle pastel nail colours. Think candy pinks, sky blues and sunshine yellows for a subtle summer style. You could also add a touch of sparkle with a coat of glitter.

### GLAMOUR KITTEN

Extend lashes with lengthening mascara, using eyelash curlers before application. Fake lashes are essential for evening events! Powerful straightened locks are great or for a more effortless finish leave your hair down with some tussled waves. You can always add volume for extra glamour in the evening. For your nails, choose bold block tones such as dark reds, deep purples and edgy black.

# Trillionaire's shortbread

A chocolaty base, a rich and easy caramel layer and a topping of three different types of chocolate swirled together take this version of millionaire's shortbread up a few notches.

## MAKES 18

| | **Caramel layer** | **Topping** |
|---|---|---|
| 225g plain flour | 100g butter, softened | 150g plain dark chocolate |
| 100g golden caster sugar | 75g light soft brown sugar | 150g white chocolate |
| 225g butter | 2 x 397g cans Carnation Caramel | 100g milk chocolate |
| 80g cornflour | or dulce de leche | 60g butter |
| 20g cocoa powder | generous pinch of salt | |
| pinch of salt | | |

Preheat the oven to 160°C, fan 140°C, gas mark 3, and line a 20x30cm baking tin with nonstick baking paper.

Pulse the flour, caster sugar, butter, cornflour, cocoa and salt together in a food processor to form a sandy dough. Press this mixture evenly over the base of the lined tin and prick all over with a fork. Bake for about 25 minutes until firm and lightly browned. Set aside to cool.

To make the caramel layer, place the butter and brown sugar in a saucepan and warm through gently until the sugar has dissolved. Add the caramel and stir until the mixture is hot and smooth but not boiling. Stir in the salt and beat until incorporated.

Pour evenly over the cooled base and leave to cool and set for about an hour.

Melt the 3 chocolates separately in 3 heatproof bowls set over a saucepan of gently simmering water, making sure the water does not touch the bowls. Stir one-third of the butter into each bowl, then spoon the melted chocolate mixtures over the caramel layer in large, alternating 'splodges'. Use a spatula or spoon handle to marble the 3 colours together. Leave to set in a cool place for at least an hour before slicing into 18 small bars. Store in an airtight container in a cool place for up to 5 days.

# Twisted candy cane biscuits

Winter wonderland festive biscuits that are great for the ski season.

## MAKES ABOUT 20

225g butter, softened
100g caster sugar
60g icing sugar
1 egg
pinch of salt
2 tsp vanilla extract
1 tsp peppermint extract
310g plain flour, plus extra for dusting
red or pink food colouring gel
50g candy canes, broken up
75g granulated sugar

Beat the butter in a large mixing bowl for 1 minute using a wooden spoon. Add the caster sugar and icing sugar and beat until light and fluffy. Beat in the egg, salt, vanilla extract and peppermint extract. Sift the flour into the bowl and mix gently to make a soft dough.

Divide the dough in half and wrap one portion in clingfilm. Add a few drops of food colouring to the remaining dough and knead until it is evenly coloured. Wrap in clingfilm and chill both portions in the refrigerator for 1 hour.

Preheat the oven to 190°C, fan 170°C, gas mark 5, and line 2 large baking sheets with nonstick baking paper.

Take a large tablespoonful of the plain dough and roll it under your fingers on a lightly floured work surface to make a cylinder about 12cm in length. Do the same with the coloured dough, then twist the two together to make a twisted rope. Roll a bit to lengthen and bind them together, then curve one end round into a cane shape and lay on one of the lined baking sheets. Repeat with the remaining dough, spacing the biscuits well apart. Bake for about 10 minutes until pale golden.

Meanwhile, blitz the candy canes and granulated sugar together in a food processor to make a fine pink powder. As soon as the biscuits come out of the oven, sprinkle the pink sugar over them, pressing gently so it sticks and melts a bit. Cool on the baking sheets for 10 minutes, then transfer to wire racks to cool completely. Store in an airtight container for up to a week.

# Mini Nutella meringue kisses

**Pucker up! These tiny treats are so cute you'll want to give them to a special someone.**

### MAKES ABOUT 14

.........................................................................................

4 large egg whites
pinch of salt
100g caster sugar
100g icing sugar
1 tsp cornflour
1 tsp white wine vinegar
1 tsp vanilla extract
100g hazelnuts, toasted and finely chopped
70g Nutella or other chocolate-hazelnut spread

.........................................................................................

Preheat the oven to 120°C, fan 100°C, gas mark ½, and line 2 large baking sheets with nonstick baking paper. Use an electric whisk to whisk the egg whites, salt and caster sugar together until stiff peaks form. Sift the icing sugar and cornflour into the bowl and continue to whisk for 3–4 minutes until the mixture is very stiff and shiny, then whisk in the vinegar and vanilla extract.

Arrange dessertspoonfuls of the meringue mixture, spacing them well apart, on the lined baking sheets, or transfer the mixture to a piping bag fitted with a 1cm round nozzle and pipe small mounds. Bake for about 45 minutes until set but hardly coloured. Leave to cool on the baking sheets.

Arrange the chopped hazelnuts on a plate. Spread a scant teaspoonful of Nutella or other chocolate-hazelnut spread on the flat side of one of the meringues, then sandwich together with another meringue. Roll the sides in the chopped hazelnuts to coat and repeat with the remaining meringues.

Store the unfilled meringues in an airtight container for up to 5 days. Once filled, eat within 24 hours.

# *Giant meringues*

These meringues are very large, but if you prefer them smaller, simply divide the mixture into 16 mounds and cook for about 1 hour. You can use a spoonful of instant coffee, ground to a powder, a little sifted cocoa or some chopped pistachios in place of the fruit if you prefer.

## MAKES 8

8 large egg whites
240g caster sugar
220g icing sugar
1 tsp cornflour
1 tsp white wine vinegar
scraped seeds from 1 vanilla pod or 2 tsp vanilla extract
red food colouring gel
4 tbsp powdered freeze-dried red fruits
ice cream or softly whipped double cream, to serve

Preheat the oven to 120°C, fan 100°C, gas mark ½, and line 2 large baking sheets with nonstick baking paper. Use an electric whisk to whisk the egg whites and caster sugar together until stiff peaks form. Sift the icing sugar and cornflour into the bowl and continue to whisk for 5 minutes until the mixture is very stiff and shiny, then whisk in the vinegar and vanilla seeds or extract.

Use a metal spoon or a spatula to marble in a few drops of food colouring and the fruit powder, barely mixing them through to create bold streaks. Spoon 8 large mounds of the meringue mixture, spacing them well apart, on the lined baking sheets, trying not to disrupt the streaks. Bake for about 1 hour 20 minutes until firm underneath but still soft and mallowy inside and hardly coloured. Leave to cool on the baking sheets. Serve with ice cream or cream.

# *Plain macarons*

These light, crisp dark chocolate macarons have a creamy white chocolate filling. You'll need to start this recipe a day, or at least a few hours, ahead to 'age' the egg whites for the perfect macarons.

## MAKES ABOUT 40

........................................................................................

144g egg whites
115g ground almonds
230g icing sugar
72g caster sugar

........................................................................................

Place the egg whites in a mixing bowl and leave uncovered for at least 4 hours, or preferably overnight. Line 3 baking sheets with silicone liners (for the flattest surface) or nonstick baking paper.

Place the ground almonds and icing sugar in a food processor and pulse in short bursts for 1–2 minutes until very fine.

Add the caster sugar to the egg whites and use an electric whisk to whisk together until stiff peaks form. Sift the almond mixture into the bowl and fold in thoroughly with a spatula or large metal spoon. After 40–45 folds, the mixture should flow slowly from the spoon like molten lava.

Transfer the mixture to a piping bag fitted with a 1cm round nozzle and pipe 3–4cm rounds, spacing them well apart, on the lined baking sheets. Rap the baking sheets sharply 4–5 times on a hard surface to dislodge any air bubbles in the macarons, then set aside in a dry room for 1–3 hours to form a skin on top. This will help create the classic bubbly 'foot' on baking. When the macarons no longer feel sticky to the touch, preheat the oven to 150°C, fan 130°C, gas mark 2.

Bake for about 15 minutes, in batches if necessary and swapping the sheets round halfway, until risen and firm but not coloured. Test to see if you can lift one cleanly off the baking sheet: if you can, they are done, but if the base gets left behind, return them to the oven for 2 minutes and then test again. Leave to cool on the baking sheets.

# Double chocolate macarons

**Super chocolatey, but super light. Make a selection of macaron flavours for a really impressive PARDY spread.**

## MAKES ABOUT 40

144g egg whites
115g ground almonds
230g icing sugar
72g caster sugar
1 tbsp cocoa powder

### White chocolate ganache
100g white chocolate, chopped
100ml double cream
5g butter
1 tsp vanilla extract

Follow the instructions on page 84 for making, baking and cooling the macarons, sifting the cocoa powder in with the almond mixture.

To make the ganache, place the chocolate in a heatproof bowl. Bring the cream and butter to the boil in a small saucepan over a medium heat, and as soon as it begins to bubble, add the vanilla extract. Pour the mixture over the chocolate and leave for 30 seconds, then stir until smooth. Cover and chill in the refrigerator for 1 hour.

To assemble, transfer the ganache to a piping bag fitted with a 1cm round nozzle and pipe a ring of ganache on the flat side of one macaron, then sandwich together with another, allowing the filling to bulge out slightly. Repeat with the remaining macarons. Serve immediately, or if you like macarons with very soft and chewy centres, place in an airtight container and chill overnight. Store in an airtight container in the refrigerator for up to 3–4 days. Once coated, store for up to 2 days only.

# Peppermint candy cane macarons

These pretty pink macarons have a white chocolate and peppermint filling.

## MAKES ABOUT 40

144g egg whites
115g ground almonds
230g icing sugar
72g caster sugar
red or pink food colouring gel

### White chocolate and candy cane filling
60g candy canes
75ml double cream
100g white chocolate, chopped
few drops of peppermint extract
40g butter, cubed

Follow the instructions on page 84 for making, baking and cooling the macarons, adding a few drops of food colouring to the whisked egg whites and whisking for another minute before sifting in the almond mixture.

To make the white chocolate and candy cane filling, place the candy canes in a plastic bag and crush with a rolling pin. Place half the crushed candy canes in a small saucepan over a medium-high heat until melted and beginning to caramelize. Heat the cream in a separate saucepan, then add to the melted candy canes and swirl the pan to mix. Add the chocolate and peppermint extract, stirring until melted, then add the butter and stir again until smooth. Cover and chill in the refrigerator for an hour to firm up.

Mix 2 tsp of the food colouring with a few drops of water to make a liquid 'paint'. Use a pastry brush to lightly swipe a streak of colour across the top of each cooked and cooled macaron, then leave to dry for a few minutes.

To assemble, transfer the filling to a piping bag fitted with a 1cm round nozzle and pipe a ring of filling on the flat side of one macaron, then sandwich together with another, allowing the filling to bulge out slightly. Repeat with the remaining macarons. If you like macarons with very soft and chewy centres, place in an airtight container and chill overnight. To serve, place the remaining crushed candy on a plate and roll the sides of the macarons in the candy to coat. Store in an airtight container in the refrigerator for up to 3–4 days. Once coated, store for up to 2 days only.

# Black raspberry macarons

For these stylish black macarons, you will need extra-strength black food colouring gel, available online or from a specialist cake-decorating shop, to get a really intense colour.

**MAKES ABOUT 40**

144g egg whites
115g ground almonds
230g icing sugar
72g caster sugar
black food colouring gel

### Raspberry filling
100g white chocolate, chopped
100g mascarpone, at room temperature
30g butter, softened
1 tbsp icing sugar, sifted
2 tbsp crushed or powdered freeze-dried raspberries

Follow the instructions on page 84 for making, baking and cooling the macarons, adding about ½ tsp of black food colouring gel to the whisked egg whites and whisking for another minute before sifting in the almond mixture.

To make the raspberry filling, melt the chopped chocolate in a heatproof bowl set over a saucepan of gently simmering water, making sure the water does not touch the bowl. Stir and set aside to cool slightly. Whisk in the mascarpone, butter, icing sugar and raspberries until well combined.

To assemble, transfer the filling to a piping bag fitted with a 1cm round nozzle and pipe a ring of filling on the flat side of one macaron, then sandwich together with another, allowing the filling to bulge out slightly. Repeat with the remaining macarons. Serve immediately, or if you like macarons with very soft and chewy centres, place in an airtight container and chill overnight. Store in an airtight container in the refrigerator for up to 3–4 days. Once coated, store for up to 2 days only.

# COOL STUFF

# Cherry and cream ice pops

The most sophisticated ice pop in town. You can use any traditional flavour combination here, but cherry and cream is so classic we can't resist.

**MAKES 8**

275g ready-made cherry compote
80g icing sugar, sifted
175g ready-made fresh vanilla custard
60ml milk
8 lolly sticks

Blend the cherry compote and 50g of the icing sugar together in a food processor until smooth. Push the mixture through a sieve with the back of a spoon to remove any lumps, then set aside. Whisk the custard, milk and remaining icing sugar together in a jug.

Divide half the cherry mixture between 8 ice lolly moulds, about 60ml each, then top with half the custard mixture. Repeat the layers to fill the moulds and then insert a lolly stick into each. Freeze the lollies for at least 4 hours, or preferably overnight.

To serve, run the outsides of the moulds under hot water for 10 seconds to release the lollies.

# Tropical ice cream sundaes

You can vary the fruits used in these sumptuous desserts: kiwis, lychees and bananas all make great additions.

## SERVES 4

2 tbsp dried coconut flakes
1 ripe mango, peeled, halved and stoned
120ml ready-made butterscotch sauce
1/2 small pineapple, peeled, cored and diced
4 large scoops of coconut or vanilla ice cream
4 large scoops of mango sorbet
140ml double cream, lightly whipped
2 tsp edible glitter (optional)
4 café curls or ice cream wafers

### Mango and passion fruit sauce
3 large passion fruit, halved
1 ripe mango, peeled, stoned and roughly chopped
3 tbsp caster sugar

To make the sauce, place the seeds and pulp from the passion fruit in a blender with the chopped mango and caster sugar and blend until smooth. Pass through a sieve to remove the bits of seed if you like, or leave them in. Cover and chill in the refrigerator for 20 minutes, or up to 3 days until needed.

Preheat the oven to 160°C, fan 140°C, gas mark 3. Spread the coconut flakes out on a baking sheet and bake for about 5 minutes until just golden at the edges. Keep an eye on them, as they burn easily. Set aside to cool.

Finely dice half the mango and slice the other half into fine wedges for decoration. Layer 4 sundae glasses or bowls with the fruit sauce, butterscotch sauce, diced pineapple and mango, coconut or vanilla ice cream and mango sorbet, alternating the layers as you like. Finish with a spoonful of whipped cream, a sprinkling of the toasted coconut flakes and a pinch of edible glitter, if liked. Stick a few mango slices and a café curl or ice cream wafer into the top of each portion and serve immediately with long spoons.

# A DAY OUT ON THE KING'S ROAD, CHELSEA

### BREAKFAST

Start your day at My Old Dutch pancake house (221 King's Road). Go for Jamie's favourite pancake, the Chocolate Sprinkles, or the Fresh Fruit Salad pancake for the more health-conscious kitten with a sweet tooth.

### SHOPPING

Once you've filled up on your pancakes you're ready to shop! First, head to Duke of York Square for staple high street brands and exclusive boutiques. From there, wander over to the Saatchi Gallery for a cultural break in your hectic day of shopping.

### LUNCH

For an exclusive lunch, try Jamie's favourite, Bluebird (350 King's Road). Refuel on a light salad or a delicious grill, depending on how much of an appetite you've worked up.

### MORE SHOPPING

Take time to browse the designer pieces at The Shop at Bluebird. Why not treat yourself to something special? You're in Chelsea after all!

### DINNER

Your feet are tired and your arms are weighed down with shopping. Fill up and wind down at the famous Big Easy Bar.B.Q & Crabshack (332–334 King's Road). Make sure you book in advance, as their yummy steaks and juicy seafood selection is always in high demand.

# Apple and elderflower jellies

So refreshing! Roll out the taste of summer and serve these on the terrace.

**Makes 6**

. . . . . . . . . . . . . . . . . . . . . . . . . . . . . . . . . . . . . . . . . . . . . . . . . . . . . . . . . . . . . . . . . . . . .

10 gelatine leaves
450ml apple juice
200ml elderflower cordial
300ml sparkling water
½ Granny Smith apple, very finely sliced horizontally

. . . . . . . . . . . . . . . . . . . . . . . . . . . . . . . . . . . . . . . . . . . . . . . . . . . . . . . . . . . . . . . . . . . . .

Place the gelatine in a small bowl with plenty of cold water and set aside for about 5 minutes to soften.

Place 250ml of the apple juice in a saucepan and heat through gently, but don't let it boil. Squeeze the excess water from the softened gelatine with your hands and add to the hot apple juice, then remove from the heat and stir until the gelatine has dissolved.

Add the remaining apple juice and the elderflower cordial and stir well. Slowly add the sparkling water, then divide the liquid between 6 glasses or cups. Chill in the refrigerator for 30 minutes until thickened. Add the apple slices, pushing them down into the viscous jelly. Cover and chill the jellies for another 2–3 hours until set. Store in the refrigerator for up to 3 days.

# Peach melba

The classic version of this dessert is served with ice cream instead of cream; choose whichever you prefer. Use the leftover vanilla poaching syrup as an ice cream sauce or a cocktail base. You can also drizzle a little over the peaches before serving.

### SERVES 4

. . . . . . . . . . . . . . . . . . . . . . . . . . . . . . . . . . . . . . . . . . . . . . . . . . . . . . . . . . . . . . . . . . . . . . . . . . . . . . . . . . .

200g caster sugar
500ml water
1 vanilla pod, split lengthways
4 ripe but firm peaches (or nectarines)

### To serve
150g fresh raspberries
8 soft amaretti biscuits
280ml single cream

. . . . . . . . . . . . . . . . . . . . . . . . . . . . . . . . . . . . . . . . . . . . . . . . . . . . . . . . . . . . . . . . . . . . . . . . . . . . . . . . . . .

Place the sugar and water in a medium saucepan over a low heat and stir occasionally until the sugar has completely dissolved. Add the vanilla pod and increase the heat slightly, but don't allow the syrup to boil.

Add the whole peaches (they should be mostly submerged in the liquid) and poach gently for 5 minutes. Turn the peaches over and poach for another 2 minutes. Remove from the heat and leave the peaches to cool in the syrup.

Peel the peaches and halve and stone them if you like. Serve each peach with a handful of raspberries, 2 soft amaretti biscuits and a good pouring of cream.

# Lime and watermelon ice pops

WHAA! Two totally cool Candy Kitten flavours in one frozen mix.

## MAKES 8

.........................................................................................

550g watermelon flesh, seeds removed
110g caster sugar
pinch of salt
juice and finely grated rind of 1 large lime
8 lolly sticks

.........................................................................................

Blend the watermelon, sugar, salt and lime juice in a blender at high speed until smooth. Pour into a jug and stir in the lime rind.

Divide the mixture between 8 ice lolly moulds, about 80ml each, and insert a lolly stick into each. Freeze for at least 4 hours, or preferably overnight.

To serve, run the outsides of the moulds under hot water for 10 seconds to release the lollies.

# ... try these extra flavours

Try using other types of melon - cantaloupe or honeydew are great choices.

........................................................................................

Pineapple works brilliantly instead of watermelon, and adding a dash of coconut milk gives a totes tropical twist.

........................................................................................

If you love berries, then blitz 550g of your choice of berries instead of watermelon. If the berries contain a lot of seeds, pass the mixture through a sieve before pouring into the moulds.

........................................................................................

If you like all the ideas above, you could always combine them for two-tone pops. Simply choose your two favourites and make half the suggested quantity of each. Divide the first flavour between the moulds so they are half full and freeze for 2 hours. Then pour in the second flavour and return to the freezer to set completely.

........................................................................................

Try out your own flavour combinations, but make sure you taste the mixture before freezing. You may need to add more sugar for a sweeter taste or more lime juice if the mixture is too sweet. For a cool drink, crush the ice pops and serve in glasses.

**PARDY** DRINKS

# Raspberry and lemon grass bubble tea

**Tapioca pearls are available in a range of fun colours - white and black look particularly good in this deep red bubble tea.**

## SERVES 6

300g caster sugar
400ml water
4 fat lemon grass stalks, bashed with a rolling pin
400g fresh or frozen raspberries
150g quick-cook tapioca pearls
milk, chilled water or cold tea of your choice, for topping up
condensed milk, to taste (optional)
ice cubes, to serve

Place the sugar and water in a medium saucepan over a low heat and stir occasionally until the sugar has completely dissolved. Add the lemon grass and simmer for 5 minutes. Add the raspberries, remove from the heat and set aside for 20 minutes to infuse.

Strain the mixture through a sieve, pressing gently to release all the liquid. Measure 400ml of the resulting syrup into a large bowl and set aside the remaining syrup in a jug.

Simmer the tapioca pearls in a saucepan of water for 5–10 minutes until tender but not mushy. Drain the tapioca and tip into the bowl with the syrup.

Divide the tapioca and syrup in the bowl between 6 large drinks cups or glasses and add a generous spoonful of ice cubes to each. Top up each glass with milk, chilled water or cold tea. Add a dash of condensed milk, if liked, and extra syrup from the jug to taste. Serve immediately with colourful straws.

# Passion fruit and mango bubble tea

If you don't like the taste of tea, simply replace it with another 125ml of mango and passion fruit juice or milk in this refreshing drink.

## SERVES 4

150g quick-cook tapioca pearls
150g light soft brown sugar
220ml cold water
1 black, red or green tea bag
250ml boiling water
250ml mango and passion fruit juice
200ml milk, chilled
2 handfuls of crushed ice

Simmer the tapioca pearls in a saucepan of water for 5–10 minutes until tender but not mushy. Drain the tapioca and tip into a large bowl.

Place the sugar and cold water in a saucepan over a low heat and stir occasionally until the sugar has completely dissolved. Turn up the heat and simmer for 1 minute. Pour the syrup over the tapioca, cover and chill in the refrigerator for an hour.

To make the tea, place the tea bag in a jug with the boiling water and leave to steep for 5 minutes. Remove the tea bag, allow the tea to cool and then cover and chill in the refrigerator for an hour.

To assemble the drink, place the juice, milk, chilled tea and ice in a cocktail shaker or large jar with a lid and shake vigorously until frothy. Divide the tapioca and syrup between 4 large glasses, top up with the juice mixture and stir well. Serve immediately.

# *Bubble coffee*

**Black tapioca pearls look most striking in this sophisticated iced drink.**

## SERVES 2

. . . . . . . . . . . . . . . . . . . . . . . . . . . . . . . . . . . . . . . . . . . . . . . . . . . . . . . . . . . . . . . . . . . . .

120g quick-cook tapioca pearls
1 tbsp light soft brown sugar
200ml strong, freshly brewed coffee, cooled
1 tbsp sweetened condensed milk, plus extra to serve
mugful of ice

. . . . . . . . . . . . . . . . . . . . . . . . . . . . . . . . . . . . . . . . . . . . . . . . . . . . . . . . . . . . . . . . . . . . .

Simmer the tapioca pearls in a saucepan of water for 5–10 minutes until tender but not mushy. Drain the tapioca and tip into a large bowl, then stir in the brown sugar.

To assemble the drink, place the coffee, condensed milk and half the ice in a cocktail shaker or large jar with a lid and shake vigorously until frothy. Divide the tapioca and remaining ice between 2 large glasses, top up with the coffee mixture and stir well. Serve immediately, with extra condensed milk to taste.

# Rhubarb and custard milkshakes

Creamy milkshake and rhubarb purée are swirled together for the ultimate treat. Use forced pink rhubarb for the best colour. This quantity makes two large or four small milkshakes.

## SERVES 2 OR 4

300g rhubarb, trimmed and chopped
120g golden caster sugar
1/2 vanilla pod, split lengthways
2 tbsp water
300ml full-fat milk, chilled
4 scoops of vanilla ice cream
handful of ice

To make the rhubarb purée, place the rhubarb, sugar, vanilla pod and water in a saucepan over a medium heat and simmer gently, stirring often, for 10–15 minutes until soft and pulpy. Remove from the heat and leave to cool, then remove the vanilla pod. Blend the purée in a food processor if you want it completely smooth.

To make the milkshakes, blend the milk, ice cream and ice in a food processor until smooth. Layer the milkshake and rhubarb purée in 2 large or 4 small glasses, then stir briefly to create a marbled effect. Serve immediately with colourful straws.

# Lemonade ice cream float

You will end up with a little more lemon syrup than you need for this recipe. The leftover syrup can be stored in the refrigerator for several weeks. Dilute it with sparkling water or lemonade for a refreshing, zesty drink.

## SERVES 2

......................................................................................

2 large scoops of vanilla ice cream
2 large scoops of lemon sorbet
2-4 tbsp lemon syrup (see below)
traditional-style lemonade, for topping up

### Lemon syrup
150g caster sugar
finely grated rind of 1 lemon, plus extra fine strips to decorate,
and the juice of 3 lemons
150ml water

......................................................................................

To make the lemon syrup, put the sugar, grated lemon rind and water in a saucepan over a low heat and stir occasionally until the sugar has completely dissolved. Turn up the heat and boil for 30 seconds, then remove from the heat and leave to cool. Stir in the lemon juice. Cover and chill in the refrigerator until needed.

To make the floats, place a scoop each of vanilla ice cream and lemon sorbet in each of 2 large glasses and drizzle with 1–2 tbsp of lemon syrup. Slowly add lemonade to top up and decorate with a few fine strips of lemon rind. Serve immediately with straws.

# HOW TO MAKE A FRIENDSHIP BRACELET

**THESE PRETTY BRACELETS MAKE PERFECT PRESENTS OR GOODIE BAG FILLERS FOR YOUR CANDY KITTENS PARDY.**

**1** Choose three colours of thread to make your bracelet. Kitten favourites are candy pink, sky blue and cute cream.

**2** Take two strands of each colour of thread and knot them all together at one end. Separate the three colours at the other end.

**3** Get a friend to hold the knotted end of the bracelet and start plaiting the three colours together.

**4** Once the bracelet is long enough to go round your wrist, tie a knot in the other end and snip off any straggly ends.

# *Ultimate hot chocolate*

Using a mixture of dark and milk chocolate makes for a rich, smooth drink. If you would prefer something a little more grown up, use all dark chocolate instead.

## SERVES 6

......................................................................

1 litre full-fat milk
1 vanilla pod, split lengthways, or 2 tsp vanilla extract
150g plain dark chocolate, finely chopped
150g milk chocolate, finely chopped

### To serve
handful of mini marshmallows
whipped cream (optional)
chocolate shavings (optional)

......................................................................

Place the milk in a heavy-based saucepan over a medium heat until almost boiling. Remove from the heat, then scrape the seeds out of the vanilla pod, if using, and add to the pan with the pod, or add the vanilla extract, and set aside for 10 minutes to infuse.

Remove the vanilla pod and reheat the milk, then add the chocolates and whisk gently until melted and frothy. Divide between 6 mugs or cups and top with mini marshmallows. Add a generous swirl of whipped cream and a few chocolate shavings, if liked. Serve immediately with spoons.

# Homemade orangeade

This is perfect for sharing with friends - just add hot sunshine, cool tunes and you've got yourself an instant PARDY!

## SERVES 8-10

300g caster sugar
450ml water
400ml freshly squeezed orange juice
juice of 2 lemons
1.3 litres sparkling water, for topping up
ice cubes, to serve

Place the sugar and water in a medium saucepan over a low heat and stir occasionally until the sugar has completely dissolved. Turn up the heat and boil for 3–4 minutes, then remove from the heat and leave to cool.

Mix the syrup with the orange and lemon juices, then cover and chill in the refrigerator until needed. To serve, pour the syrup into a large jug and top up with the sparkling water. Serve with plenty of ice. The syrup can be stored in the refrigerator for up to 2 weeks.

# Index

# Acknowledgements

**Candy Kitten Contributors:** Edward Williams, Warren Crane, Erin O'Connor

**Commissioning Editor:** Eleanor Maxfield
**Editors:** Alex Stetter & Katy Denny
**Copy Editing:** Jo Smith
**Deputy Art Director:** Yasia Williams-Leedham
**Design and Art Direction:** Jaz Bahra
**Illustrations:** Abigail Read
**Assistant Production Manager:** Caroline Alberti

**Food Photography:** Charlotte Tolhurst
**Lifestyle Photography:** Ruth Rose
**Models:** Katie McNaughton, Robyn Bevan, Rosana Dimmick & Natalie Hepworth
**Food Prop Styling:** Tamsin Weston
**Wardrobe Styling:** Sarah Katchis
**Make-up:** Sabina Ventriglia
**Hair Styling:** Zoey Olachnowicz
**Flowers:** Leanne Roberts-Hewitt/Wildabout